UNIVERSITY OF KNOWLEDGE

GLENN FRANK, B.A., M.A., LITT.D., L.H.D., LL.D., *Editor-in-Chief*

PRINTED AND BOUND IN THE UNITED STATES
OF AMERICA BY THE CUNEO PRESS, INC.

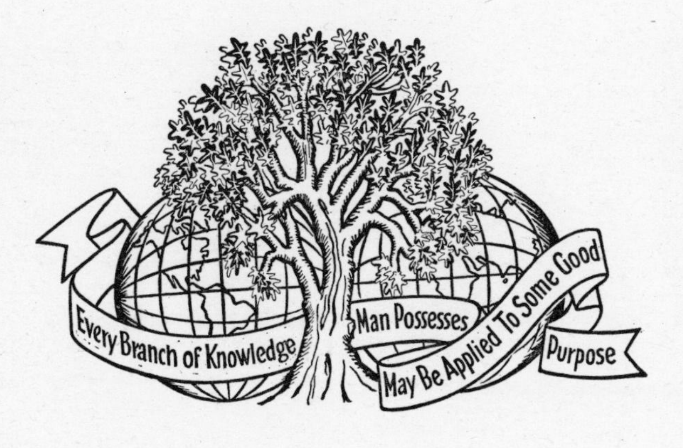
Every Branch of Knowledge
Man Possesses
May Be Applied To Some Good
Purpose

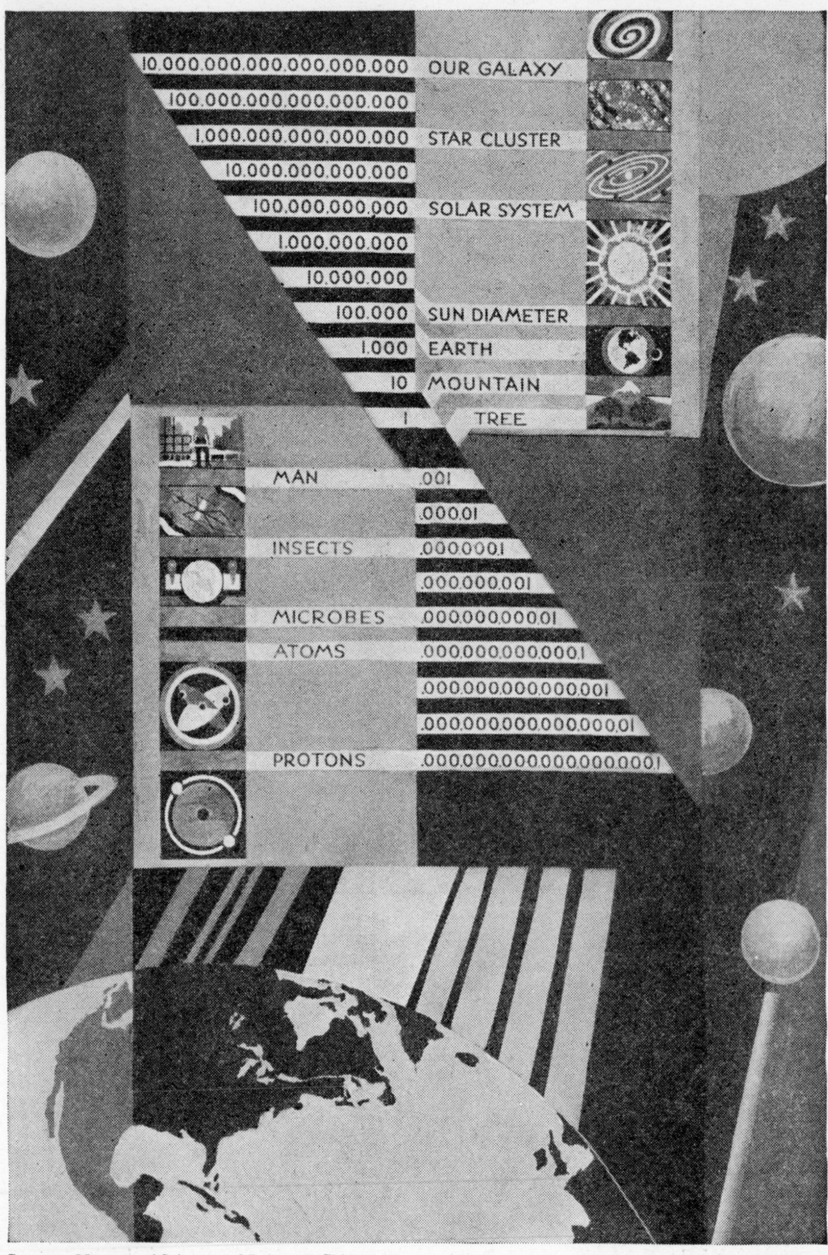

Courtesy Museum of Science and Industry, Chicago

A MURAL SHOWING COMPARATIVE DIMENSIONS OF NATURAL OBJECTS IN MILES

THE UNIVERSITY OF KNOWLEDGE
WONDER BOOKS

GLENN FRANK, EDITOR-IN-CHIEF

EARTH AND SKY
MARVELS OF ASTRONOMY

WONDERS OF THE UNIVERSE

BY

CLARENCE R. SMITH, B.S., M.S.

Professor of Physics and Astronomy
Aurora College, Aurora, Illinois

AND

ASSOCIATES

•

UNIVERSITY OF KNOWLEDGE, INCORPORATED
CHICAGO

1941

GLENN FRANK
Editor-in-Chief

INTRODUCTION

With the earth beneath his feet and the sky above his head, man lives his brief moment in a world he can see and touch and come to know, but sublime mystery shrouds his coming and his going.

His twofold passion is to penetrate the mystery and to perfect the mastery of life.

This volume on earth and sky does not pretend to penetrate the mystery of the man's story before birth or after death. It seeks only to help him become better acquainted with the earth on which he lives, with the universe in which the earth moves, and with inconceivable reaches of space where his universe is but one of many universes.

Our animal needs can be satisfied by adapting ourselves to the world around us. But living means more than eating, working, playing, and sleeping. A mind that is alive, vibrant with the very pulse of life, never ceases in the attempt to break the chains that bind it to earth. The body is bound by physical laws, but the mind can project itself to the farthest frontiers of a boundless universe.

This book is an astronomical journey. It begins with a consideration of the earth as a small planet swinging around the sun. In its pages we may study the earth's atmosphere, its surface, and its core. We then turn to the moon, the sun, the planets, and the constellations of stars. Beyond our universe we encounter still other universes, galaxies, and super-galaxies.

Geology and astronomy are sciences which can help us on our way to an understanding of man's true place in a system that seems almost beyond comprehension.

The geologist takes the whole world for his laboratory. Abysmal chasms that scar the earth; mountains hidden in the clouds; plains, hills and cliffs; boulders, pebbles and sand; rivers, lakes, and oceans—all are grist for the geologist's mill. We need not be scientists to look upon the earth's wonders with eyes that really see and with minds that understand.

The astronomer gives us another way to study the small planet upon which fate has ordered our existence. The earth is part of a vast and varied astronomical system. All objects in that system are made of similar materials. The meteors that blaze brilliantly through the atmosphere; the comets that rush madly through space; the billions of flaming suns; the uncountable clusters of stars; the obscuring clouds of cosmic dust—all these are composed of the same elements as our own planet.

The astronomer toys with figures that defy the imagination. Our sun, less than a hundred million miles away, is a close neighbor. The brilliant points of light we see overhead are suns vastly larger than our own. These stars are so far away that their distances can scarcely be understood by minds accustomed to measuring in inches, feet and miles. The telescope gathers light from stars so distant that thousands of years are required for it to reach the earth. Millions of stars, so large that the earth in comparison is but a speck of dust, crowd the heavens. But the unending expanses of space are so vast that even the largest stars are but tiny objects drifting in a boundless ocean.

Man might seem to be reduced to utter insignificance in this limitless cosmic scheme. Thus far science has found no evidence that life as we know it exists anywhere but on this planet. Man is the highest form of that life. He alone has the gift of comprehension. He alone must seek the answers to the eternal questions of Whence, Whither, and Why. We cannot study the earth and the countless stars and suns scattered through space without a vital quickening of the imagination. Life itself takes on a new meaning.

GLENN FRANK, *Editor-in-Chief.*

PREFACE

The earth and sky as a theme for writing—what scope for the imagination and how obligingly flows the pen! These pages are written in the faith that the general reader, whether in field, office or store, has lurking in his mind a desire to know more about the natural world around him. He wants to know the meaning of the stars and what is in the deep interior of the earth. He wants to share a little of the thrill of those who make explorations and discoveries.

Authors of textbooks may feel the obligation of writing what needs to be taught and they may realize that their pages may often be read by those whose urgings are other than pleasure, but the writer of popular science can dare to hope that his pages will be read for the joy of reading and the pleasure of learning. Science of nowadays owes its advancement mostly to men who work in strange laboratories and in mountain-top observatories, and these men who are spending their lives in this serious business of science will record their findings in highly technical journals and in the transactions of learned societies. This cannot be otherwise but there is need for writing that will glean from the more technical records the essential and interesting facts and present them in a manner that the average man can enjoy. Such is the attempt of this book.

The man whose daily occupation is in an office wants to read at home for pleasure and to keep abreast of the times. Moreover, he wants to gain a fuller appreciation of nature itself. In looking out at the glowing stars he wants to know the story they try to tell, he wants to know whether the brightest stars are the largest, why some are tinted red and others blue, what and where are the galaxies and super-galaxies, whether the sun is going anywhere, what are shooting stars, and what are the marks on the moon? These questions and many others of equal interest are taken up in what we hope is easy style and with the utmost care as to accuracy of statement.

The section regarding the earth treats of the atmosphere with its life-giving oxygen and its clouds, the mighty depths of the sea, the land on which we dwell, and methods of studying the interior of the earth far below the penetration of the deepest wells ever drilled.

Perchance this book may fall into the hands of some who would go so far as to make a hobby of their science of the earth and the sky. The United States Weather Bureau gets much of its valuable data regarding temperature, clouds and rain from enthusiastic and capable observers whose livelihood occupations are far removed from science of any sort.

Who would not wish to know the constellations? There is here included a description of the more conspicuous ones so that they can be readily identified. It seems almost pathetic that many persons of intelligence and with useful attainments walk under the star-studded skies every night of their lives and yet do not recognize even Orion and the Swan!

What can be more inspiring than to know some of the more important constellations and watch them through the changing seasons; to recognize Arcturus, whose light requires forty years to reach the earth; or to find the great nebula of Andromeda, the most distant object the human eye ever looks upon without a telescope; to learn that this nebula is so vast that the entire solar system would be lost in it as a speck of dust!

The great nebula of Andromeda is just barely visible to the unaided eye but even a small spy glass or opera glass will show it clearly, while a telescope with a three- or four-inch objective lens will reveal this nebula in grand display.

Much astronomy can be learned from the sky without a telescope, and a section of this book has been especially written for aid on that line. Much can be gained with even the smallest and cheapest of telescopes and the amateur astronomer is pretty sure to purchase one of some sort.

As his hobby becomes more fascinating, the amateur will buy a better instrument and at no great outlay of money, or indeed he may find himself bitten by the "bug" of making telescopes for himself. If the reader is susceptible to such urges he may begin a new chapter in life for, among others, the pages on amateur astronomy are calculated to stir up enthusiasm. Once you start this telescope-making business you may as well resign yourself to seclusion and have your family and neighbors and friends clear the way. You will be spending hours and hours in your basement, walking around a barrel grinding your mirror, a smell of pitch will fill the air, your hands will be illuminated with bright red rouge, and there will be a fire in your eye. This telescope-making bug bites to the bone.

A number of persons have aided the author in making this volume possible. Dr. Arthur R. Sayer and David Hamlin of Dearborn Observatory; Mr. Charles Hetzler of Yerkes Observatory; Mr. Frank M. Preucil, one of the foremost amateur astronomers; Mr. Jerome Wolff, and Mr. E. C. Martz have contributed information and drafts of some of the manuscripts. Others who have contributed in an equally helpful manner are Messrs. Fritz Leiber, Jr., Charles Hopkins, Donald Morris, Lewis Herman, and Jay S. Seeley.

Mr. Charles W. Paape has helped the author in the preparation of this volume from its first outline to its final editing. To him and to those mentioned above I am grateful for assistance rendered.

The manuscript has been checked and rechecked, and while the author scarcely dare hope that no errors have escaped his notice, the book is now ready to be placed before its audience "with good omens and a fair breeze."

Aurora College
January 19, 1938

CLARENCE R. SMITH

ACKNOWLEDGMENT

From the very earliest times the sky had a great fascination for men. Its beauty and its mystery have influenced humanity very much. Poets have sung about the heavens with joy, and scientists have studied them with eagerness. So closely is man related to the earth that we frequently speak of her as "Old Mother Earth." We have tried to have the pictures in this volume present the glories of the heavens and the grandeur of earth. Practically all of the pictures used in the sections dealing with astronomy are reprints of the plates the astronomers themselves have studied.

We desire to acknowledge our gratitude to:

Field Museum of Natural History, Chicago
Yerkes Observatory, Williams Bay, Wis.
Lick Observatory, Mount Hamilton, Calif.
Mount Wilson Observatory, Pasadena, Calif.
American Museum of Natural History, New York City
Bausch and Lomb Optical Company, Rochester, N. Y.
Carl Zeiss, Inc., New York City
Mr. Frank M. Preucil, Joliet, Ill.
Northern Pacific Railway
Chicago, Milwaukee, St. Paul and Pacific Railway
Rosenwald Museum of Science and Industry, Chicago
Gaertner Scientific Corporation
The Bauer Type Foundry, New York City.

J. Bradford Pengelly
Picture Editor

TABLE OF CONTENTS

Courtesy Lick Observatory

THE GREAT NEBULA IN ANDROMEDA
The farthest object that the unaided human eye can see.

EXPLORATIONS IN TIME AND SPACE

"When I, sitting, heard the astronomer, where he lectured
with much applause in the lecture-room,
How soon, unaccountable, I became tired and sick;
Till rising and gliding out, I wander'd off by myself,
In the mystical moist night-air, and from time to time,
Look'd up in perfect silence at the stars."

—Walt Whitman

MAN HAS burrowed deep into the earth and soared high into the rarefied stretches of the stratosphere. He has explored the far-flung wastes of the desolate Arctic and Antarctic and the steaming, impenetrable jungles of the tropics. He has brought light into the dim, dark morasses of the hitherto unknown. Intrepidly, he has extended the last outposts of civilization to the jumping-off places, the edges of the world. By means of powerful telescopes, he has even projected his knowledge to take in the stars and planets that glimmer fitfully, billions times billions of miles away in space. Yet, in spite of his seemingly far-reaching explorations, he has scarcely scratched the surface of the sum total of knowledge concerning the earth on which he lives and the universe of which his earth is an infinitesimal atom.

Three-fourths of his earth, for instance, is submerged under water. The submarine mountains and valleys and jungles of the ocean bed have been explored and exploited only in the least degree. Even after he has disinterred these secrets from their water-grave, even after he has mapped and charted every inch of the earth's surface, man will have explored only one room of his enormous house. For the earth's crust, which he has merely punctured with mile-deep mines and two-mile deep well holes, is four thousand miles from the center. No one knows what lies beneath this thin crust. Perhaps there is molten lava, solid rock, or even a core of iron.

But suppose man does eventually learn the entire composition of the earth; suppose he does uncover the secret of every nook and cranny that has thus far eluded him; suppose he knows everything that there is to be known about the planet on which he lives—how great will be his knowledge in relation to the vast expanse of the universe?

THE INFINITELY SMALL AND THE IMMEASURABLY GREAT

The smallest particle known to man is the electron, which revolves around a slightly larger nucleus called a proton. The two combined form an atom so small that several thousand of them could be gathered on a pin-point. These atoms, in turn, combine to make up a molecule, the smallest recognizable division of matter as we know it to exist in the form of man, beasts, vegetable matter, minerals, liquids and gases. Analogously, the earth on which man lives is an electron whirling around the protonic sun to form a solar system which, in turn, is part of a star cluster comparable to the molecule. This molecular star cluster is, in itself, part of a galaxy, the aggregate in the unlimited, unmeasured vastness that is the universe. Man's complete knowledge of his earth in relation to his knowledge of the universe is like the knowledge of one electron among the billions and billions and billions that compose the earth.

But although we have not learned all there is to be known about the earth, even with the aid of powerful microscopes, sensitive cameras, and ingenious spectroscopes, we have been able to learn much about the multitudinous other worlds that accompany our little world in its eternal journey through the heavens. And this has been done in spite of the enormous distances that separate us from them. Recently, with the aid of the spectrograph and infra-red photography, astronomers discovered a new star behind the star Epsilon Aurigae, eighteen quadrillion miles distant from

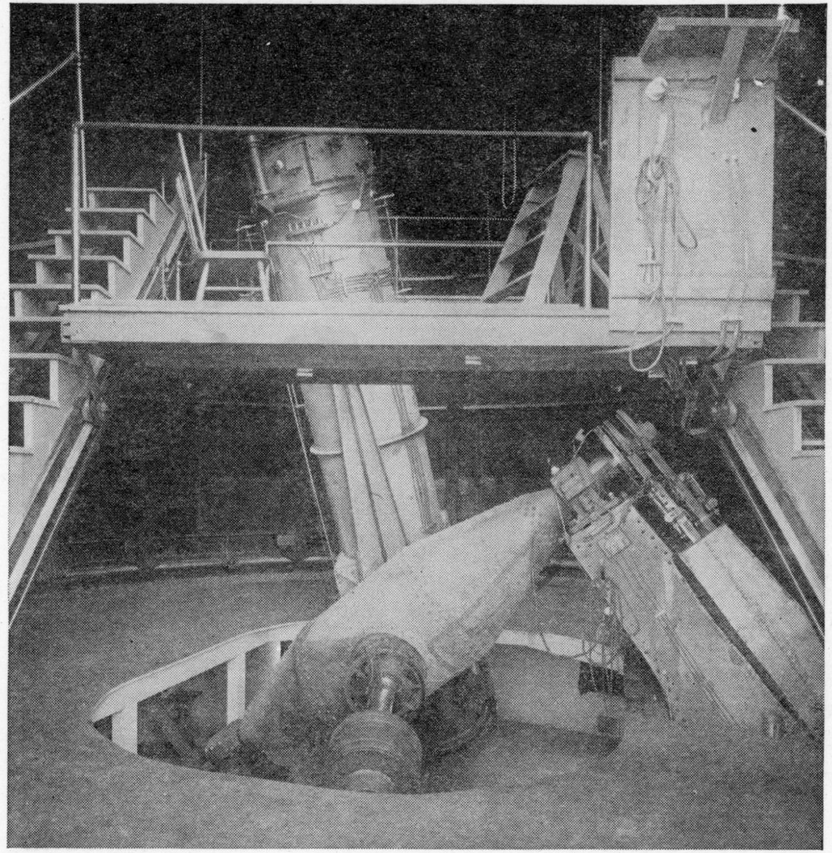

Courtesy Lick Observatory

THE MECHANISM OF A TELESCOPE
Complicated machinery is necessary to keep telescopes aimed at the stars, and timed with their movement.

the earth. They know, too, that this star is two billion miles in diameter, has a temperature of 2,500° Fahrenheit and has a shell of ionized gas revolving around it somewhat like the atmosphere around the earth. By means of the spectroscope, astronomers have been able to determine that the elements of which the new star is composed are essentially the same as those that compose the earth. Spectrographic deductions have already been made of more than fifty-seven thousand similar binary or twin stars, and astronomers claim that soon they will have completed the spectra of two hundred thousand stars.

Courtesy Yerkes Observatory

A "BIG GUN" OF THE SKIES
On clear evenings this telescope is put into action, that man may learn what lies beyond his limited vision.

ANOMALIES OF TIME AND PLACE

An amazing sidelight regarding these enormous distances that separate us from the distant stars is the fact that what we are now viewing through a telescope actually happened hundreds and thousands of years ago. Were the newly discovered star behind Epsilon Aurigae suddenly to explode into star-dust today, we would still continue to see it for three thousand years. At that future time, were we to be watching it through a telescope, the extinction of this gigantic star which is almost as large as our entire solar system, would appear to be simply the sudden blackening of a white speck of light. The interval occurs because light travels at one hundred and eighty-six thousand miles a second, six trillion miles a year, and the new star is three thousand light years away from the earth.

Since the development of the theory of the fourth dimension, another amazing factor has come to light regarding the things we see in the heavens. Not only is it possible that the star we see no longer exists, but, in all probability, it actually never was where we saw it. Astronomers have proved that rays of light are "bent" by the layer of atmosphere around the earth; therefore, the North Star, for instance, would actually be in a much lower position than we see it to be. Water refracts light in a similar manner; the phenomenon has been observed by anyone who has peered over the edge of a fishbowl and has seen two fish where there was actually only one.

In spite of the tremendous distances that separate us from the other eight planets which form our solar system, we have come to know a lot about them. For instance, we know that the side of the moon not facing the sun reaches a temperature of 100° below zero Fahrenheit. We know that Mercury, the smallest of the planets but the closest to the sun, experiences temperatures on a midsummer day ranging from 90° above zero to well over 1,000° Fahrenheit. Of the planet Venus we have learned that, of all the planets, it would be the most suitable to sustain life as we know it. At one time it was thought that the planet Mars showed signs of a network of canals, perhaps man-made, but now it seems more probable that these green strips are immense forests of trees growing in swamp lands irrigated by the melting of polar icecaps.

Galileo, with his crude telescope, was the first to identify four of Jupiter's nine moons. With our modern scientific implements, we have been able to deduce that Jupiter is a whirling ball of less density than aluminum. Galileo, too, was the first to identify the rings around Saturn which we know to be huge, flat bands of material ranging in size from dust grains to boulders a mile in diameter. Uranus, we know, experiences two sunsets in twenty-four hours, has a probable noonday temperature of 340° below

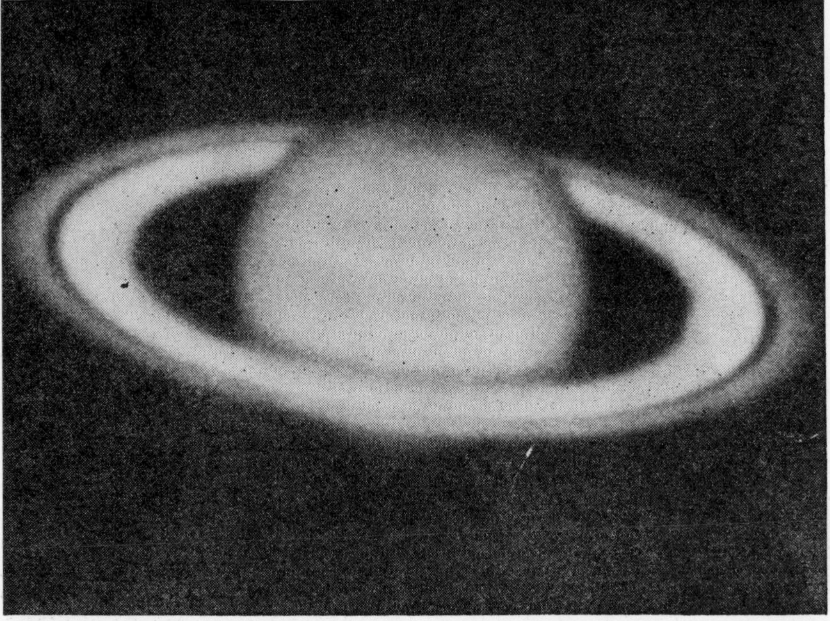

Courtesy Yerkes Observatory

THE PLANET WITH RINGS

Probably the most interesting of the planets is the sixth one, glorious Saturn with its mysterious "rings." No other astronomical body yet discovered by man is comparable to this one, and no one yet knows the cause of the circles or rings that surround the planet.

zero and, like Jupiter and Saturn, is relatively light in weight. Because it rotates on its axis in an opposite direction from that of the earth, we know that on Neptune the sun rises in the west and sets in the east. Although it was not actually seen until twenty-five years later, the planet Pluto was discovered in 1905 by Percival Lowell through the medium of mathematical calculations.

OF MEN AND STARS

Almost as startling as the universe itself is man's ingenuity in unlocking its secrets. As early as 2000 B.C. the Egyptians were recording the movements of the planet Venus, and, by 600 B.C., they were able to calculate the positions of the sun and moon and foretell solar eclipses. Thus they were the first to practice what we know now as scientific astronomy. Even the supposedly barbaric Aztec Indians of Mexico, separated from the European centers of science by oceans of water and centuries of civilization, cunningly devised a calendar stone which indicates that in 1100 A.D. they possessed an amazing knowledge of astronomy. Copernicus, the Polish mathematician, solely by mathematical calculations, was the first to advance the theory that the earth was a part of a system of planets which revolved around the sun, and thus paved the way for the modern and true conception of the universe.

Until the time of Galileo, all of these astronomical discoveries had been made without the telescope, simply because man had learned to reason truths from patient observations. With his new telescope, Galileo was able to pull aside the veil that distance had cast about the heavens. He saw, not a "man in the moon," but craters and mountains; he astounded contemporary scientists by stating categorically that the planet Jupiter possessed four separate moons of its own; he broadened the vistas of sight and bridged the limitless stretches of infinity with knowledge.

From then on the astronomers began to reach across the millions of miles that separated them from the rest of the universe, cornering its myriad of stars and planets and dead worlds into the eyepieces of their telescopes. Telescopes were improved and the millions of miles became billions; photography was adapted to use in astronomy; the spectrograph was invented; and the billions of miles became trillions. The completion of the new two-hundred-inch telescope in California, in about 1940, will throw the cold, searching light of astronomical knowledge yet farther into the depths of infinite space.

Yet, strangely enough, many of these astral explorations have been made without the use of a telescope. Seated in a tiny cubicle, using only charts and graphs and astronomical treatises, men have been able to discover the existence of stars without ever having seen them. Both Leverrier and Adams discovered the planet Neptune, independently of each other, simply by mathematical calculation and deduction. In the same way, twenty-five years before

GALILEO DEMONSTRATES HIS TELESCOPE

The astronomer was acclaimed by distinguished citizens of Venice when he demonstrated his first telescope from the tower of St. Marks.

Courtesy Lick Observatory

LICK OBSERVATORY ON MT. HAMILTON, CALIFORNIA

it was first seen by man, Lowell calculated the approximate position of the ninth planet, Pluto. More recently, the giant twin of the binary star Epsilon Aurigae was seen by means of the spectroscope and high-speed infra-red photography only after its position had been foretold and charted by mathematics. The giant swing of the universe has been confined to the limits of a mathematical formula.

The spectroscope has been one of the great boons to astronomers. With this device, which breaks up the spectrum of light into its component colors by means of a series of prisms, they have been able to identify the materials that go to make up a star trillions of miles away. The process is simple. All materials have characteristic spectra. The lines of color projected by the spectroscope, when it is pointed at a star, vary according to the star's material content. Thus, astronomers were able to discover the gas, helium, in the sun before it was discovered on earth.

OF STARS AND MEN

Out of the early studies of the stars came not only the true science of astronomy but also the pseudo-science of astrology. The Babylonians believed that the position of the stars and planets at the birth of a king foretold the future of that king. Out of these beginnings grew a mass of zodiacal claptrap and magical abracadabra that spread through Greece, Rome, Europe, and the Americas. It still has millions of adherents who live and breathe according to the position of the stars. Trading on the credulity of the early ignorant mass mind, the astrologers proved they could foretell the movements of the heavenly bodies. From that beginning it was a simple step to prove also that they could divine the future of human beings. Horoscopes are now being prognosticated by weighing machines which spew forth a detailed character analysis, advise the best time of the year to seed corn, tell you the kind of wife to choose, direct your energies into a more lucrative line of work, and even tell you the most propitious day for betting on the horse race—all as if it were ordained by the stars. Astrology is not a science; it is a phase in the development of astronomy that men should have outgrown.

However, certain kinds of divination are possible by means of astronomy. The surface of the sun is pocked with what are

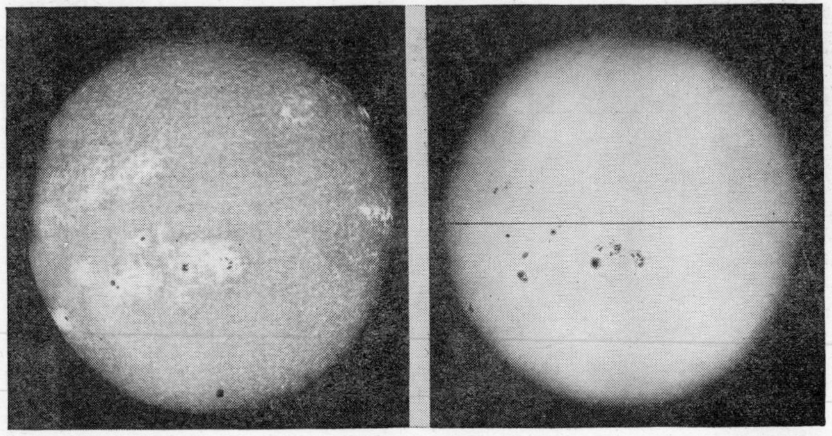

Courtesy Yerkes Observatory

TWO VIEWS OF THE SUN

Right, an ordinary photograph; left, a spectro-heliograph.

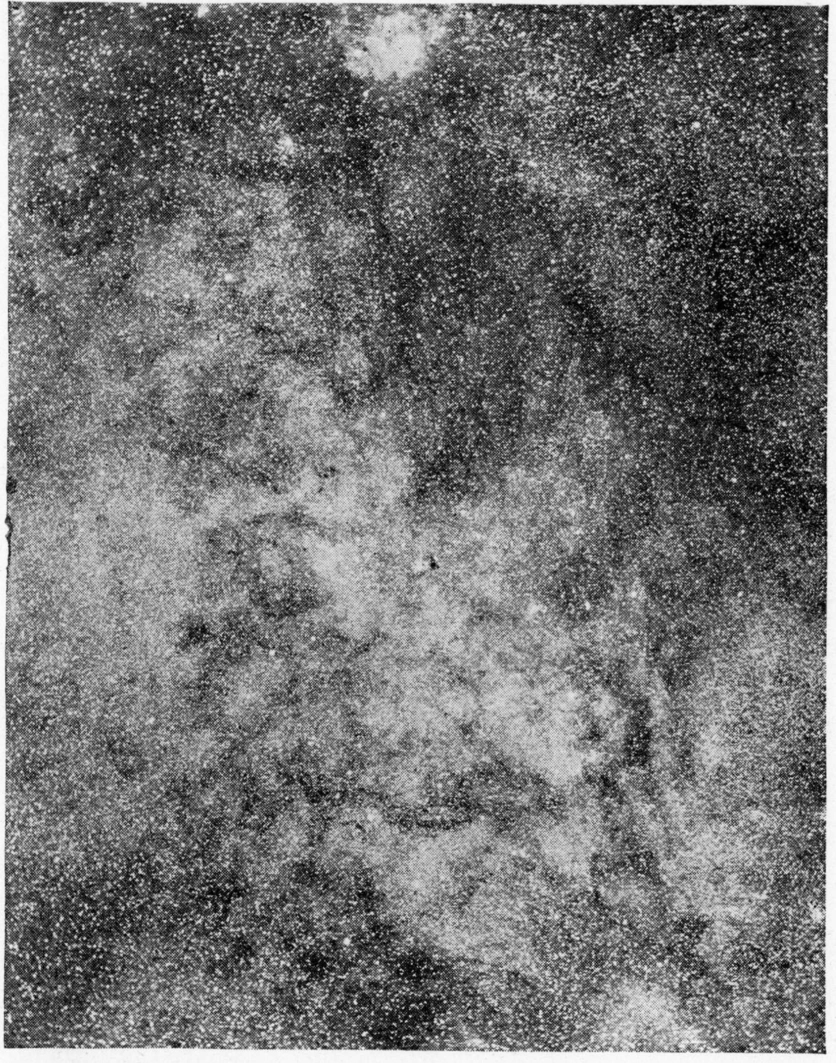

Courtesy Yerkes Observatory

THE GREAT STAR CLOUD IN THE CONSTELLATION SAGITTARIUS
Invisible to unaided eyes, but discernible through a powerful telescope, the distant stars appear as dense smoke clouds.

known as sun spots. To us on earth they appear to be spots, but actually they are disturbances in the photosphere layer on the sun that create holes large enough to engulf the earth. The position and size of these spots vary and, to these changes, some astronomers have attributed crop failures, wars, birth rate drops, magnetic storms, and a number of other physical phenomena. Actually, these spots affect the weather on earth and the reception of radio waves by radio sets. By studying them the astronomical weather man is able to foretell, to a certain degree, the weather conditions that will prevail in the future. But, as yet, comparatively little has been uncovered about these solar phenomena. The new two-hundred-inch telescope should aid in solving many of their mysteries.

THE IMPONDERABLE NUMBERS OF ASTRONOMY

Perhaps the greatest wonder of the universe is born of the enormous numbers that are used to measure distances, weights, temperatures and sizes. We on earth are comparatively small inhabitants of the universe. A trip around the world represents a long distance to us; a skyscraper is a vast bulk; a "heat wave" of 100° or a "cold spell" of 15° below zero is almost insufferable; a mountain of rock is an awesome weight. But compared with similar factors in the universe, our lives and environmental conditions become insignificantly diminutive.

Just this same condition prevails concerning our ideas of the age of the universe. To us whose span of life seldom exceeds eighty years, the age of the earth, approximately five billion years, is a fantastic figure that is incredible. But in the scheme of the universe, the age of the earth is lost in the immeasurable number of years that preceded its birth. A graphic illustration of such a fantastic amount of time can be obtained from a fable that is told to illustrate the meaning of eternity. Imagine a mountain of sand as high as the highest mountain in the world. Once every year a little bird comes to this mountain of sand and carries away one single grain of sand in its beak. By the time the bird has carried away that enormous mountain of sand, one second of eternity will have passed.

Five billion years ago the earth was first formed. Five hundred thousand years ago, more or less, men first roamed its valleys. Five thousand years ago, they began to look up—and to record their thoughts about the other worlds that showed themselves each night.

BUTTER BOWLS AND LAMPS

OUT OF THE DARKNESS

TODAY MAN KNOWS that the stars are gigantic incandescent worlds, moving through space at such vast distance from the earth that they appear as mere pin points of light. There was a time when man thought of them as lamps hanging down from the dark undersurface of a great inverted bowl. This seems a crude explanation but, considering the scanty knowledge possessed by primitive man, it was not an unclever one. At an even earlier date man had no explanation at all. He probably thought that just as there were leaves on trees, animals in forests, birds in the air, and grains of sand in the desert, so there were stars in the sky. He accepted the fact. That was all. According to the way he probably looked at it, animals and birds and stars just happened to be where they happened to be! As far as the stars were concerned, they were less interesting to him in a practical way than the others. The stars did not help or interfere with his doings and he probably returned the compliment by not looking at them very often.

Such a state of affairs did not last very long after man began to reason and link together the various events and happenings that made up his experience. He noticed that during the daytime he could usually see the sun in the sky. Therefore, he came to believe that the sun was the cause of the daylight. This may seem so absurdly simple as not to deserve the name of reasoning, but it was not a simple problem for primitive man. He knew nothing

Courtesy Yerkes Observatory

AN ANCIENT IDEA OF THE UNIVERSE

The Egyptians thought the universe looked like this, with the sky upheld by lofty mountains surrounding the earth.

Courtesy Buffalo Museum of Science

THE STARS EXCITED THE WONDER OF PRIMITIVE MEN

Limited in knowledge and equipment, and bound by superstition, the ancients could but gaze in awe upon the majesty of the star-swept skies.

of our theories of light; the very concept of light was outside his comprehension. He had to solve the problem of those cloudy days in which there is light but no direct sign of the sun. It is most difficult for the modern mind to imagine the pit of utter ignorance out of which man has climbed. The simplest deductions were his first steps.

FEARS IN THE SKY

The more man reasoned, the more suspicious he became of things in the sky. Thunder and lightning came from above; perhaps, he reasoned, the stars had something to do with that. As the lush greens of summer melted into the rich reds and yellows of autumn, and as they, in turn, gave way to bleak, freezing winter, he noticed that the sun climbed less and less high. Perhaps there was a tall tree in front of his cave and he got into the habit of noting how high above the treetop the sun appeared at midday. As autumn wore along, he noticed that there was less and less space between treetop and sun. Finally came a day when the sun barely reached the top, then a day when it was hidden altogether. At this point fear entered his heart. He did not know that the phenomenon was due to the shifting of the angle of the earth with respect to the sun, in the course of its annual revolution around that great flaming disk. All he knew was that the sun was going away and leaving the earth to freeze to death; not only was the sun lower in the sky, but also the days were shorter. In spite of memories of other winters successfully passed, the first primitive observer of the sun's annual movement must have felt that the end had come. There was a worrying and a shaking of heads and an offering of sacrifices. Finally the sun began to swing higher; eventually it began to appear above the top of the tree once more. In spite of the fact that the bite of winter was even sharper, man rejoiced, for he knew that the beneficent sun was coming back, and that spring would follow.

In the course of centuries, the precise date of the sun's lowest swing was more and more accurately determined. This date, which we call the winter solstice, and which falls on December 21 in the Northern Hemisphere and on June 21 in the Southern,

A COMET SEEN THROUGH EVENING CLOUDS

Daniel's Comet as it appeared September, 8, 1907.

Courtesy Yerkes Observatory

became a time of celebration and sacrifice for primitive man. Eventually he believed that his sacrifices were the cause of the sun's return. He confused the cause with the effect.

In ways such as this, fear and awe began to dominate man's attitude toward the heavens. He peopled the sky with alien minds, with demons and with gods, any of whom might strike back if offended. The unexpected terrified him. A flashing meteor would send him running for shelter; he thought that a star had fallen, that the demons of the sky were at war, and that it was time for puny man to hide. A glowing comet was a dire portent, the phases of the moon a matter for grave concern. An eclipse of the sun was worst of all, for it betokened a catastrophe to the greatest god of all, the ruddy giver of life. Some ancients thought that at such times a dark god was attempting to eat the sun; they watched the sudden drama of an eclipse, the gradual disappearance and the last minute rescue, with a more terrified intent than that with which any modern watches a melodramatic motion picture.

Man was beginning to understand the importance of the great universe around him, but he made the mistake of thinking, like a child lost in a dark forest, that every noise, every shape and every event was meant as a threat or a warning for him alone.

THE OLD SHEEP AND THE HEAVENLY FLOCK

More than four thousand years ago the shepherds of the Euphrates Valley began to study the heavens in a more regular fashion than had other men. Out in the lonely night tending their flocks they turned to the stars as to a kind of serious and dignified pastime, even as an unoccupied modern might turn to chess problems or cryptograms. They noted that, as the night passed, the stars moved in slow curves across the blue-black heavens. They began to keep special watch on certain stars because of their unusual brightness or color; reddish Antares, yellow Capella, icily scintillating Sirius, and others that stood out from the majority. They called them all "the heavenly flock," perhaps because their own sheep stood out like dim white patches against the dark earth and air of night, perhaps because it was the readiest analogy at hand. The sun they called "the old sheep." Since he was biggest, they reasoned he was oldest.

Even as a person looking steadily at vaguely patterned wallpaper begins to make out faces and fancies he sees the outlines of men and animals, so the shepherds and other ancient stargazers saw forms in the host of stars. A few that were bright and close together would suggest the framework of a pattern; three stars in a line might suggest a spear, or a shepherd's staff, or a belt; four in a rectangle might bring to mind the outline of the body of an animal, or a box, or the positions of the hands and feet of a man. Very bright stars would tend to suggest eyes staring down. The lesser stars would serve to fill in the details of a figure.

After this fashion the sky was peopled with men and women and animals, hunters, charioteers, fish, serpents, bulls, rams, ships, altars, weapons, and birds. Since the sky was considered an important and holy locality, the figures were named after the notable demigods, monsters, and divinities of mythology and religion.

THE CONSTELLATION SAGITTARIUS, THE CENTAUR-ARCHER
Shepherds of the Euphrates valley, studying the stars while their flocks grazed by night, peopled the heavens with gods and demigods, as well as men, women, animals and other familiar objects. From these imaginative creations of the ancients we get many of the names of the various astronomical bodies.

This custom eventually gave rise to the belief that the various star-patterns, or constellations, as they are called, actually *were* the heroes and beasts of mythology, given immortality in the heavens.

The constellations were only the result of centuries of man's imagination playing with the chance patterns of the stars as they appear from this earth. Today we have difficulty in seeing the same forms, even as forms in wallpaper appear differently to different people. Nevertheless, the constellations were very helpful to early astronomy in that they served as signs and guide posts. The ancient shepherds found it easier to remember a particular star because it represented the tooth of a horse or the head of an arrow. Moreover, by growing familiar with set patterns, they became more able to note changes in those patterns.

WANDERERS AMONG THE STARS

One of the first fruits of man's knowledge of the patterns of the stars was the discovery that, while the vast majority remained stationary with respect to one another, certain bright stars moved from night to night and from season to season. The shepherds called these "the old-sheep stars," the chief companions of "the old sheep," the sun, since even as he, they slowly moved through the fixed stars. The Greeks eventually called them the planets, or wanderers, and that is the name by which we know them. The brightest evening and morning "star," Venus, was probably discovered first. There followed Jupiter, Saturn, Mars, and finally Mercury, a planet that can be seen for only a few moments at sunrise and sunset, and then only on certain days. Its discovery constitutes an undying testimonial to the patience and sharp eyes of the early shepherd astronomers.

With these men astronomy ceased to be a matter of chance observations of startling occurrences and obvious changes; it became a customary matter of systematic study. A father would hand down his knowledge of the sky to his sons and grandsons. In this fashion there came into being a technique of study suitable to the slow and stately progress of the heavens. A shepherd was able to say, "See, the yellow old-sheep star (Jupiter) passes near

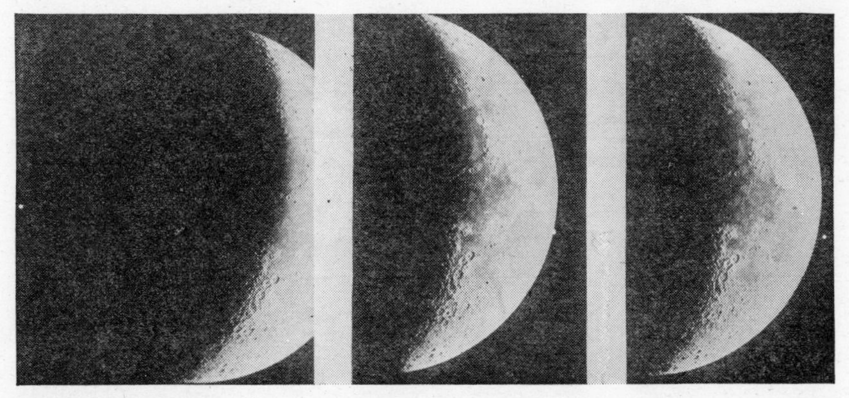

Courtesy Yerkes Observatory

CONJUNCTION OF THE MOON AND A STAR

The white dot at the extreme left is Aldebaran just before immersion. In the center the star may be seen as it reappeared, and at the right as it looked immediately after reappearance. Ancients believed the passage of a star behind the moon portended evil.

the angry red eye of the Scorpion; in my father's day it passed closer to the sting. But in his father's day it passed near the eye, even as it does now. There is an order in the wanderings of the old-sheep star; after a number of years he returns to the beginning of his old path and begins to travel it anew."

The old sheep, the sun, was studied in the same way. The constellation that rose in the east just before the sun was noted; the constellation that appeared in the west just after sunset was observed. Thus the shepherd was able to reason, "The rising of the fish (the constellation Pisces) warns us today of the coming of the old sheep; the terrible bull (the constellation Taurus) follows him down into the west. Six months ago, when the old sheep was elsewhere, I observed that the ram (the constellation Aries) was between the fish and the bull. Indeed, in the memory of my fathers, it has always been there. So now the old sheep must be in the same place as the ram, although we cannot see the ram because of his brightness. Let us hope they do not quarrel."

Courtesy Yerkes Observatory

THE CONSTELLATIONS OF THE ZODIAC
From a compilation made in 1520.

In the course of many centuries it was discovered that the wanderers in the sky—the sun, moon, and planets—were never seen far to the north or the south. Mars never came close to the polestar, Venus never crossed the Dipper. They kept to a broad band of constellations, which forms the equator of the sky, and was called the zodiac. The twelve constellations, or vague star-patterns, that make up the band, were called the signs of the zodiac. The early shepherds made their eyes see twelve constellations, instead of eleven or thirteen, in order that the constellations might conform in number to the months of the year—they had chosen an arbitrary and convenient number of months for the year. A year consisted of the length of time it took the sun to pass through all the signs of the zodiac.

The body of astronomical knowledge built up by the shepherds and other early observers constituted an invaluable heritage for mankind. It gave future students a chart to find their way through the confused patterns of the stars and the planets. It was man's first grand effort to orient himself in the universe. Indeed, the very word "orient" means "to turn toward the east." The stars were not only interesting subjects for study and mythological speculation; they also provided men with signs and guide posts for making their way about in the world. The polestar infallibly indicated the north; the same constellation gleamed down on one side of a mountain as on the other; the early Phoenician skippers dared occasionally to lose sight of land, because they had a knowledge of the sky.

THE UNIVERSE IN A BOX

The body of astronomical information gathered by the shepherds was expanded, refined, further systematized, and recorded by the men of Babylonia. They adopted a year of 360 days, adding an extra month every few years to keep their calendar from getting seriously out of order. For each year they made accurate predictions of the phases of the moon and the motions of the planets and inscribed those predictions on clay tablets. They even mastered the schedule of that dreaded phenomenon, the eclipse; they discovered that the moon returns to a starting posi-

Courtesy Yerkes Observatory

THE CHALDEANS' IDEA OF THE UNIVERSE
The sky was held in its place by a great rim of mountains.

tion in the heavens in the course of eighteen years and eleven days. Thus, knowing the date of one eclipse, they were enabled to predict the next time the moon would obscure the sun, or the earth's shadow the moon. However, they did not yet realize the cause of the latter; they did not know that the earth cast a shadow.

Having considerable knowledge of earth and sky they sought to organize it. They depicted the whole universe as a box. The floor was the earth, with central snowy mountains serving as the source of the Euphrates. The sides consisted of much higher mountains, which in turn supported the top of the box. The top was the sky. In it were fixed the stars. The whole box was perhaps pictured as being tucked away in a corner of the home of the great gods; perhaps man's thought was satisfied not to go beyond its six sides.

The early Egyptians had much the same view. Only they made the box oblong, modeling it after the shape of their own narrow land along the fertile Nile. This mighty river they pictured as running through a great gulley that went from one end of the box to the other. Round about the land was a band of sea, and from the other side of the sea the heavens rose in a great dome or roof, from which the lamps that were the stars were hung on cables.

These pictures of the universe now seem crude and childish. Their most obvious fault is the complacent way they take for granted that the observer's own country is the center of everything, a tendency that man has always had a hard time in outgrowing. However, the person of today knows the right answers to all the obscure problems that perplexed the ancients, and is therefore apt to underestimate the difficulties. How were the ancients to know that the stars were as big as, or bigger than, the sun? They looked much smaller. How were the ancients to know that the earth was a sphere suspended without support in space? They would have labeled such a notion as nonsense, since their daily experience taught them that objects without support fall immediately to the ground. How were they to know that the earth was round? Anyone could see it was flat. Truth is seldom

Courtesy Yerkes Observatory

THE EGYPTIAN BOAT OF THE SUN

obvious and often startling. The truths of astronomy are more than startling; they are paradoxical. Man had to revise his whole concept of matter before he could accept them. Therefore, the ancient notion of a box-shaped universe was by no means ridiculous. It at least fitted some of the known facts.

Nevertheless, it did not explain them all in a satisfactory manner. It had a hard time explaining how the sun and stars got under the solid earth in the course of their daily revolution. It did not tell how the planets moved among the stars. It did not say what was outside the box. Centuries of attempts to get around these difficulties led eventually to our modern point of view, which pictures the earth as a mote in an immeasurably vast universe. Even today we have not satisfactorily solved the problem of the sides of the box. We do not know whether the universe is boundless or bounded, or indeed, if the question has any answer at all. Such unanswered questions may accompany man forever in his endless quest for knowledge and truth.

Courtesy Buffalo Museum of Science

EGYPT, WHERE THE GREEKS LEARNED TO APPLY MATHEMATICS TO ASTRONOMY

THE GREEKS PUT THEIR MINDS TO WORK

The practical knowledge of the heavens, gained by the shepherds and consolidated by the Babylonians, filtered across the island-fretted Mediterranean to where a new spirit of free and sceptical inquiry was being born. A man named Thales went to Egypt. He studied the methods of the swarthy, somber surveyors of the Nile farmlands and generalized them into the beginnings of geometry, a name which means "the measuring of the earth." He accepted the general picture of the universe in a box, but conceived of the earth as a flat disk floating on water. Another Greek, Anaximander, changed the disk to a flattened cylinder. Yet another, Anaximenes, pictured the earth as floating in air rather than water. Slowly these men were cutting out from under the earth the props that the ancients had considered necessary. Anaximander was one of the first men to maintain that the stars move around the earth in great perfect circles which have the polestar as the mark of their axis.

THE MUSIC OF THE SPHERES

However, even the Greeks did not eliminate all magic and mysticism from astronomy. Pythagoras of Samos, who lived about five hundred years before Christ, believed that *number* was the basis of the universe. He considered that ten was the perfect number and therefore tried to reduce the universe to ten bodies. Since the five known planets, together with the earth, the moon, and the sun, totaled only eight, he lumped all the fixed stars together for the ninth, and then hypothesized an unseen "counter-earth" to make up ten.

In order to explain why the various heavenly bodies moved without falling, Pythagoras pictured each as being imbedded in a transparent crystal sphere. The fixed stars were on the outside and the earth at the center of these spheres, which were arranged like a nest of boxes. The movement of the crystal spheres was the cause of a wondrous music; they sounded the chord of the universe.

ANCIENTS FEARED ECLIPSES

A battle between the Medes and Lydians was arrested by a solar eclipse.

Courtesy Yerkes Observatory

These theories seem unnecessarily artificial and poetic, yet they represented a great advance. They were the first serious attempt to explain why the planets did not fall, why the heavenly bodies moved in circles. If Pythagoras had stuck to matters of experience he would probably have thought the earth flat; but because he sought after perfection, he pictured the earth as a sphere, and thus hit on the approximate truth.

Other Greeks adopted Pythagoras' general views, after weeding out much of the mystical element. The main difficulties they encountered were the movements of the planets Venus and Mercury. These disturbing bodies did not circle the earth neatly.

JUNO AND PALLAS GOING TO THE ASSISTANCE OF THE GREEKS
Greek poets represented the gods as living in the sky.

Instead, they moved both backward and forward, and never were seen very far away from the sun. The simplest way of explaining these movements was to assume that they revolved around the sun. This step was taken by a man named Heraclides. Others, however, did not follow him. Heraclides was also one of the first men to maintain that the earth rotated once every day and that the stars only seemed to move in circles during that time. This view became general.

WHAT IS THE CENTER OF THE UNIVERSE?

Aristarchus of Samos, who lived in the third century before Christ, anticipated our modern notions in an even more startling fashion. The first part of his work was practical. By observing eclipses of the moon and certain other phenomena, he deduced that the sun is about seven times as big as the earth. Seven was much too small a figure, but it was a step in the right direction. Considering that he worked with the crudest instruments, he could not have hoped for results more accurate.

Having proved that the sun was larger than the earth, Aristarchus made a bold step: he took the sun as the center of the universe, the point around which all the planets, *and the earth,*

THE DESCENT OF PALLAS OVER ITHACA

revolve. This view retained the advantages of Heraclides' theory and also helped to explain some of the irregularities in the movements of the other planets, Mars, Jupiter, and Saturn. However, it put a tremendous strain on man's imagination: he not only had to conceive of the solid earth as moving at high speed, he also had to believe that the high speed did not disturb the atmosphere or produce the slightest noticeable vibration or shaking. It was like telling a man he could ride in a chariot and not know he was moving.

Nevertheless, Aristarchus' fellow investigators and philosophers would not ultimately have balked at the fact, paradoxical as it seemed. They gave his theory fair consideration and then proceeded to disprove it, like good modern scientists, by experimentation. Most of them had long discarded the theory that the stars are set in the surface of a sphere; they conceived of them as being, like the planets, bodies at varying distances. If the earth moves, they argued, then the nearer stars would seem to change position in relation to the farther ones. There would be an apparent shifting in the patterns of the stars due to the actual movement of the earth. Therefore, they looked closely at the stars. They determined their positions at different times of the year with crude sextants. They did not find any shift. Hence, they decided that Aristarchus was wrong. He defended himself by arguing that the stars were at such great distances that their shift was too slight to be seen. They dismissed this explanation as being overly artificial. Aristarchus' opinion has today been proved true, but his contemporaries would have been bad scientists if they had accepted it. The evidence was insufficient. The Greeks have been criticized for devoting too much time to theorizing and too little to scientific observation. This is at most only relatively true; they did well with their crude instruments.

THE GREEK KNOWLEDGE IS CONSOLIDATED

Before barbarian invasions and internal discord had plunged into chaos the Roman Empire of which the Greek states became a part, the great School of Alexandria collected and unified almost all the facts known about the heavens. In the second century A. D., Claudius Ptolemy published an encyclopedia of astronomical information that was afterwards known under the Arabic name *Almagest.* The moving spirit behind this volume, the man whose inclusive views it chiefly expressed, did his work three centuries before. His name was Hipparchus.

He was a great organizer. He revised the calendar of his day and prepared tables to illustrate the movements of the planets. He catalogued the positions of over a thousand stars, dividing them up into six classes, according to their brightness. He invented the astrolabe, a device for measuring the angular altitude of heavenly bodies. Like the others, he discarded Aristarchus' theory; the earth was the center of his system of the universe. He accounted for the irregularities in the movements of the planets by devising the theory of epicycles. Imagine a bit of mud on the rim of a rotating wheel. Then imagine the whole wheel being carried in a great circle around a central point. That was Hipparchus' theory. The earth was the central point. The planet was the bit of mud, moving at the same time in two circles, one small and one great. It was a complicated idea, but it explained the known facts.

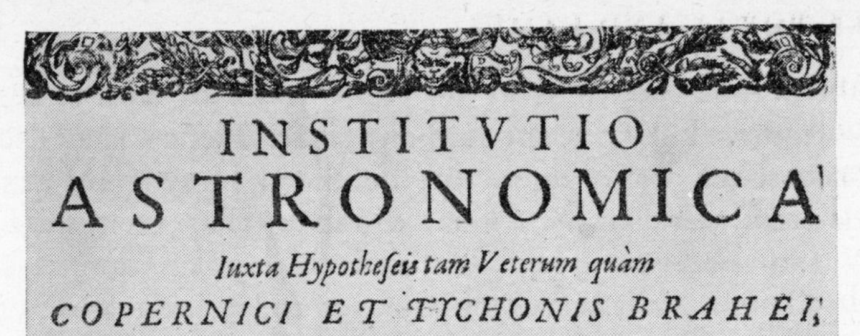

INSTITVTIO ASTRONOMICA

Iuxta Hypotheseis tam Veterum quàm

COPERNICI ET TYCHONIS BRAHEI,

CAPVT PROOEMIALE.

QVAM Plato Astronomiam, alij plærique Veterum etiam Astrologiam dixere. Ex quo autem Chaldæi suas nugas in Doctrinam hanc invexerunt, est ferè Astrologiæ nomen tributum Genethliacæ (quæ & Iudiciaria ferè appellatur.) Astronomia verò nuncupata est, quæ in contemplandis, dimetiendisque Astrorum motu, distantia, ordine, magnitudine, luce, adjunctisque cæteris consimilibus occupatur.

Originem ipsi fecit admiratio; tum nimirùm, cùm homines præter splendorem, varietatem, multitudinem, amplitudinem Siderum, obseruârunt in ipsis motum tam constantem, tam regularem, tam incessanter diei, ac noctis, æstatisque, & hyemis vicissitudines inducentem.

Commendat illam summoperè dignitas subiectæ materiæ, quæ non alia est, quam amplissima, nobilissimáque totius Mundi regio; Cælestis nempe, quam homines vt contemplentur, tum obtinere oculos, tum erectos habere vultus à Sapientioribus dicuntur.

Certant de eius inuentione, & antiquitate Babylonij, ob authorem Belum; Ægyptij, ob Mercurium; Mauri, ob Atlantem, & Herculem; Græci, ob Iouem, Orpheum, & Atreum; Scythæ, ob Prometheum, &c.

Quorum supersunt Obseruationes, antiquissimi Babylonij sunt; nimirùm habet Ptolomæus aliquot Eclipseis ab iis obseruatas annis paullò plus ante Christum septingentis. Quod de vlterioribus memorant, aut nullo probatur monumento, aut fabulam sapit.

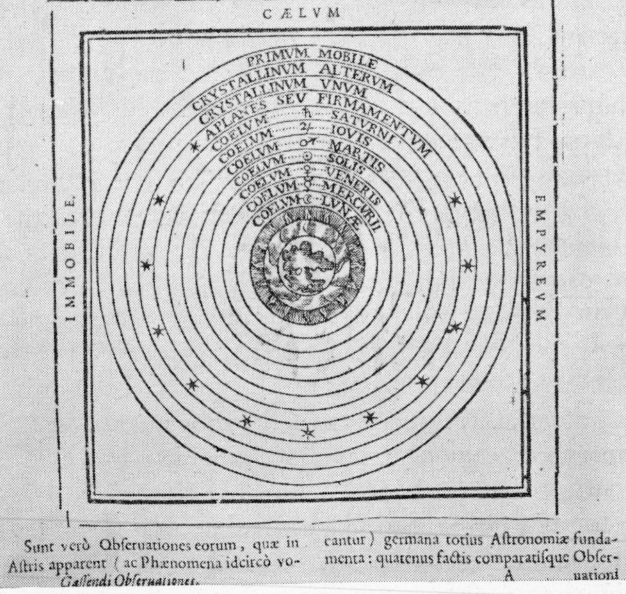

Sunt verò Obseruationes eorum, quæ in Astris apparent (ac Phænomena idcircò vocantur) germana totius Astronomiæ fundamenta: quatenus factis comparatisque Obser-

Gassendi Obseruationes. A uationi

Courtesy Yerkes Observatory

PTOLEMY'S DRAWING OF THE SOLAR SYSTEM

Reproduction of the first page of a book by Gassendi, published in 1658 A. D. Note Ptolemy's order of the orbits.

Eratosthenes, another early member of the Alexandrian school, did much to give man an idea of the limits of his environment. He measured the size of the earth. First, at Alexandria, he determined the elevation of the sun at noon on the day of the summer solstice. On the same date but in a different year, he made the same observation at Syene, Egypt. He discovered a difference between the elevations observed at the two different localities, and he measured that difference. Knowing the distance between Alexandria and Syene, he was able to determine the circumference of the earth. His answer was within eight hundred miles of the truth, a lasting testimonial to the accuracy of his work.

The legacy the ancient astronomers left for the future was no slight one. When Columbus sailed into the uncharted West, certain men had been believing for two thousand years that the earth was round. The spirits of Pythagoras, Aristarchus, and Eratosthenes sailed with him. The *Almagest* of Ptolemy preserved for future students the observations of the Babylonians and the carefully reasoned theories of the Greeks.

MEN OF ANOTHER AGE TAKE UP THE TORCH

As the Western world struggled through the confusions that came with the fall of Rome, there was small advance in astronomical knowledge. Whatever work was done was due mainly to the activities of the Arabs, a people who had something of the traditions of the early shepherds. Moreover, the Arabs preserved the *Almagest* as well as other books of the ancients. They named or renamed many stars, and it is difficult to estimate the extent of their work. Be that as it may, the Western world ceased to a large extent its studies of the sky.

Then, in the sixteenth century, a studious man named Nikolaus Koppernigk reaffirmed the old idea of Aristarchus, claiming that the sun was the center of the universe. He had no better evidence for his view than had his ancient intellectual forebear. His chief argument was that it was a simpler view—it needed fewer epicycles to explain it. However, it did need some epicycles. Man was still trying to reduce the movements of the heavenly bodies to circles and combinations of circles. Koppernigk, more

NIKOLAUS KOPPERNIGK

Courtesy Yerkes Observatory

famous under his Latinized name, Copernicus, was one of the first to take the torch from the ancients. The new spirit of Europe was soon shown by his follower, Giordano Bruno, who maintained that the universe was an infinite scattering of stars, in which our own earth and sun were but tiny bits of matter. For some reason this idea, abhorrent to the Babylonians and the early Greeks, had become acceptable. The evidence for it was slight, but infinity was coming into fashion.

Shortly after Koppernigk died, there was born in Denmark the man who was to study the stars more accurately than had anyone before him, Tycho Brahe. An imaginative boy, he early developed an interest in astronomy. His uncle wanted him to become a lawyer, but young Brahe preferred to look at the stars. He stole from

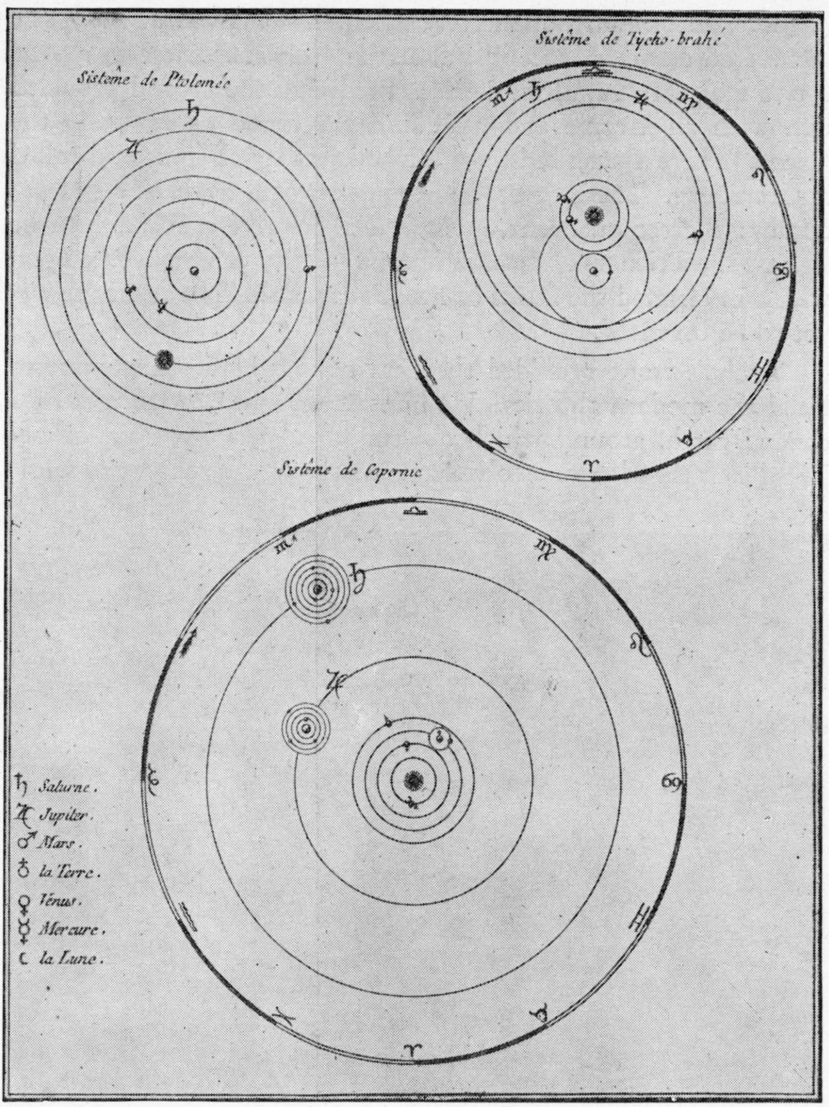

Courtesy Yerkes Observatory

THE SOLAR SYSTEM ACCORDING TO PTOLEMY, BRAHE, AND KOPPERNIGK

his bed and peered thoughtfully at the stars. Even as a boy, he discovered errors in accepted tables and charts. Later in life he found means to fulfill his desires. Frederick the Second provided him with an income and gave him the island of Hven in the Sound. There Tycho built a great observatory of stone and called it Uraniborg. There he used instruments of a novel size and accuracy: a great quadrant, along whose massive movable arm he sighted the altitudes of various stars; a mighty celestial globe upon which he charted the fruits of his observations. The telescope was yet to be invented.

Tycho's work provided the data upon which others were to build the modern theories. He himself returned to the idea of a central earth, around which the sun revolved; however, he believed that the planets revolved around the sun. Tycho was a sensi-

TYCHO BRAHE

Courtesy Yerkes Observatory

JOHANN KEPLER

Courtesy Yerkes Observatory

tive man. His face had been mutilated in a duel; to conceal this he wore an artificial nose made of gold and silver. His wife was a peasant girl. Typical of the difficult rebirth of science was his lonely life in Uraniborg, the "fortress of the heavens."

A NEW THEORY AND A NEW INSTRUMENT

Tycho's accurate observations were not lost to the world. Johann Kepler, one of his students, used them to solve the problem of the wanderers of the skies, the problem that had first been set by the early shepherds. Kepler sought to prove that the planets moved in circles, but his calculations would not agree with

Tycho's figures. He tried to work out a suitable theory of epicycles; but, without bringing in tremendous complexities, it still would not agree with Tycho's figures. Finally the truth dawned upon him. The planets did not move in circles at all! They moved in ellipses, with the sun at one of the foci. Only ellipses would satisfy the observations made by Tycho. The perfection of form exhibited by the circle had misled men for ages. By patient study Kepler arrived at the truer view, which formed a bulwark to the theory of Aristarchus and Koppernigk. Man was beginning to realize his place in the universe.

At about the same time, an instrument was being devised that was to revolutionize astronomical methods of observation. That instrument was the telescope.

For some time it had been known that a lens would magnify nearby objects; spectacles were commonly constructed to aid people who had difficulty in reading and seeing things close at hand. However, since a single lens does not make a telescope and since the very idea of the telescope was foreign to man's mind, it took an accident to discover it. Tradition tells us that at the beginning of the seventeenth century a Dutch spectaclemaker happened to be holding a lens in either hand. Turning momentarily from his work, he glanced idly through the nearer one. There was nothing unusual about his action. Spectaclemakers had done it countless times. But this time there was a difference. The two lenses happened to be in a line with one another; the line happened to point through an open window toward a church tower; the lenses happened to be just the right distance apart. As a result he received a shock. It looked to him as though the church tower had rushed up upon him; it was much closer than it should be. He had discovered the telescope.

The principle of the instrument was relatively simple. The first lens cast an image of the church tower; in other words, it formed close at hand a visual miniature of the church tower, an image that the spectaclemaker could have seen directly by darkening the room and putting a piece of paper behind the first lens for a screen. The second lens magnified that image, precisely as though it were a nearby object. When the spectaclemaker recovered from his surprise, he set the two lenses in a tube in order that he might permanently keep them the right distance apart. He had constructed the first telescope.

News of this strange instrument spread abroad and came to the ears of a progressive Florentine scientist named Galileo who, knowing much more of optics than the lucky spectaclemaker, immediately constructed one for his own use. But he did not confine his observations to church towers. His object was to unravel the secrets of the sky. When he was sure of the principles, he began constructing more powerful telescopes, using larger and more carefully ground lenses. When he turned these instruments upon the heavens, he made discoveries that threw the intellectual world of his day into confusion.

The intellectual world had forgotten that the *Almagest* and other Greek writings were only a record of progressive discoveries

GALILEO, INVENTOR OF THE TELESCOPE

Courtesy Yerkes Observatory

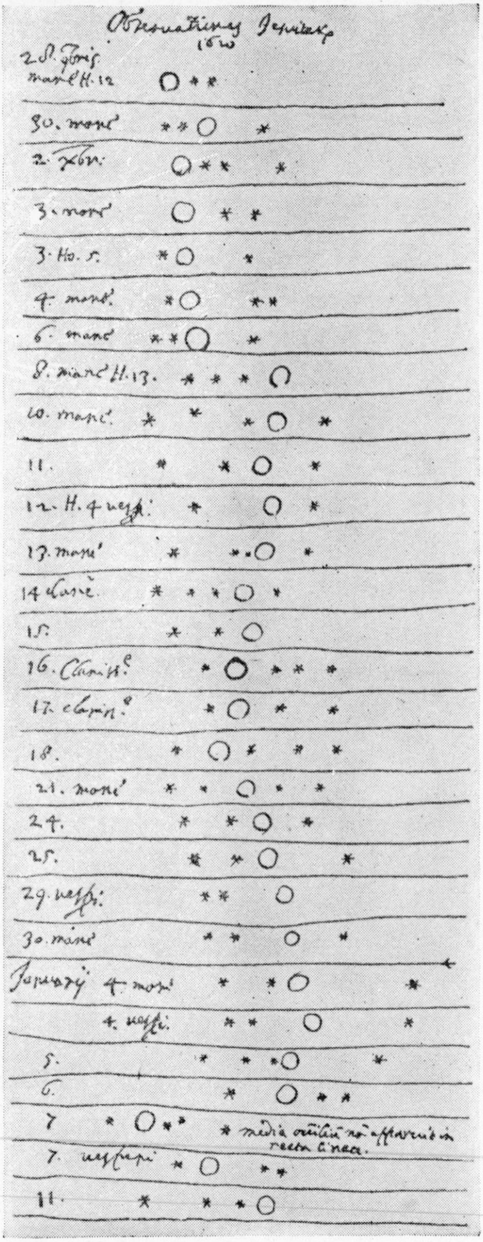

Courtesy Yerkes Observatory

GALILEO'S DIAGRAMS OF THE POSITIONS OF THE MOONS OF JUPITER

and unfinished business. Under the influence of a stern and conservative church, they had come to believe that the unfinished business was a statement of final and ultimate truths. Galileo discovered that there were mountains on the moon; this indicated that the moon was not a smooth-surfaced sphere. Galileo discovered that there were four little moons revolving around the planet Jupiter; this proved that there were more bodies in the universe than the ten upon which Pythagoras had originally insisted. Galileo turned his telescope upon the sun and, protecting his eye with some such thing as smoked glass, discovered that there were dark spots upon it; and he dared to affirm that the sun was not undefiled fire.

Men were afraid of new knowledge. They were angry with it. They did not want to face the task of reconstruction. One of Galileo's learned colleagues refused point blank to put his eye to the telescope. Another went to the Grand Duke and attempted to prove on logical grounds that Jupiter could not have any moons at all; certainly not four. Not all men took this unreasonable attitude. The Grand Duke of Tuscany provided Galileo with money to carry on his investigations. But eventually Galileo encountered opposition from the Church which, he offended by writing a satire. He was hailed before a tribunal and forced to recant many of his scientific opinions, among them Koppernigk's belief that the earth revolved around the sun.

A NEW PHYSICS FOR A NEW ASTRONOMY

The aged Galileo may have recanted his views, but no inquisition could make the world recant. The spirit of free and skeptical inquiry was once again abroad.

As we have noted, early man's conception of matter hindered him from arriving at the truth about the heavens. Experience taught him that bodies fell to the earth. He did not seek to discover the cause of their falling; he took it for granted that falling was an ultimate property of all bodies. The more sophisticated Greeks found it hard to understand why the planets did not slow down and cease to move. They believed that some constant force, such as that exerted by the crystal spheres, was necessary to keep them moving. Kepler's laws did not explain planetary movement. They only described Galileo's discovery that, except for wind resistance, all bodies fall to earth at the same speed, but did not state the cause of falling. A new physics, or knowledge of matter, was needed to explain the new astronomy, from which the central earth and crystal spheres had vanished.

The firm foundations of the new physics were laid down by the Englishman Isaac Newton. When London was suffering the great plague of the seventeenth century, this man was grappling with the problems of the material universe. He accepted the universe as boundless, a box without sides. Here and there in the infinity of space were the stars and, at one spot, our own sun with its family of planets. Why did they move without appreciably slowing? Because there was nothing to stop them, no friction in space to stay their course. If there were only one sun in the whole universe, how would it move? In a straight line. Why a straight line? Because there would be no outside force to change its course. It would take an outside force to make a body move in a curve. What could be the source of such an outside force? Another sun, or another heavenly body of some sort. Perhaps there was a force of attraction between any two suns, causing them to move toward each other. Perhaps there was an attraction between any two pieces of matter in the universe.

So Newton puzzled and reasoned. If there was an attraction between the sun and the earth, why didn't the earth fall into the sun? Perhaps because the earth was always tending to move away from the sun in a tangent straight line, like a stone swung at the end of a string. And perhaps the pull of the sun was just sufficient to overcome that tendency and make the earth move in

ISAAC NEWTON

Courtesy Yerkes Observatory

a continuous ellipse. Newton conceived, most daringly, that the earth was eternally falling into the sun and eternally moving away from it, and that the two forces, the centrifugal and the centripetal, just balanced one another. Similarly Newton explained why a ball tossed up into the air tends to fall. The tendency was not an innate property of the ball. If there were no earth the ball would keep on moving in a straight line. It was because of the attraction between the earth and the ball. It was because *every body of matter in the universe attracts every other body with a force proportional to the product of their masses and inversely proportional to the square of the distance between them.*

Newton tested his theories by seeing if they were in harmony with the general laws of movement and planetary movement observed by Galileo and Kepler. They were. From his theories and assumptions he could even deduce those observed laws directly.

After Newton, the activities of scientists and astronomers became legion. Indeed, it would take a long time to discuss the many experiments and discoveries that Newton himself made. The great universe was opening to man, a boundless scattering of titanic stars. Every day new telescopic lenses were being ground, new observations were being made, new theories were being pondered. After the foundations were laid, the building began to go up with rapid progress.

THE MYSTERY OF THE STARS' MESSENGER

Light is the messenger of the stars. It brings us all the information we have concerning the universe beyond the atmosphere.

Ancient man had no clear conception of light. Newton thought it consisted of particles. Huygens, his contemporary, believed that it consisted of a wave motion. This latter view gained greater credence. Today scientists believe that both views are partly true.

Some men thought that the movement of light was instantaneous, that it was no sooner emitted by its source than it was received by our eyes. Other men thought that it traveled at a definite speed. Galileo sought to determine this speed by signaling with lanterns from one hilltop to another. He failed, and decided that his method was too crude to check on the speed of light. In 1676,

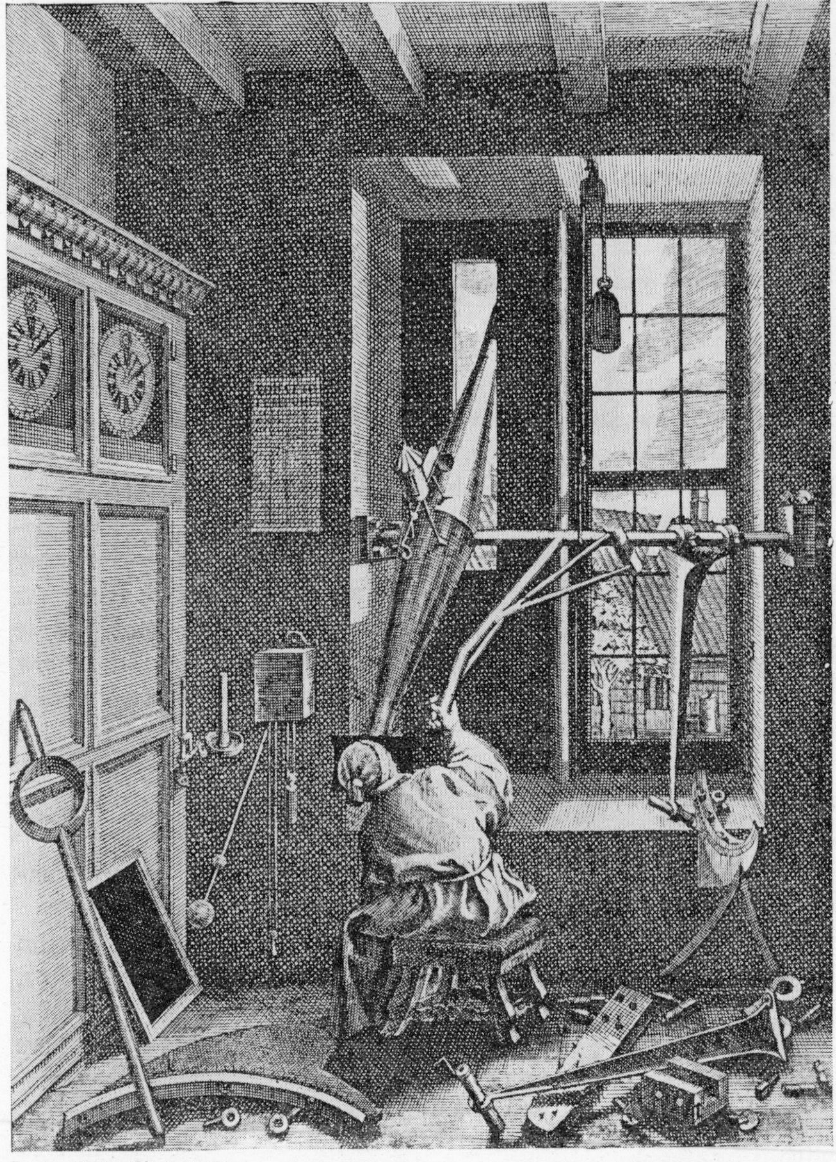

Courtesy Yerkes Observatory

ROEMER'S TELESCOPE, WHICH LED TO THE DISCOVERY OF THE SPEED OF LIGHT

the Danish astronomer Olaus Roemer was studying the eclipses of the moons of Jupiter; he was noting down the exact time at which the moons disappeared behind the mother planet. He noticed that as the earth moved away from Jupiter the eclipses kept occurring a little later each day. When the earth approached Jupiter, the opposite was true. It occurred to him that the difference was due to the time it took light to travel across the great sweep of the earth's orbit. On this assumption he calculated the speed of light and found it to be approximately 190 thousand miles a second. Small wonder that Galileo had failed!

Roemer's determination was very close to the truth. Astronomy was paying back its debt to physics. Newton had given astronomy a new conception of matter and now astronomy was giving physics valuable information about light. The two sciences worked hand in hand.

LIGHT IS A WANDERER

Aristarchus' theory that the earth moved was discarded by his contemporaries because they could see no yearly shift in the relative positions of the stars. Now, armed with the telescope, astronomers considered the evidence anew.

In the eighteenth century James Bradley, a famous English astronomer, took up a different phase of the same problem. He asked himself the question "How can we measure the distances between the earth and the stars?" There was no way of pacing out such distances; there was no way of using a tape measure. This fact, however, gave Bradley no essential difficulty. For a long time man had known how to measure the distances to inaccessible places on earth, such as to rocky islands lying in the midst of offshore reefs. The method was to lay out a straight base line on the nearby shore, and sight a point on the island from each end of the line. Knowing the length of the base line and the angles made with it by the lines of sight, it was possible to calculate the lengths of the lines of sight and thus the distance to the island.

Already astronomers had calculated the distances to the moon, sun, and planets by similar methods. Two men, at places widely

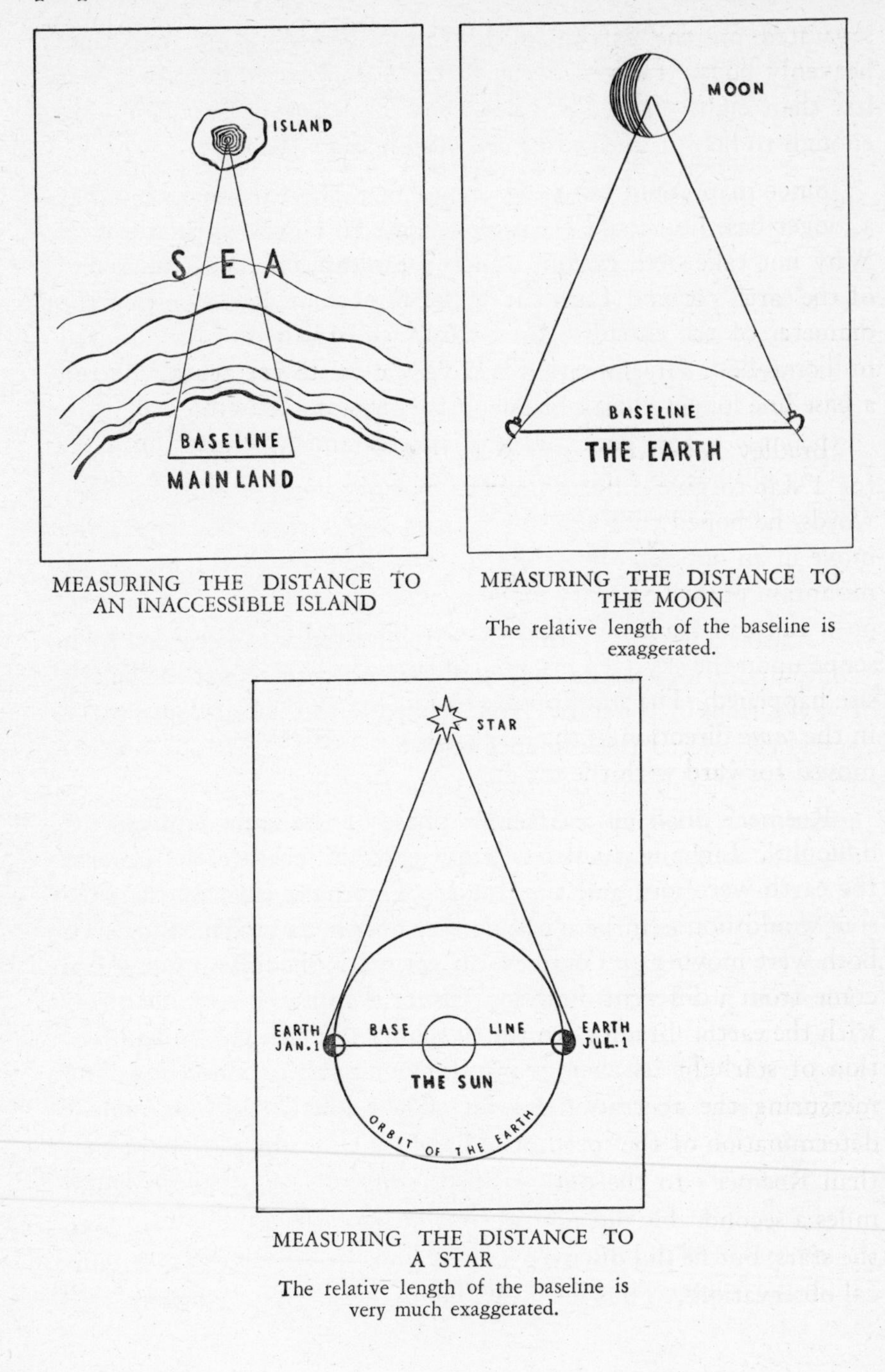

MEASURING THE DISTANCE TO AN INACCESSIBLE ISLAND

MEASURING THE DISTANCE TO THE MOON
The relative length of the baseline is exaggerated.

MEASURING THE DISTANCE TO A STAR
The relative length of the baseline is very much exaggerated.

separated on the earth, would simultaneously sight the same heavenly body. However, the farthest they could get apart was less than eight thousand miles. Such a base line was not long enough to help in measuring the distances to the stars.

Since man could not leave the earth it seemed impossible that a longer base line could be found. Bradley, however, had an idea. Why not take observations of the same star from two extremes of the earth's orbit? Then the length of the base line would be the diameter of the earth's orbit, a distance of almost two hundred million miles. Thus, without leaving the earth, Bradley discovered a base line longer than any possible on the earth itself.

Bradley hoped that this base line would be sufficiently long for a star to give different angles of sight at each end; in other words, he hoped that the star he was observing would appear to move in an opposite direction to that taken by the earth, even as mountain peaks appear to move backward when viewed by a man on a railroad train. With this in mind Bradley turned his telescope upon the sky. To his great surprise he found that the opposite happened. The star appeared to move, all right, but it moved in the *same* direction as the earth. It was as if the mountain peaks moved forward with the train.

Roemer's discovery helped Bradley to explain this unexpected difficulty. Light had a definite speed; so did the earth. If either the earth were motionless or the speed of light infinite, then the star would not seem to move forward with the earth. But since both were moving at a definite rate of speed the light appeared to come from a different direction; the star appeared to move along with the earth. Bradley named this apparent change in the direction of starlight its aberration, which means its wandering. By measuring the aberration he was able to make an independent determination of the speed of light. His determination was closer than Roemer's to the one accepted today—about 186 thousand miles a second. He did not succeed in measuring the distances to the stars, but he did discover a great source of error in astronomical observations. Thus he aided the men that followed him.

WILLIAM HERSCHEL

Courtesy Yerkes Observatory

SOLVING ARISTARCHUS' PROBLEM

Among those who profited from Bradley were the Herschel family—Sir William, his sister Caroline, and his son Sir John. Their work extended over the seventeenth and eighteenth centuries. William worked as a musician, but his real interest in life was astronomy. In 1781 his persistent observations were rewarded by a lucky find. He discovered a new wandering body in the heavens. At first he thought that it was a comet; but careful study of its course showed it to be a planet, the first to be discovered since the days of the sharp-eyed men of Babylonia. It was given the name Uranus. Its discovery won Herschel not only fame, but a pension from the king.

Thereafter he and his sister turned to the problem of stellar distances. They sought to use the method originally suggested by Aristarchus: a search for changes in the relative positions of stars. To simplify their work, they chose pairs of stars that looked to be close together in the heavens—double stars. Since the Herschels assumed that all stars were evenly distributed throughout space, they took for granted that such double stars were not actually close together—they only appeared to be so when viewed from the earth, even as a steeple may be in line with a mountaintop when viewed from a train.

By studying the relative positions of double stars, the Herschels thought to eliminate the effects of aberration. They reasoned that the light from each star would be displaced to the same extent, and that any changes of relative position would therefore be observable in spite of aberration. They were right. Nevertheless,

Courtesy Yerkes Observatory

HERSCHEL'S 40-FOOT TELESCOPE—AN EARLY GIANT

Courtesy Yerkes Observatory

FRIEDRICH BESSEL

they were unable to observe any annual changes in the relative positions of the double stars they studied. They felt that they had failed. Eventually, further research transformed this disappointment into jubilation. It turned out that most double stars actually were neighbors, that they not only seemed but were the same distance from earth. It was found that many double stars revolved around each other—a new proof of Newton's law of the universal attraction between bodies. Another seeming failure had paved the way for discovery.

In 1838 Friedrich Bessel, a German astronomer using Bradley's method, managed to measure the distance to the star called 61 Cygni. Far from finding it a matter of millions of miles, it was a matter of many millions of millions. Indeed, the nearest star ever discovered, Proxima Centauri, is twenty-four million million miles away— a distance so great that it takes light more than four years to travel from it to earth, remembering that light can go seven times around the earth in a second and can come from the moon to the earth in less than two seconds. Small wonder that Aristarchus' colleagues failed to find a shift in the stars! Moreover, the angle that Bessel measured was more than fifty times smaller than the angle of aberration. It is easy to understand why Bradley failed to find what he was after!

MAN'S PICTURE OF THE UNIVERSE

With the growth of astronomical knowledge, man's feelings toward the heavens have changed. No longer does he feel, like the Babylonian, that a snug little sky bends close above the mountaintops. No longer does he listen, like the Pythagorean, for the music of a perfect and limited number of invisible crystal

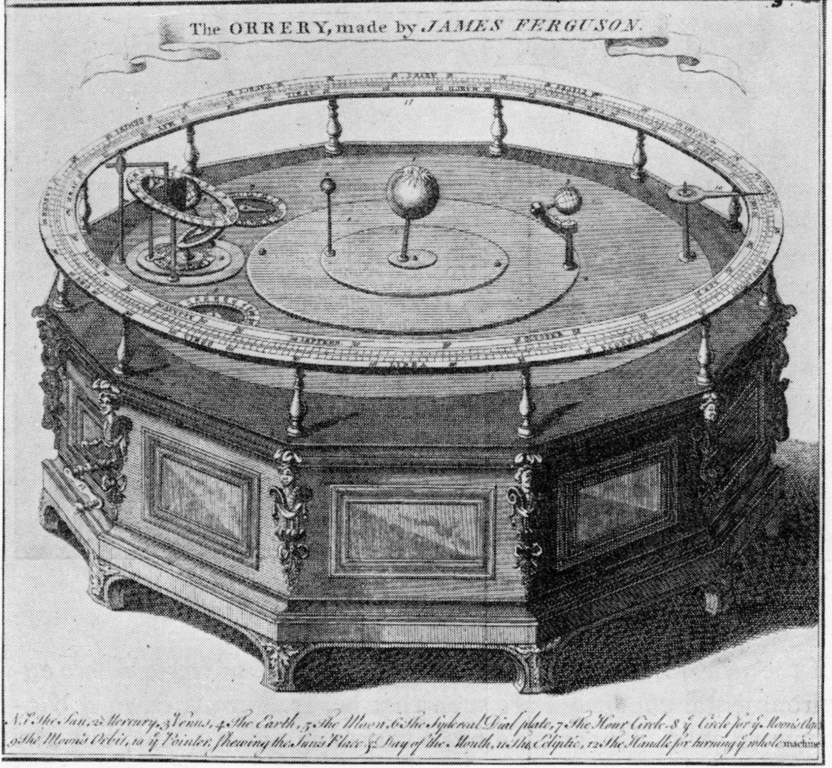

Courtesy Yerkes Observatory

AN EIGHTEENTH-CENTURY MODEL OF THE SOLAR SYSTEM

spheres. No longer does he think of the stars as lamps hung on cables. No longer does he see mighty gods in each planet and star. No longer does he feel that he sits serene and all-important in the center of a diamond-studded globe hardly bigger than the flat disk of earth itself. Today he knows that he is living on the surface of a tiny mote, delicately poised in a vast universe of titanic suns and immeasurable reaches of extra-galactic space. The props have been cut from under earth and sky.

With the new universe has come new understanding. Astronomers and other scientists are studying the behavior of the planets that are earth's brothers, the stars that are great suns, and the other bodies that move through the universe. They are learning about their habits, the ways they move, and the influences they exert on each other. Man is arriving at a better understanding

Courtesy American Museum of Natural History

THE HAYDEN PLANETARIUM IN NEW YORK

of the world he lives in, the tiny section of the universe where environmental conditions are such that he, frail creature, may continue to exist. Understanding is banishing ancient fear, but awe remains and even increases. Man is only beginning to realize the number of limitless mysteries that surround him and give to his existence a sense of adventurous expectancy.

Only in one place does man still picture the sky as an inverted bowl—in the planetarium. Almost as long as man has studied the universe, he has sought to draw diagrams or make models of the universe. In these things can be traced his changing conceptions of the cosmos. First came pictures carved in stone and charts inscribed on papyrus. Then star maps such as those used with the astrolabe. Then the armillary sphere, a skeleton globe made up of interlocking rims, each rim representing the course of a heavenly body. Then models of the solar system, in which little metal planets revolved on rods around a central metal sun. Finally came the Zeiss planetarium, in which a central projector casts points of light upon a hemispherical ceiling, to be viewed by the audience from below. The points of light represent stars and other heavenly bodies. The projector was devised by Dr. Oscar von Miller of Munich. Today there are several in the United States. Within the circular walls of the planetarium, men may watch the movements of the sun, moon, planets, and stars as if in a miniature sky. In one moment, years of planetary movement may flash before their eyes. Thus has the inverted bowl survived—not as a symbol of truth, but as a device for furthering man's understanding of the infinite and exciting universe around him.

Courtesy Adler Planetarium, Chicago

THE PROJECTOR USED IN A PLANETARIUM

Courtesy Yerkes Observatory

THE STARS CAN BE COUNTED!

You can know the approximate number of stars in this picture by counting those in one square inch, then multiplying this figure by the total number of square inches in the picture. Astronomers use a similar method in counting the stars in the sky.

A STARRY NIGHT

ASTRONOMY WITHOUT A TELESCOPE

AND WHAT OF THE NIGHT? From horizon to horizon there sweeps the glory, the beauty, and the splendor of the silent stars—argosies of silver spray that twinkle at us from the spangled bowl of heaven. To us who watch from beneath the smoky, dusty skies of cities, those lights are dimmed, or even hidden; but seen from the clearness and solitude of mountain peaks and lonely plains they are distant worlds that sparkle brilliantly at men who strive patiently to solve their riddles.

Even without the aid of telescopes and perfect skies, we can aid in the solution of some of the riddles the universe has put to us. By naked-eye observations of meteors, the discovery of "new" stars, and the study of such peculiar phenomena as the aurora and the zodiacal light, we can aid science, and in so doing gain the enjoyment of a fascinating hobby. However, to do work of value, we must first learn to understand the relationships of the various heavenly bodies to each other as they appear to us in the sky. To create a basis for such an understanding, we will introduce this section with a consideration of the relative *apparent* motions of the sun, moon, and stars, and follow it by a brief discussion of the major constellations.

Courtesy Yerkes Observatory

THE PATH OF A METEOR THAT PASSED IN THE NIGHT

STARS AND PLANETS WE CAN SEE

As we watch from night to night, our eyes see a multitude of stars of varying brightness and color. These range from brilliant points in the sky, which look almost like arc lamps or electric bulbs viewed from a distance, to momentary glimmerings of light so faint that we can hardly be sure we have really seen them. Estimates indicate that there are about five thousand of these stars visible to the naked eye under good conditions. Since the earth is a sphere, and we can observe from only one side of it at a time, this means then that not more than twenty-five hundred stars are visible at any one time. Thus, we find that the usual impression of "millions" of stars being visible in the heavens is an optical illusion, brought about largely by the close packing of certain major groups of relatively bright stars. Of course, the application of the telescope and photography brings vastly many more stars into view; but for our purposes we will consider only those visible to the naked eye, or that may be seen with small opera glasses.

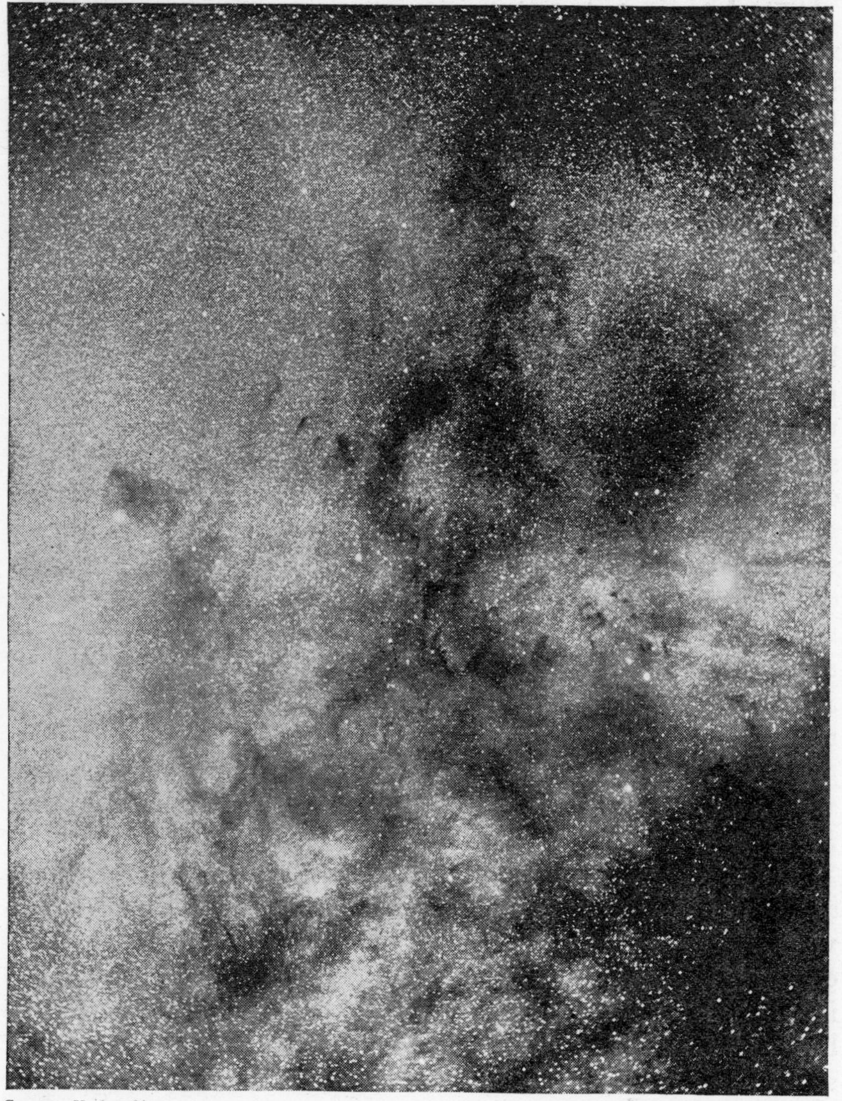

Courtesy Yerkes Observatory

A SECTION OF THE MILKY WAY

This picture of the region north of Theta Ophiuchi shows the rich detail of the starry field contrasted with obscuring matter.

The vast majority of stars are quite comparable in average size, brightness, and physical constitution to our own sun, which is itself a star. However, other stars are at infinitely greater distances from the earth than is our sun, and thus appear much fainter. If we watch any given group of stars all night, we will find that it will not change its position with respect to other groups of stars; but that the whole hemisphere of stars has a uniform apparent motion from east to west during the night.

In addition to the stars, there are often visible in the night sky five brilliant objects which are frequently confused with the brighter stars in the constellations. These are the five brightest planets: Mercury, Venus, Mars, Jupiter, and Saturn. These objects, though often brighter than the brightest stars, are, however, much smaller. They are illuminated by reflection of the light from our own sun, and do not shine by their own light. Their great brightness, although they are smaller than the stars, is due to their proximity to the earth; their distances are of the same order of magnitude as that of the sun from us. They are, of course, much smaller than our "Day Star." The planets can be differentiated from the stars by their relatively rapid motions; the stars appear almost "fixed" with respect to each other, but from night to night and month to month, we can see the planets change their positions with respect to the constellations. Sometimes they disappear from our sight, only to reappear a few months later, and go through the whole cycle once again.

There are only about twenty of the brightest stars in the whole sky which might be mistaken for planets; fifteen of these are visible in the northern hemisphere. However, the stars lack apparent motion relative to each other and are different from the planets in color and luster. Also, to observers in the North Temperate latitudes, the planets will always be between the zenith and the southern horizon. They will never appear in the northern part of the sky.

REAL AND APPARENT MOTIONS

The ". . . inconstant moon, that monthly changes in her circled orb," is as well known to us as the sun. Though the moon, when full, appears nearly the same size as the sun, it is actually much

Photo by Frank M. Preucil

THE FULL MOON

Its seas, craters and mountains are visible to the unaided eye on clear nights.

smaller; but it is so close to the earth that its diameter seems about the same as that of the sun, which is larger but farther away. In effect the moon is a small planet, and is illuminated, as are the other planets and satellites, by the light of the sun. Like the stars, the moon appears to move from east to west in the sky each night. At the same time there is a constant drift of the moon toward the east which causes it to rise and set an hour later each night. Along with this eastward drift, the complete cycle of which takes one lunar month of twenty-eight days, there is the waxing and waning of the moon, followed by invisibility for a few days. This cycle has occurred over the same length of time throughout all recorded

THE CHANGING MOON
Observers on the earth see only that portion of the moon which is illuminated by the sun.

Photo by Frank M. Preucil

history. The change of apparent shape of the moon is due to the varying angle between the light rays which come from the sun to illuminate the moon, and the line of sight joining the observer on the earth with the moon. Thus, at full moon, the sun is directly behind the observer, "in back of" the earth, and illuminates the full disk of the moon we see. At half or crescent phase, the sun is still illuminating a whole hemisphere of the moon, but because of the changed position of the moon with respect to the earth, we see only a portion of that illuminated hemisphere. This assumes the shape of a crescent because of the roughly spherical shape of the moon, upon which the sun's light is falling and being reflected toward the earth.

If we watch the sun, moon, and stars throughout the year, we find they all have other changes in their relative positions aside from those described so far. These changes are cyclic in character, and are repeated in periods of one year. Thus, the moon, in its nightly journey from east to west with the stars, also has a slower motion from west to east *among* the stars, and in one month's time will have completely made the circuit. The sun has a similar motion from west to east among the stars but requires a full year to make the circuit. There is also a north to south shifting of the sun from summer to winter.

The daily east to west motion of all the heavenly bodies is due to the rotation of the earth in the opposite direction; and the monthly variations of the moon are due to its revolution about the earth; and finally, the seasonal eastward motion of the sun is due to the revolution of the earth about the sun. The apparent motions of the planets in the sky with respect to the stars are more irregular than the motions discussed above. These planetary motions occur in intervals of time called "synodic periods," and vary for the different planets; they are due to the combined effect of the planet's own revolution about the sun, and the earth's revolution about the sun.

We have used the term "apparent motion" a number of times. The stars themselves are moving, relative to each other, at high rates of speed; but they are so far from the earth that the angular change in position between any two stars is too small to be determined by the unaided eye within the lifetime of any single individual. Such motions are discovered only by instruments of precision and data extending over long periods of time.

THE CONSTELLATIONS

To judge accurately the changes of position of the sun, moon, and planets with respect to the stars, the observer must have some fixed set of reference points. Basically, these reference points are the "fixed" stars themselves. These stars, particularly the twenty brightest, are usually referred to by classical Arabic names, such as Algol, Vega, and Deneb. These names and the Greek constellation names come from the peoples who were the first systematic observers of the planetary, lunar, and stellar motions. It is obvious that with the large number of stars visible in the sky we should

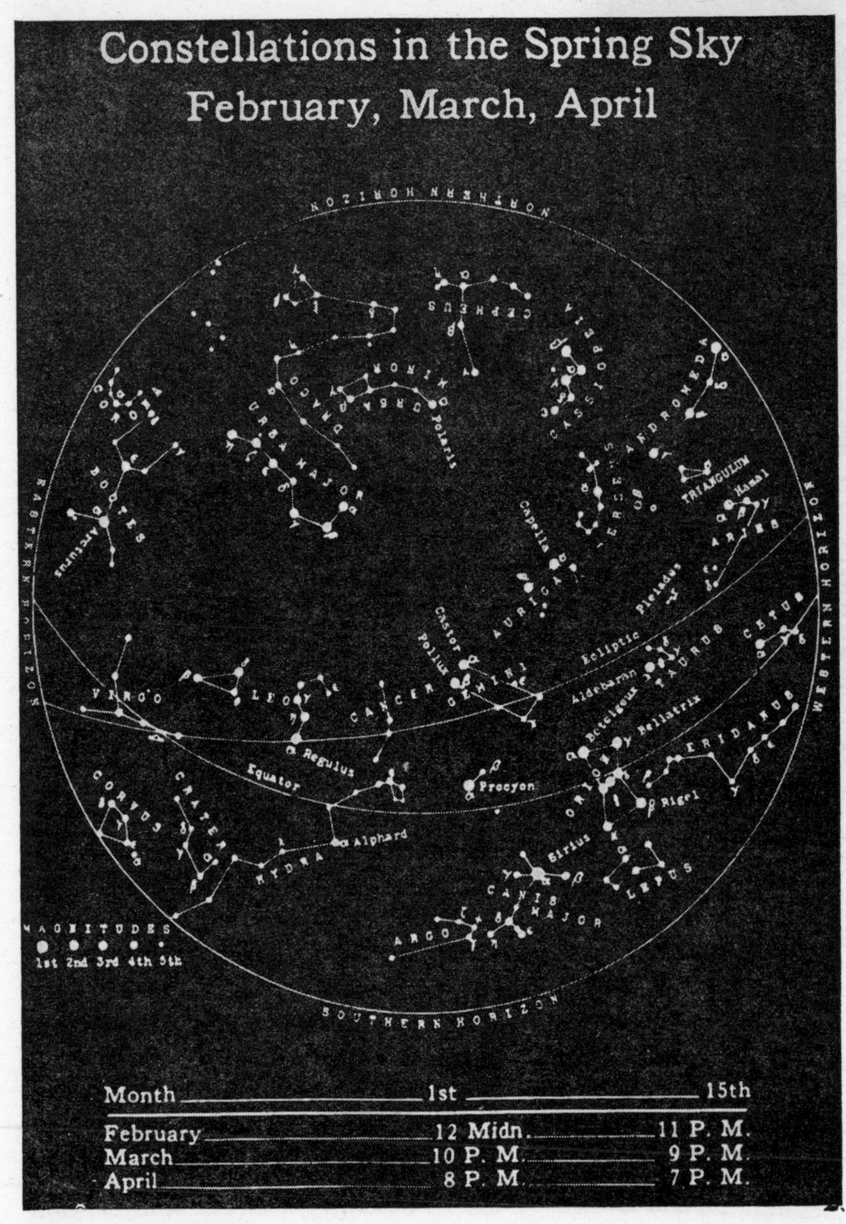

Courtesy Yerkes Observatory

before long run out of names, so it has long been the custom to designate successively fainter stars in each constellation by the successive letters of the Greek alphabet—Alpha, Beta, Gamma, Delta, etc. Thus, Sirius, the brightest star in the whole sky, which is in the constellation Canis Major—the Great Dog—is also designated as Alpha Canis Majoris, which indicates that it is the brightest star in that constellation. With the application of telescopes and modern photography, the number of known stars has been so increased that very faint stars are designated by rather complex systems of letter and number combinations.

The obvious step after naming individual stars was to divide them into groups which were relatively close together in the sky. This was done by the early races at the same time that names became attached to the brightest stars. Early astronomy developed as a result of the astrological attempts of the Chaldeans, Egyptians, and Greeks, so the popular mythologies and legends of these peoples influenced the naming and grouping of the constellations. Thus it is that our constellation names come from the gods, goddesses, and other characters of ancient mythology.

Knowledge of the constellations and identification of the stars can come readily by a little practice in locating them in the sky itself. Everyone can find the seven stars in the northern sky known as the Big Dipper or Ursa Major—the Great Bear. Watch these seven stars throughout one night, and you will discover the east to west motion that all the stars have. However, the stars in the northern sky do not go directly from the eastern horizon to the western, but appear to rotate around a center, which is called the north celestial pole. Near this pole in the sky is a fairly bright star, Polaris, which appears to be nearly stationary. It may be identified by extending an imaginary line outward through the two stars in the side of the Dipper's bowl opposite the handle, to a distance of about five times their separation from each other. This star is always directly north of the observer, and at a height above the horizon equal to the observer's terrestrial latitude in degrees. In the case of an observer near Chicago, this height is about forty-two degrees, or a distance in the sky about equal to eight times the separation of the two stars, the "pointers," in the side of the Big Dipper. The usual unit of rough measure in the sky

Courtesy Yerkes Observatory

THE STARS OF THE BIG DIPPER

is the *degree*. For comparison with other star separations, which we will give later, the distance between the two "pointer" stars in the Big Dipper is about five degrees. Thus, the distance from Alpha Ursae Majoris, the second of the pointers, to Polaris is about thirty degrees.

Because of the westward drift of the stars, the position of the Dipper will vary for the same hour of the night at different seasons of the year. In July the Dipper is west of the polestar at nine o'clock in the evening and stands on end, with the handle reaching upward. In January, however, the Dipper at the same hour is seen east of the polestar and with its handle extending downward. In the Spring and Fall it will take intermediate positions above and below the pole, respectively, thus illustrating the general counter-clockwise rotation of all the star pattern around the North Star through the change in seasons.

Most of the stars of Ursa Major never set below the northern horizon, for observers in the North Temperate latitudes. However, all other stars, save the strictly circumpolar ones, do set, and are not visible at certain seasons of the year. This is again due to the constant westward seasonal drift of all the stars in the sky. Thus, we will briefly consider the major constellations, easily visible overhead during the four different seasons of the year. Our guide will be the Big Dipper and the polestar, which are always visible to us.

THE STARS OF WINTER

If we extend an imaginary line from Epsilon Ursae Majoris—the star in the Big Dipper where the handle joins the bowl—through the polestar, and to the Milky Way, we will find a large W-shaped group of five bright stars, which will, however, be upside down at nine P.M. in the winter, and will look more like a sprawling M. This is the constellation Cassiopeia. Farther east, along the band of the Milky Way, are six fairly bright stars marking the spine of the Milky Way, and bending in a smooth curve to a very bright yellow star above Polaris. This star is Capella, in Auriga; and the stars pointing to it are a part of the constellation Perseus. Now, if we return to Ursa Major and prolong a line through the star where the handle joins the bowl of the Dipper, and the first star of the "pointers," diagonally opposite to it, for about forty degrees in the general direction of Capella, we find two bright stars separated by about five degrees. They are Castor and Pollux, in the constellation Gemini, the "Twins."

Directly south and well up in the sky, is the brilliant constellation Orion. Three bright stars close together and in a perfect straight line are the most prominent. Below them, to the south, are three fainter stars forming another straight line at an angle to the first. The first three form the belt of Orion—the Hunter—and the second three form his sword. Around the middle of the haziest of the stars is the awe-inspiring Great Nebula of Orion. This constellation has somewhat the appearance of a dipper, and is often mistaken by novices for the Little Dipper, though, of course, it is in the opposite part of the sky. To the northeast and above Orion, is a brilliant red star, Betelgeuse; and diagonally opposite it, on the lower southwest side of Orion, is the bright bluish star, Rigel. About thirty degrees east of Orion and a little below, is Sirius, the brightest star in the whole sky. When observing these southern portions of the heavens one must be careful not to mistake a bright planet for a bright star, or vice versa. The planets move with relation to the stars as the month progresses; and their change of position is quite marked from week to week.

Now let us run another imaginary line, this time from Sirius through the three bright stars of the belt of Orion. About the distance between Sirius and Orion, but beyond Orion and above it, we find a small V-shaped group of fainter stars, with the V pointing South. This is the Hyades cluster. Its brightest star is Aldebaran. If we extend the imaginary line about half again as far in the same direction, we reach the small group of the Pleiades —the Seven Sisters. Actually only about six faint stars in this cluster are usually visible to the unaided eye, unless one has exceptional eyesight. Both the Pleiades and the Hyades lie in the constellation Taurus—the Bull.

THE STARS OF SPRING

At about nine o'clock on a night in spring the Big Dipper is upside down in the northeastern sky. If we extend a line from the two stars in the bowl of the Dipper opposite the pointers, upward and southward for about fifty degrees, we come to a group of six stars curving into a large question mark but without the dot beneath it. The constellation is Leo—the Lion. Let us find Orion again, now low in the western sky, and extend a line from Betelgeuse, the bright red star near it, eastward to Regulus. About half-way to Regulus, just below or south of the imaginary line, is the bright star Procyon. A line down from Procyon and through Betelgeuse will fall on the somewhat fainter star, Bellatrix, just above Rigel. Half-way between Regulus and Procyon and south of them about half their distance apart, is Alphard, which shines almost alone in the constellation of Hydra. Regulus, Alphard, Procyon, Sirius, and Betelgeuse form a very large W in the southern sky, and are the brightest stars in the region with the exception of Rigel. Constellations which we identified in the winter sky are still present in the west, but we need not mention them again.

THE STARS OF SUMMER

From Ursa Major in the northwest sky at nine P.M., let us extend a long, sweeping curve out along the handle of the Dipper westward as far as its total length. There in Boötes is Arcturus, the bright orange-red star of Chicago World's Fair fame. About the same distance farther, in a curve from Arcturus, is the bright

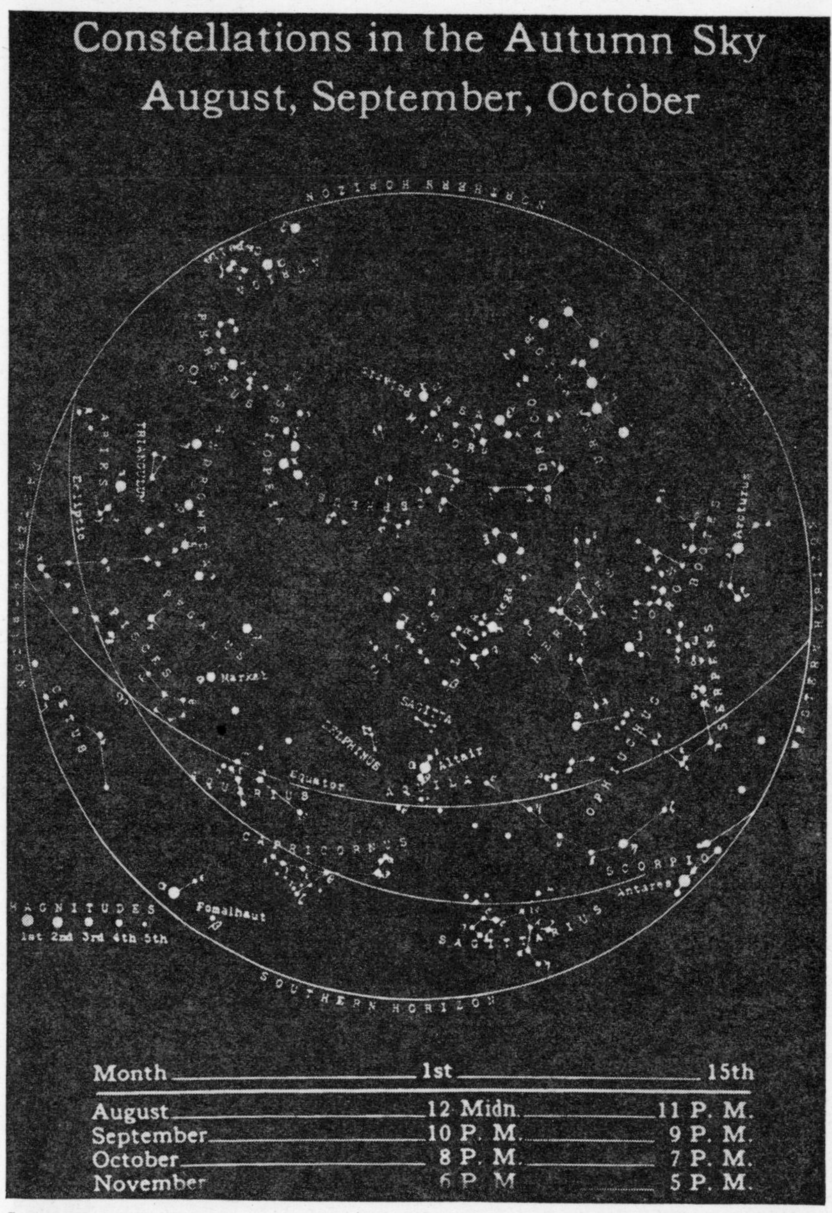

Month	1st	15th
August	12 Midn.	11 P. M.
September	10 P. M.	9 P. M.
October	8 P. M.	7 P. M.
November	6 P. M.	5 P. M.

Courtesy Yerkes Observatory

Black Star, copyright by Wurts Bros.

THE CONSTELLATION GEMINI, THE TWINS
The bright stars are Castor and Pollux.

Black Star, copyright by Wurts Bros.

THE CONSTELLATION TAURUS, THE BULL

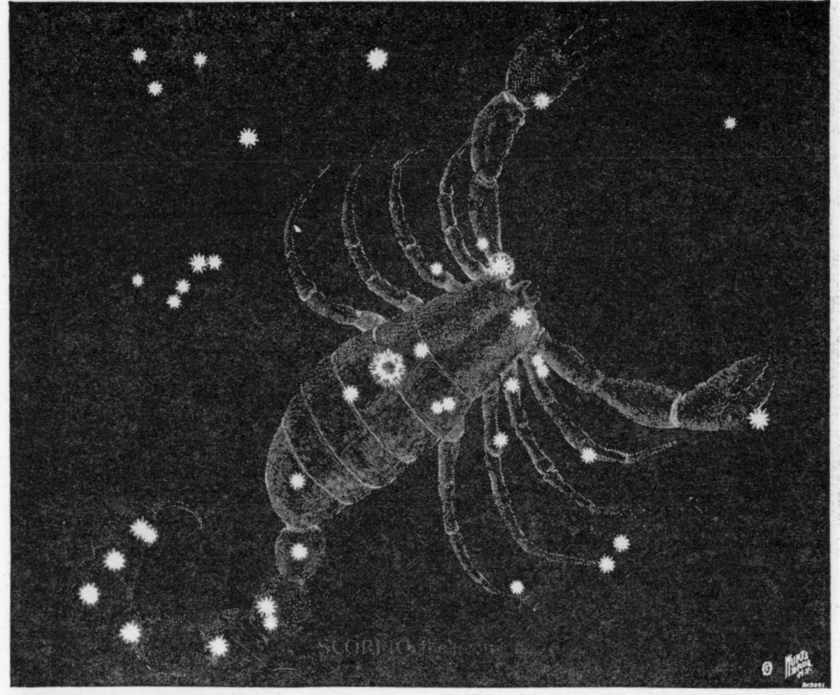

Black Star, copyright by Wurts Bros.

THE SCORPION—THE CONSTELLATION SCORPIO
The formation bears an unusually close resemblance to the animal from which its name is derived.

white star Spica, in the constellation Virgo. Again, from the handle of the Dipper in a straight line about the length of the Dipper itself, is a group of six stars in a half-circular arc, resembling half of a crown. This is the constellation Corona Borealis—the Northern Crown.

Far to the south of the Great Dipper's handle is the most brilliant of the summer constellations, Scorpio—the Scorpion. Unlike most constellations, Scorpio really looks a little like what it is named after: a great scorpion, with its tail curling up over its back, and a bar of four stars at the base of the body for the forepincers. A very red and brilliant star, Antares, is situated in the center of the body of the scorpion.

A little later in the summer, at 9:00 P.M., the very brilliant

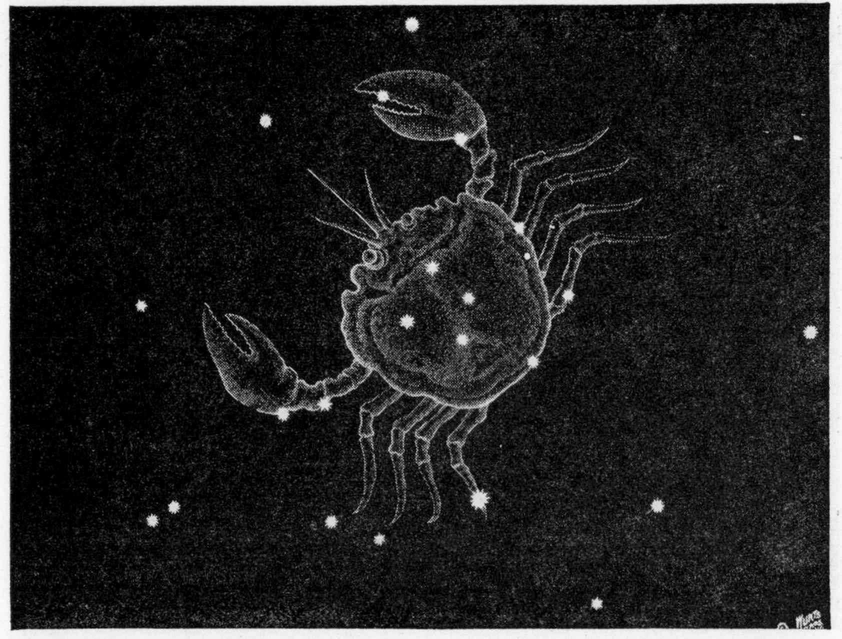

THE CONSTELLATION CANCER—THE CRAB

blue-white star Vega is nearly overhead in the constellation Lyra. With the exception of Sirius, it is the brightest star in the northern heavens. Two faint stars just east of Vega, and quite close to it, form a little triangle with it. The northernmost of these two stars is Epsilon Lyrae, a double star of which we will say more later. About twenty degrees east of Vega is another bright star, Deneb. This forms the top of a large cross composed of six fairly bright stars, with the longer axis of the cross pointing southward directly down the path of the Milky Way. This is the constellation Cygnus—the Swan—more commonly known to us as the Northern Cross. It is a more perfect cross than is the famed Southern Cross.

On the eastern edge of the Milky Way and forming a triangle with Vega and Deneb, is the bright white star Altair. This is the head of the constellation Aquila—the Eagle—which forms a very rough cross of five stars along the plane of the eastern lane of the

Milky Way, and parallel to the Northern Cross. About twenty degrees west of Vega is the constellation of Hercules, which spreads over wide expanse. The most important part, however, is the crude square which lies midway between Vega and Corona Borealis. This is composed of four fairly bright stars, but the sides are far from being equal to each other.

THE APPARENT MOTIONS OF THE PLANETS

We have already discussed briefly the monthly motions of the moon in its revolution around the earth. Both the planets Mercury and Venus appear to us to oscillate back and forth from one side of the sun to the other. The greatest distance that Mercury ever reaches on either side of the sun is about twenty-eight degrees, and that of Venus, forty-eight degrees. The interval of this extreme separation is about six weeks for Mercury. It is thus an evening star for about two weeks; it then continues its movement, passes the sun invisibly, and six weeks later it appears as a morning star. Of course, as with Venus, the best time to view Mercury is when it is farthest from the sun. There will be no difficulty whatever in recognizing Venus as either a "morning star" or an evening star; it is then, with the exception of the moon, the brightest object in the sky. It looks like a brilliant arc-light well above the horizon.

For the greater part of the year the planet Saturn moves eastward among the stars at the average rate of one degree in about eight days. Jupiter moves similarly, but covers a degree in about four days. However, about seventy days before Saturn reaches a position in the sky opposite the sun, and hence directly south of the zenith at midnight, it slows down and finally stops its apparent motion to the east, just at opposition. Then, for 143 days Saturn moves westward. This westward movement is called retrogression. Jupiter slows down about sixty days before its opposition, and then begins its retrograde motion just after opposition; it moves westward for 122 days. At the end of these periods of retrogression, both Jupiter and Saturn become momentarily stationary, and then begin to move eastward again to repeat the cycle. For Jupiter the total cycle, or synodic period, takes 399 days, and for Saturn, 378 days.

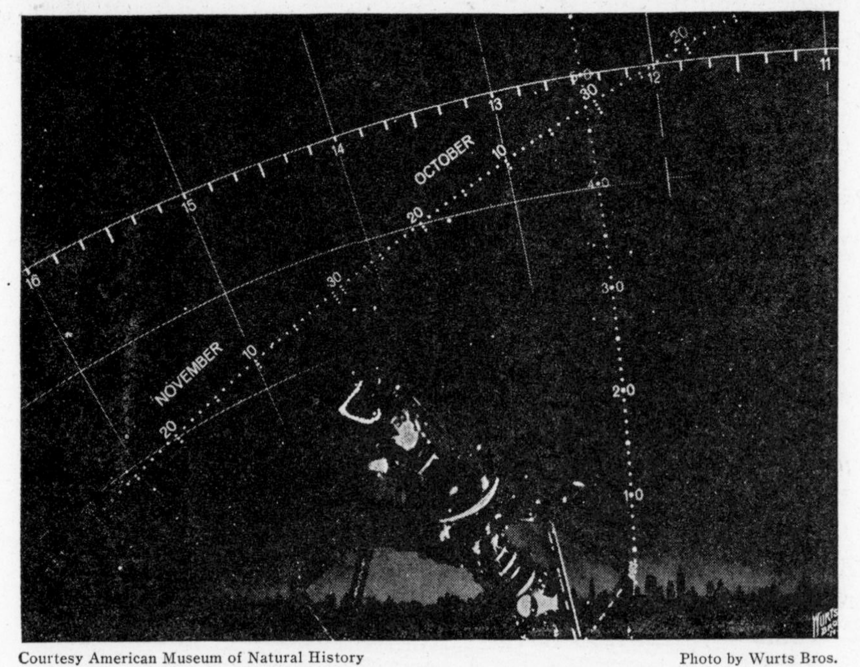

Courtesy American Museum of Natural History Photo by Wurts Bros.

WHERE YEARS BECOME MINUTES

In a planetarium it is possible to reproduce the complicated apparent motions of the planets in a few minutes, although the time actually required is a year or more.

The total synodic period of the planet Mars is 780 days, during 710 days of which it moves eastward. Then, it retrogresses and moves westward for seventy days, covering a distance in the sky of about sixteen degrees. The rate of Mars's eastward motion among the stars will be found to be nearly one degree a day. This is quite rapid, so for a large part of the 710 days Mars is too close to the sun to be seen in the night sky. Once every two years when it is at opposition, Mars is favorably placed for observation. The next opposition of Mars occurs in August, 1939.

These synodic motions of the planets have much historical and archaeological interest because several ancient races, including the Mayas and the Babylonians, carefully observed and recorded them. Their observations were remarkably accurate considering their crude equipment; and, in many cases they have in their manuscripts and on their monuments complete records of the planetary and lunar motions. Since we know the cycles of the planets and eclipses, it is often possible to compute the dates of many of the historical events of the Mayas and the Babylonians.

VARIABLE STARS

The novae brighten up suddenly and unexpectedly, but another class of stars, the variables, brighten and fade periodically. Most of them have their periods of variability well determined, so that we can predict just how bright a certain variable will be at any given time. The most striking variable star that can be seen by the naked eye is Algol, in Perseus; it lies half-way on a line between the Pleiades and Cassiopeia, directly opposite the star Capella, which we have previously identified. Algol is as bright as the stars in the Cassiopeia "W" for two and one-half days; then it fades for four and one-half hours until it is nearly invisible; and then returns in the same period of time to its original brightness. Other easily seen variables are Mira, in Ceti, which has a period of nearly a year; Beta Lyrae, with a thirteen-day period; and Delta Cephei, which has a period of five and one-third days.

THE STRUCTURE OF THE MILKY WAY

In the rural areas the fortunate observer can see the true beauty and magnificent undulations of the Milky Way, as it coagulates here and there into brilliant areas, or at another place is obscured by dark spots and hazy filaments. The exquisite Milky Way photographs taken by Barnard and Ross have in the main superseded the scientific value of naked-eye drawings of its faint channels and broad bands; but the amateur observer may still enjoy following out its mysteries, and noticing outlines of its different regions. To see the faintest portions of the Milky Way, the observer must be in almost total darkness, and shield his eyes from extraneous light.

STAR-TESTING YOUR EYES

The human eye is very sensitive to slight variations of intensity. However, not all eyes are equally acute; some see certain types of objects, such as white dots on a dark background, much better than black dots on a white background. The person with

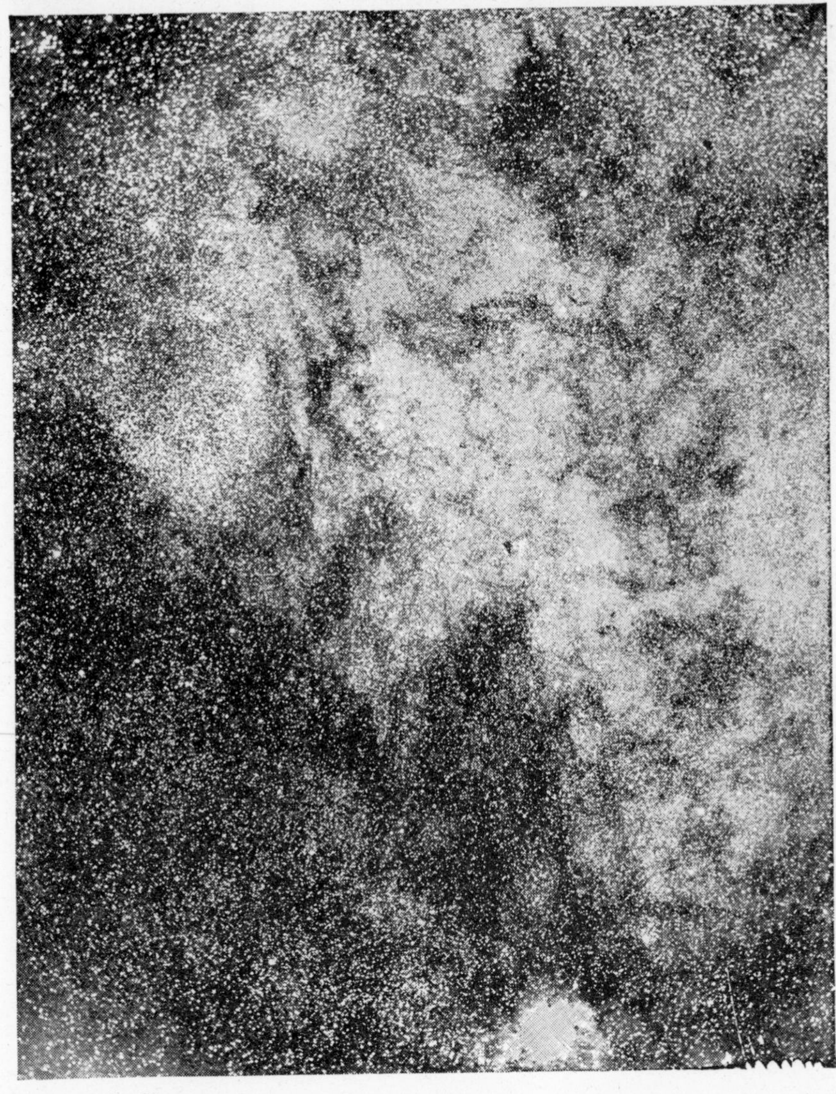

Courtesy Yerkes Observatory

THE MILKY WAY THROUGH A TELESCOPE

The hazy band resolves itself into countless stars when viewed through a modern telescope.

the first type of vision may test his eyes by finding out how many stars he can see in the Pleiades, or by trying to separate close double stars. Those who are better at finding black on white can test their eyes by trying to pick out the very fine detail on the bright disk of the moon. On a good night, one should be able to make out at least six stars in the Pleiades. Indeed, some astronomers of excellent vision, including Percival Lowell and W. H. Pickering, have been able under perfect sky conditions to see as many as thirteen to sixteen with the unaided eye. Another test is the double star Mizar and Alcor, the second star from the end of the handle of the Big Dipper, at the bend. These are wide apart and most people can see them easily. Just a little to the east of the brilliant star Vega, are two faint stars, forming a small triangle with it. The northernmost of these fainter stars is a fairly close double star, Epsilon Lyrae. If one can see it clearly as double, on a good night in the summer when Vega is overhead, one's eyes' "resolving power" is good.

WATCHING THE SUN

During a period when the great storms or spots on the sun are at a maximum of intensity, they often attain a size large enough to be seen with the unaided eye. The brilliant illumination must be reduced by looking through a piece of smoked or colored glass, or an over-exposed and developed piece of photographic negative film.

It takes about twelve days for a spot near the sun's equator to move from one limb of the sun to the other limb. This is because the rotation period of the sun is about twenty-five days, and we see only one hemisphere at a time. The periods of great sun-spot activity usually reach their peaks at about eleven-year intervals.

THE MOON AND LUNAR ECLIPSES

The changing phases of the moon are always fascinating, largely because of their effect on the brightness of its surface. It is particularly interesting to watch the *mana* of lunar seas become darker and darker as the moon changes phase. The craters of the moon are also often visible to the unaided eye.

THE SURFACE OF THE MOON
On clear nights it is possible to distinguish as many as a dozen places on the moon.

Courtesy Lick Observatory

While lunar eclipses are not as fascinating as total solar eclipses, they occur under more favorable conditions. One may learn when to watch for them by consulting almanacs, astronomical journals, and newspapers. Most interesting in an eclipse of the moon is the gradual diminution of light as the disk is eclipsed by the shadow of the earth, and the coppery pall thrown over it.

THE PLANETS

We have already discussed briefly the motions of the planets in the sky among the stars. Following these relative motions from night to night throughout the year will give the amateur observer more knowledge about the planetary paths than any amount of reading.

Venus is the only star which is bright enough to be seen in broad daylight. If one wishes to have the experience of seeing this star in daylight, one should first note the variation in brilliancy of Venus as an "evening star" and "morning star" and choose a season when it is brightest, then look for it approximately overhead at noonday. It is then quite easy to find if one is persistent, if there is no sky haze, and if one looks in the right direction. This direction is about forty-five degrees either east or west of the sun, along the path of the ecliptic which the sun follows in the sky. This is the position of Venus when it is near "greatest elongation" from the sun, and its dates are given in many almanacs. It is fascinating to watch Venus appear first as an evening star, brilliant and low in the west; and then a few months later as a morning star, after it has passed the sun in its path, and rises in the east an hour or so before the dawn.

Mercury, being smaller and closer to the sun, is harder to find. It is said that Copernicus died without ever seeing it, although he knew of its existence and studied its motions from observations made by other observers. However, the climate where he lived made the sky unfavorable for observation. Mercury's greatest distance from the sun in the sky is about twenty-eight degrees, and it appears as a morning and evening "star" just as Venus does. Mercury is seen best as a morning star in September and October, and as an evening star in March and April.

The planet Jupiter when at its brightest is high in the sky at midnight, and any object in its light casts a definite shadow if there is not too much haze or scattered light around the observer. Jupiter can be distinguished by its brilliancy and its soft golden-white color. Mars has a reddish glow, and Saturn a steady yellow light. In color Mercury is reddish-yellow, like Mars, and about the same average brightness; but being close to the sun, it can be seen only just after sunset or just before sunrise. Mars, on the other hand, is usually some distance from the sun and is best visible in the night sky. Similarly, Venus, which is blue-white and often brighter than Jupiter, can be seen only in the twilight

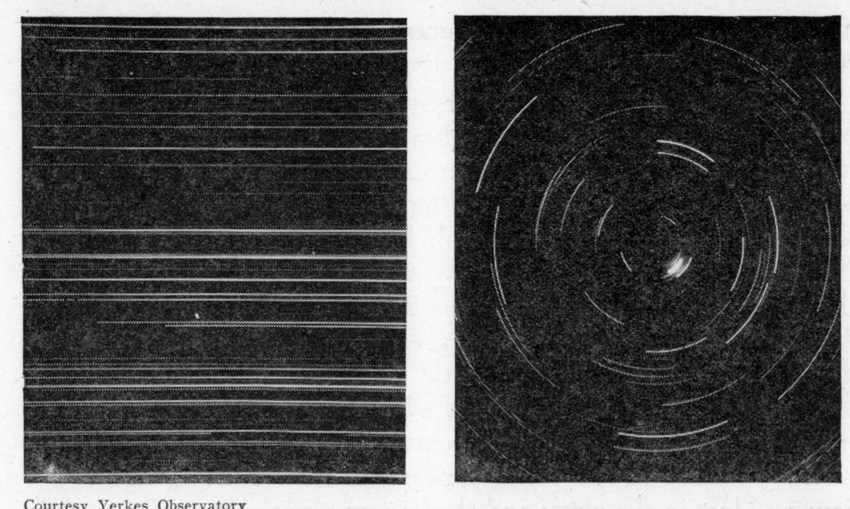

Courtesy Yerkes Observatory

STAR TRAILS AT THE EQUATOR AND THE NORTH POLE

These time exposures prove the revolution of the earth on its axis, which points toward the center of the circular star trails, known as the celestial north pole.

or before dawn; while both Jupiter and Saturn are prominent only in the night sky.

With a small hand camera, one may make many interesting experiments in simple astronomical photographs. Even a simple box camera is usable if it has a time exposure shutter release. One of the first things to attempt to photograph should be the trails of the stars as they circle the celestial pole from east to west. The camera should be set firmly on a solid support and pointed directly at the polestar. The lens should be opened as wide as possible, the focus set for the greatest distance, and the film exposed for an hour. During this time it should be shielded from light and the formation of dew. If all goes well, the path of the stars will be marked on the negatives by a series of arcs. The same process can be used for the stars overhead and those in the southern sky. Sometimes a bright meteor is recorded during the exposure. The paths of the moon and the planets can also be photographed in this manner.

THE ZODIACAL LIGHT AND THE GEGENSCHEIN

The zodiacal light is a very faint, diffuse glow that is sometimes visible under the clearest atmospheric conditions, in the western sky a little after twilight, or in the early morning sky before dawn. The base of the triangle-shaped glow is toward the sun, close to the horizon, and may often be as much as twenty-five degrees in breadth. The apex of the cone of light tapers up into the dark sky about sixty degrees. Though the zodiacal light is best viewed in the tropics, we can occasionally see it from the north if we watch carefully in good weather before dawn. Its brightness seems to vary in different seasons and different years.

The Gegenschein is a similar, but smaller glow of light, which is somewhat elliptical in shape; it is about seven degrees in breadth and travels in the ecliptic, about 180 degrees from the sun. That is, it travels in the sun's path in the sky, but directly opposite it. It is also known as the Counterglow. There are several other very

THE AURORA BOREALIS, OR "NORTHERN LIGHTS"

Often highly colored and swift-moving, the beauties of the Aurora can not be pictured. Even a color "movie" would not do them full justice.

Black Star photo by Ernst Mayer

THE EVER CHANGING AURORA BOREALIS
Incandescent mists of green and red float in the sky, continuously shifting their position and changing their appearance.

Black Star photo by Ernst Mayer

faint areas of light near the ecliptic, including the so-called "zodiacal bank," and the "lunar zodiacal light"; but they are so faint as to be seen only under the very best conditions by experienced observers.

THE AURORA BOREALIS AND LUMINOUS NIGHT CLOUDS

Although the aurorae are not strictly astronomical phenomena, they may well be observed by the amateur star gazer. They are most frequent and brilliant at the times of sun spot maxima. The position and extent of auroral displays should always be noted, as well as the colors and types of streamers. Sounds attributed to auroral displays have been reported, but have been usually discredited. Similarly, the existence of aurorae very close to the ground has been reported. Tests show that the aurorae have no appreciable effect on radio reception, despite popular belief to the contrary.

Brilliant silver-white luminous night clouds have often been reported, particularly during otherwise clear summer nights. These clouds are apparently lit up by the sun from below the horizon, and so usually appear only a little after sunset or before sunrise. They must be extremely high in the earth's atmosphere and are of interest for that reason.

HOW MAN OVERCOMES HIS LIMITATIONS

Man's chief advantage over animals is his ability to overcome physical limitations through the use of various instruments. There is, indeed, reason for his being called a tool-using animal. Through his ability to invent man has gradually won a higher position in the economy of nature. Animals change, and sometimes species disappear as they attempt to meet the demands of their environment; but man improves his mind in the manipulation of an increasingly complicated set of tools. In this way he

Courtesy Yerkes Observatory

YERKES OBSERVATORY AT WILLIAMS BAY, WISCONSIN

perceives phenomena beyond the ken of his unaided senses. The microscope expands the exceedingly minute, the telescope the exceedingly remote. Both of these are enhanced by photo-chemical and photo-electric attachments. The things man detects with these instruments he may soon put to use in the long battle against ignorance. It might be advantageous for human beings to have additional senses, such as a sixth radio sense; but the less direct, "detective" methods of instruments are no less fascinating. Let us consider, in particular, how astronomical instruments have extended man's sensibilities without changing or impeding his bodily make-up.

All of man's senses, of which so far there are five well-defined ones—namely, vision, hearing, touch, taste, and smell—are really specializations of the general sense of touch. Vision, and to a lesser extent hearing and smell, establish contact with things at a distance. How vision acts at a distance—whether light requires a medium in which to travel—is still a great mystery. It is the senses of sight and touch, particularly that of sight, which man has extended by means of instruments for use in furthering our knowledge of the heavens. Since the astronomical extensions of the sense of touch are limited to instruments sensitive to a "feeling" of heat or radiation, and do not involve actual space contact, they may be considered as extensions of the wave-length range of vision. Astronomical instruments, therefore, are concerned with extending our sense of vision by the use of instruments with extraordinary powers of gathering and analyzing light. A great variety of materials and instruments are involved, some of which we shall presently consider.

Since instruments are usually products of inventive skill and technique, let us see where invention comes into the astronomical picture. A year's astronomical progress can be conveniently divided into three general classes, more or less interrelated. Each year certain comets, novae, meteors, and eclipses are more or less accidentally favorable for observation. Some are predictable, others depend on discovery. While much depends on proper preparation, the external situation is most important. Each year new approaches, departures, and inventions reveal new things that

THE EYE-END OF A REFRACTING TELESCOPE

This is the 36-inch telescope of Lick Observatory, Mount Hamilton, California.

Courtesy Lick Observatory

have long been just as favorably located. Astronomy adapts new developments in other fields to its own use. This progress is due to invention. Each year a large amount of routine work is done which comes under the general heading of industry in astronomy. Much of this is a carrying-on of old work of proved value, which, done by alert individuals, often leads to new discoveries and inventions. Some of the results of routine industry gradually assume such immense proportions as to be almost spectacular. Their culmination sometimes becomes "news." A laborious star catalogue can be as inspiring as a new comet. The three headings of *discovery, invention,* and *industry* could probably be fitted over any of the other sciences, and, indeed, over progress in general. Not every individual is fortunate enough to be a discoverer or inventor, but everyone can be a builder by being industrious. Industry alone can make for much progress, while without it there is likely to be little discovery or invention with which we are particularly concerned here.

DEVICES THAT HELP THE EYE

Many of the ingenious astronomical instruments are products of modern research and industry in other fields, particularly the fields of chemistry, physics, and engineering. In reality they are products of the ages. They are new, but they are old, too. In fact, we add each year, in every field, only a few new patterns to the fabric woven by our past. If some of the clumsier devices of the past have been modified or dropped, they have not been with-

A 50-INCH REFLECTING TELESCOPE USED IN GERMANY

Courtesy Carl Zeiss, Inc.

out their influence, and in that sense, at least, they are a part of the newer device. Every astronomical instrument has an interesting history, with which we can not be concerned here. Let us look at some of the modern extensions of the human eye such as photographic emulsions, photo-electric cells, thermocouples, bolometers, and radiometers. The last three of these devices also extend our sensitivity to heat.

Consider first the natural sensitivity of the eye. The unaided retina is able to tune in, so to speak, upon only a very limited frequency band. It was probably not by accident that the eye was made most sensitive to the most intense part of the radiation of the nearest star, our sun, which happens to be a predominantly "yellow star." If we were associated with a red or blue star, or a double or triple one, instead of the sun, our eyes would probably be more sensitive to red or blue, or both. Since we are not likely to outgrow our parent sun, or wander very far from its friendly warmth and protection toward other stars within any readily conceivable time, our eyes are not likely to develop any different sensitivity.

CHEMISTRY'S PLACE IN ASTRONOMICAL PHOTOGRAPHY

In astronomy we wish to study not only the predominant radiation of the sun, but all its other radiations of all frequencies or wave lengths, from the shortest wave length of ultra-violet to the longest of infra-red. And we wish to study various radiations of other heavenly bodies which are predominantly more violet or more red than our sun. With the discovery that compounds of silver, especially those with chlorine, bromine, and iodine, are sensitive to light, our perception of radiation was immediately increased toward the blue, since "emulsions" of these compounds have their greatest sensitivity in that range. Gradually the sensitivity range of the simple photographic emulsion has been extended. Some substances, chiefly certain coal-tar dyes, by-products of gas and electric industries, absorb various wave lengths or colors, and, properly added to photographic emulsions, they give them various sensitivities ranging far into the infra-red. Certain fluorescent oils have been successfully used to increase sensitivity to the far ultra-violet.

The amount as well as the range of sensitivity of photographic materials is now and then increased by still other methods. Bathing the emulsions in aqueous ammonia or in mercury vapor is an outstanding example. Of course, like the retina itself, all its extensions or counterparts, such as emulsions and photocells, are greatly aided by the light-gathering power of a lens or telescope, as will presently be made clear. But since a sufficient increase in photographic sensitivity would put smaller telescopes on a par with the largest using present emulsions (for all purposes except resolving power, which depends on the lens area), it would be better to accomplish this than to build a score of two-hundred-inch mirrors. Such emulsions would make the many existing modest telescopes become immediately their equals. Finally, the time factor is probably the biggest asset of the photographic

Courtesy Northern Pacific Ry

INFRA-RED PHOTOGRAPH OF A FAMILIAR OBJECT

The image is clearer, but there is a change in color value. This is also true of infra-red photography in astronomy.

emulsion. The retina acts practically instantaneously, and nothing is gained by longer exposure—in fact, there is apt to be fatigue. But a photographic emulsion "soaks up" the light continuously, so that the effect is nearly the same whether a bright light acts for a short time or a fainter one acts for a correspondingly longer time. Hence, we can photograph with the same instrument faint nebulae and stars which we are unable to see because they are too faint.

Like the material of the human retina and the silver salts of the photographic emulsion, certain metals are markedly sensitive to light. Their reactions are electrical in nature, and the minute electrical currents which result from proper manipulation, and which are proportional to the exciting light, can be amplified by vacuum tubes, as in an ordinary radio set. The photoelectric cells, as these instruments are called, are, like the eye and photographic emulsion, sensitive only to limited regions of color. Cells employing the metal caesium are especially red-sensitive, while potassium cells are blue-sensitive, and in their special regions their sensitivity is very high. They can "see" a candle thirty miles away, or three thousand miles away, with the aid of the one-hundred-inch telescope. With their aid, for example, the fainter outlying portions of the nearest extragalactic nebula or system of stars, that in the constellation of Andromeda, have been traced to show that the nebula is comparable to the size attributed to our own galaxy.

MEASURING MINUTE QUANTITIES OF HEAT

We have already pointed out that all astronomical instruments really enhance our perception of the radiant energy of which the eye is able to perceive only a very limited range. All radiant energy, if intense enough, can be felt as heat even when not seen. There are three physical instruments used in astronomy which are able to measure minutest radiant energies as heat. In one sense they are a kind of retina sensitive to heat radiation; they make no distinction as to color, but only as to heating ability. One of these instruments, the thermocouple, is based on the principle that two different metals, if welded together at their ends, will give rise to a minute electrical current in their circuit if one junction is

Courtesy Carl Zeiss, Inc.

GREAT TELESCOPES ARE FOUND ALL OVER THE WORLD
This telescope is used by students of astronomy in Tokyo, Japan.

heated above the temperature of the other. Another, the bolometer, makes use of the variation in the resistance of a wire with temperature. A third, the radiometer, depends on the change in pressure of a gas on being heated. It so happens that these three instruments are of the same order of sensitivity; they can feel and measure quantitatively the radiation from a single candle perhaps a hundred miles away, and, of course, correspondingly farther in conjunction with a telescope, using its energy-gathering power. Being sensitive to all wave lengths, these instruments measure the total radiation of a body which depends directly upon the temperature for any given body. Thus we have here one method of determining the temperatures of the sun, the moon, the planets, and the stars.

FENCES THAT SHUT OFF LIGHT

It will have been noticed in our discussion so far that all the various retinas with which we have dealt, while sensitive to considerable ranges of radiation, are able to deal with it only compositely as bundles of radiation with a kind of average hue. The human eye, for example, sees a neon sign as red, although there are also yellow, green, and blue emanations therein, the red being merely predominant. The last three instruments take in the largest bundles of all—the total radiation. Various smaller bundles of radiation can be segregated from the larger bundles by means of fences known as "filters," since they block out or are opaque to certain wave-length regions, but allow others to filter through. These fences form more or less well-defined boundary lines within which there is a kind of average color of "effective wave length." The greenish-yellow seen through sun glasses used to cut the bluish glare of the snow is a simple example. Fences taking in a larger rather than a smaller territory are often an advantage in astronomical work. The effective wave length often gives about the same results as would the single corresponding wave length and has the asset of greater intensity, since it is a bundle of colors

Courtesy Mt. Wilson Observatory

THE MOUNT WILSON OBSERVATORY
Here men nightly study the secrets of the stars.

acting together, illustrating the original idea of the fasces—in union there is strength. This result is always desirable with regard to the relatively faint, distance-dimmed objects with which astronomy deals.

In our various terrestrial experiences we have noticed that illumination from the coals of a cooling fire is red, candle light is yellow, and tungsten filaments give off white light. By applying the same principles we may determine the approximate temperature of astronomical bodies by noting their color. The relative intensities of two or three bundles of radiation of different effective or average color suffice for such determinations. Any of the retinal instruments above (including the eye), in combination with suitable filters or fences, may be used. Platinum would melt on the surfaces of the cooler stars so far measured, while the hottest stellar surface temperature so far measured is around 180,000° Fahrenheit; the temperatures of stellar interiors are supposed to be millions of degrees. We shall find that much can be learned about the brighter stars by splitting the bundles into much smaller ones, but that belongs to the light-analyzing part of our subject. Meanwhile, let us consider light-gathering instruments, of which our corresponding bodily organ is the lens of the eye.

HOW TELESCOPES AID THE EYE

Though the big two-hundred-inch mirror now being ground is often referred to as the "giant eye," it will be clear by now that the mirror corresponds only to the lens of the eye. The pupil or opening of the eye is less than one-fourth of an inch in diameter even when looking at the night sky. The corresponding area is about four one-hundredths of a square inch. The big two-hundred-inch mirror will have an area of about thirty thousand square inches, or nearly a million times the size of the effective lens of the eye. Since all points of celestial bodies are radiating in all directions, the giant mirror will be able to reach out and gather in nearly a million times as much radiation from each heavenly point of light as does the unaided eye. In astronomical language it will be able to see fourteen to fifteen magnitudes fainter than the eye. When a telescope mirror is used in combination with a photo-

THE FAMOUS 100-INCH REFLECTING TELESCOPE AT MT. WILSON
A number of the illustrations in this book were made from photos taken through this telescope.

Courtesy Mt. Wilson Observatory

graphic emulsion, forming a complete mechanical eye, the light-gathering is increased both by taking in radiation over more space, and by using more time.

In addition to making each point of an object brighter in proportion to its light-gathering power, a telescope can be made by means of suitable eye-pieces or lenses to magnify the object, or apparently to bring it nearer by increasing the separation of points in the image. Thus the two-hundred-inch telescope can be made to bring the moon apparently only two dozen miles away, whereas its actual distance is a quarter of a million miles. With the same magnification all celestial bodies will apparently be brought to one ten-thousandth of their distances. This "reduction" of distance will make all the larger members of the solar system assume considerable proportions and show many details in their grosser features. The mountains and craters of the moon, the markings and

(Left) REFLECTOR FOR THE WORLD'S LARGEST TELESCOPE

View of the ribbed back of the reflector of the giant 200-inch telescope which will magnify the power of the eye about one million times.

Courtesy Corning Glass Works

(Below) EXAMPLES OF VARYING DEGREES OF MAGNIFICATION

The circular views are different magnifications of the towers in the center of the square picture.

Courtesy Bausch & Lomb Optical Co.

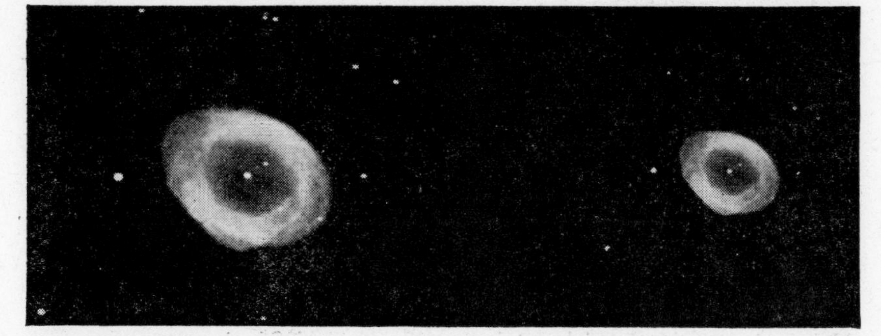

Courtesy Mt. Wilson Observatory

TWO VIEWS OF THE RING NEBULA IN LYRA
Comparison photographs taken with the 100-inch and 60-inch reflecting telescopes.

rings of Saturn, the belts and the moons of Jupiter, the polar caps and oases of Mars—all will be more fascinating than ever. But what of the stars? Even at one ten-thousandth of their distances, though they are thousands of times brighter and larger than our giant planet, Jupiter, the larger, nearer stars are still so far away that they will appear not appreciably larger than to the eye alone, though, of course, they will appear much brighter. Probably the greatest achievement of the giant mirror will be in bringing in more distant galaxies or systems of stars like our own, and in showing more detail in those now within reach.

HOW A TELESCOPE WORKS

The ability of a telescope to show sharpness and clarity of detail is known as its resolving power. The nature of light is such as to hinder detail in the image of a telescope, but this hindrance diminishes as the aperture of the objective increases in size. The image of a point source of light which is formed by a telescope is in the form of what is called the "diffraction pattern." This pattern, consisting of a tiny central disk of light surrounded by faint concentric rings alternately dark and light, seems to be due to the wavelike nature of light. This diffraction disk becomes progressively smaller as larger apertures are used; therefore, truer images may be obtained with larger apertures. With the two-hundred-inch mirror, the diffraction disks will be very tiny indeed. As a practical aid in the magnification which can make full use of the resolving power of a telescope, it is desirable to have as long a focal length as is convenient. With a reflecting-type telescope this is accomplished by reflecting the light forth and back, doubling the light on itself, making only half or less of the mechanical length necessary. The required dome or observatory is correspondingly reduced in size.

Since the telescope is the basic astronomical instrument, it will be well to dwell a little upon the relative merits of the two types which are in common use. The mirror, or reflector, telescopes can be made much larger than the lens, or refractor, telescopes. For the lens type the light must pass through the glass, or other possible refracting medium, such as quartz. This means that the glass must be particularly fine, free of bubbles and strains, and highly transparent to as wide a range of wave lengths or colors as possible. These qualifications are increasingly difficult to meet as the size of the telescope is increased. The clearest glass becomes increasingly opaque to the shorter wave lengths toward the ultraviolet band. In order to bring even a narrow range of color close to the same focus, a lens must be compounded of at least two

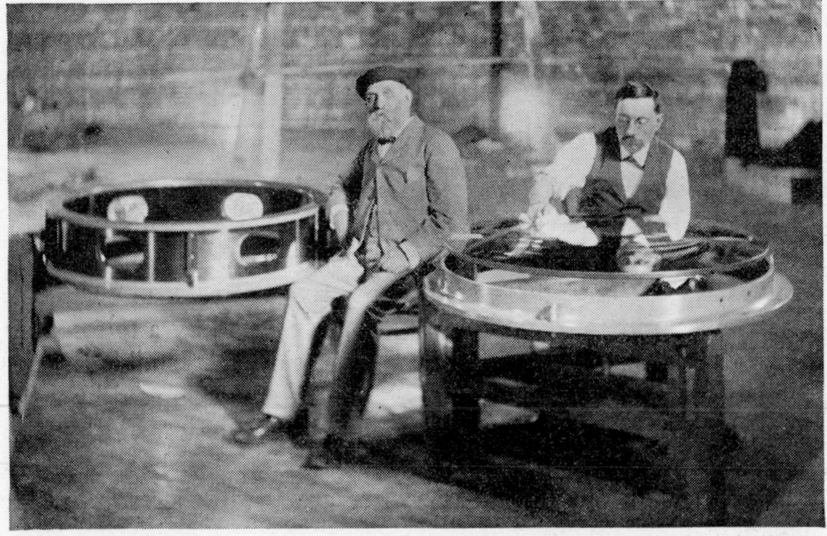

Courtesy Yerkes Observatory

THE 40-INCH LENS OF YERKES OBSERVATORY
The thin lens on the right is the largest ever made.

SILVERING A GREAT TELESCOPE
The mirrors of the 100-inch reflector must be re-silvered from time to time. The process is similar to silvering an ordinary mirror.

Courtesy Mt. Wilson Observatory

kinds of glass, each of which must have its two surfaces curved and polished with the greatest refinement. This process is very difficult, costly, and requires unusual skill. Large lenses must be made thick in order to prevent even the slightest warping when they are mounted. Increasing the thickness makes lenses more opaque, and the great weight causes them to be more subject to distortion. The great refractor at the Yerkes Observatory, largest of this type in the world, has a lens forty inches in diameter and a focal length of sixty-three feet. It is probably very near the practical limit of size for a refractor.

A mirror requires only one surface to be figured and polished. Since the light is not transmitted, the mirror can be supported over its entire back surface. The back can even be honeycombed so as to lessen the weight. For the same reason a few internal bubbles and strains are not detrimental if a good surface is assured: opaqueness is no handicap; in fact, the first reflectors were of polished metallic alloys. Aluminum, which is highly reflective to practically all wave lengths including the ultra-violet, and other metals can be electrically evaporated in a vacuum chamber and deposited upon mirrors of polished glass. This material is chosen as a support because of its rigidity and relatively small variation under variations of temperature. Mirrors also have the great advantage of focusing all colors together. All the largest mirrors, including the Mount Wilson one-hundred-inch, the eighty-two-inch McDonald, which is now being polished, and the yet unfinished Mount Palomar two-hundred-inch, are of the paraboloid mirror type.

One of the main disadvantages of the mirrors as compared with the refractors is their distortion of what is known as the "field." A paraboloid mirror can best see only straight ahead; at even small distances "off axis" the images become distorted. Mirrors are unsurpassed for certain kinds of astronomical work that can be done entirely on the axis, such as work on a single star or small point-like areas of a surface. But when a "wide field" is under investigation, astronomers give refractors more consideration. Perhaps one of the most useful of modern telescopes will be a refractor with an aperture of twenty inches and a moderate focal length. This refractor is now being made for the Lick Observatory for photographing rather wide areas of the sky and faint stars.

A rather recent development in telescopes is a kind of combination of the lens and mirror types known as the Schmidt camera. This device consists of a spherical mirror with a thin lens so placed that the light passes through the lens before being focused by the mirror. The lens is introduced to eliminate the off-axis distortion of the reflector field, which is thus made superior in several respects to that of a purely lens-type camera, particularly where great speed over a wide field is required. It is expected that a proposed Schmidt camera of fifty-inch aperture will enable certain kinds of work to be done on Mount Palomar better than with the two-hundred-inch itself. A smaller Schmidt camera on Mount Palomar obtained the first photographs of the two supernovae, the discovery of which were outstanding events in astronomy during 1937.

WRESTING SECRETS FROM LIGHT

Astronomers must depend upon the spectrograph for analysis of the radiation from astronomical bodies. The spectroscope and spectrograph are essentially instruments for placing the different colors emanating from a point of light alongside one another, like

THE SPECTROGRAPH ATTACHED TO THE YERKES TELESCOPE

Spectrographs separate and measure the colors of light, giving astronomers a key to the composition of heavenly bodies.

Courtesy Yerkes Observatory

a row of piano keys, in a spectrum. The spectroscope is used in direct observation, the spectrograph in photography. If the source has appreciable area or width, its image must first be focused on a narrow opening or slit, since unless the "lines" are very narrow the "piano keys" will overlap and blur too much. Light may be divided into its components by the use of prisms and gratings. A prism is a wedge-shaped piece of transparent material with polished faces. A grating is a series of regularly spaced parallel wires or linear rulings on polished glass or metal.

Spectrographs, like the eye, make use of the light-gathering power of telescopes. With larger telescopes it is usually possible to use spectrographs in which the colors of the light are so separated that it is relatively easy to recognize and measure the "lines." Larger telescopes are also more efficient in obtaining, though with less dispersion, spectra of fainter objects. Long experiment and spectral analysis in the laboratory have given us the keys for interpreting the light that comes from stars and planets. We know, for instance, that an incandescent solid body or liquid, or a gas under such high pressures as exist at all considerable depths in stars, give a continuous spectrum. Using our keyboard analogy, no keys are missing from such a spectrum. But a hot gas at low pressure gives a "line" spectrum, with perhaps a key or line missing here

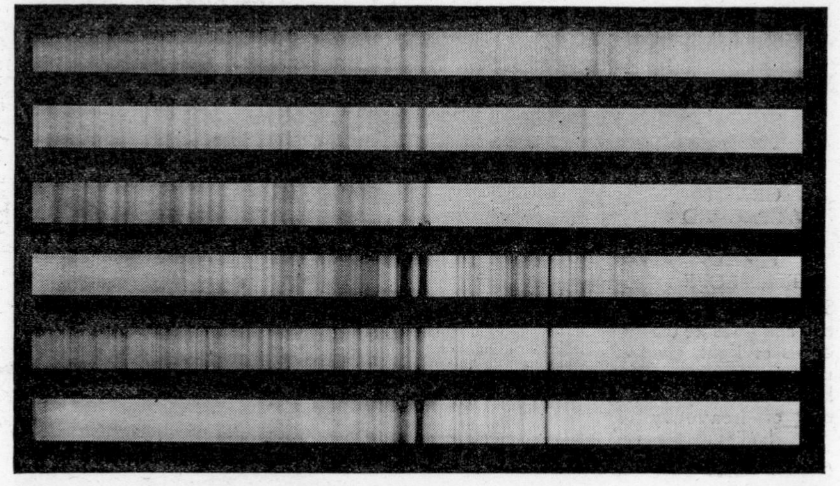

Courtesy Lick Observatory

FINGERPRINTS OF THE STARS
No two stellar spectrographs are the same.

and there. Certain gaseous nebulae give only line spectra; but practically all stars, and planets, since they reflect the light of our sun, give both line and continuous spectra. Line spectra are usually relatively darker than the continuous because the surface gases from which they arise are relatively cooler than those at greater depths. Every substance has a characteristic space distribution of its lines of energy when dispersed into a spectrum. The spectra of no two substances are alike, so we can identify the gases which compose the surface layers of the stars. This examination reveals only substances which, though subjected to different degrees of temperature and pressure, are those with which we are familiar on earth.

Besides revealing the composition, pressure, and temperature of the stars, spectral analysis tells us about the velocity and direction of a star. The whistle of an approaching train sounds higher in pitch than that of a departing train. This phenomenon is caused by the difference in the number of sound waves which reach the ear per second. Likewise, the frequency of light waves is greater for an approaching star than for one which is apparently receding. The color of a star's spectrum also yields information about its apparent direction and velocity.

Among the many other things to be learned about stars from spectral analysis is an approximation of their distances. The distances of the nearer stars may be accurately measured by using the distance across the earth's orbit as a base line. Their distances, combined with their apparent magnitudes, give their real or absolute magnitudes. It has been found that the relative intensities of certain spectral lines in stars are closely related to the stars' real or absolute magnitudes. Assuming that the more distant stars show the same relationship, which seems altogether valid, their distances are accurately determined.

PHOTOGRAPHS OF THE SUN'S SURFACE

Among the progeny of the spectrograph, with special application to the sun, is the spectroheliograph or sun spectrograph. Let us see how it differs from its parent. As already pointed out, a spectrograph forms a series of images of whatever light is focused on the slit, like a row of piano keys in different colors. If the slit is moved across the sun's image, the keyboards of the successive "slices" of the sun will all superpose and form a composite picture without detail. If we move the photographic plate or retina at the same rate as the slit, the various keyboards will overlap and blur one another. But if only one of the "piano keys" is allowed to be photographed as the slit and photographic plate are moved, a series of pictures of this key will be taken side by side, resulting in a picture of the sun in the color of this key. It is like closing one's ears to all notes except those of a single pitch, or like tuning our radio to a single frequency and eliminating all other broadcasts.

The spectroheliograph is a receiver set for light waves instead of radio waves. The method is very simple in principle. A screen is placed over all of the spectrum except for a narrow slit at the desired wave length or key. The slit is moved in exact synchronization with the slit moving over the sun's image. The wave length usually chosen is that of one of the bright lines of the surface gases of the sun, often the red line of hydrogen, or the blue line of calcium. The results are pictures of the distributions and intensities of those gases over the solar surface. Since these are continually changing, a continuous record will give us a movie of the move-

A SPECTRO-HELIOGRAPH ATTACHED TO A TELESCOPE

A development of the spectrograph, this instrument is used in making solar photographs.

Courtesy Yerkes Observatory

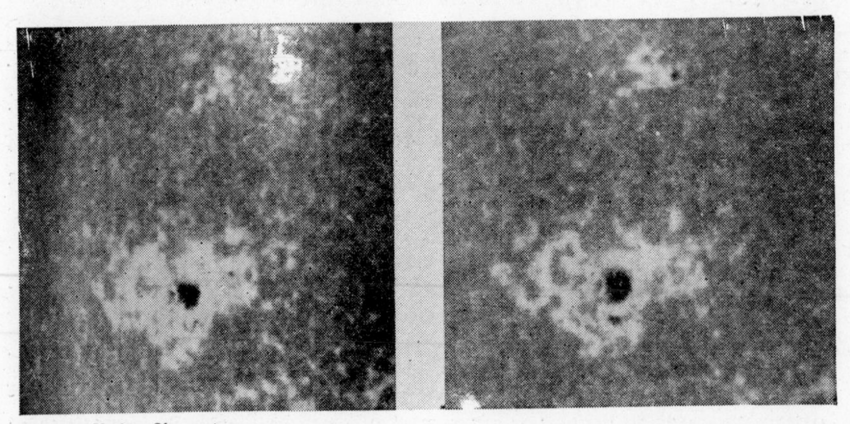

Courtesy Yerkes Observatory

SPECTROHELIOGRAMS SHOWING SUNSPOTS

ments of the solar surface gases. This is accomplished by the spectroheliokinematograph, a further adaptation of the fundamental instrument using moving picture film instead of "stills." The continuous record is much more enlightening than a succession of glimpses at less regular intervals, and through it much is learned about the nature of the solar atmosphere.

There are storms raging on the sun analogous to those on the earth. Great masses of glowing gas appear to gather and precipitate themselves upon the underlying layers, but instead of cooling rain storms, they are rains of very hot gases only relatively cooler than the photosphere itself. Stills from this very special moving picture machine, spectroheliokinematograms, sometimes show prominences or flares of hydrogen gas reaching half a million miles, or more than half the sun's diameter, above the solar disk. Speeds as great as two hundred miles per second are recorded for their movements, so they completely change shape in a few minutes. They are often seen to descend, sometimes several from different directions, into the vortices of what simultaneous direct photographs show to be sunspots. During a total eclipse of the sun, when the disk of the moon just covers the photosphere, the hydrogen prominences are often seen as great red flares projecting from the limb or edge of the sun, since red is the predominant or composite color of hot hydrogen gas as seen by the eye.

MEASURING DIAMETERS OF STARS

We have already indicated that with the two-hundred-inch telescope a few of the nearer giant stars will show apparent diameters appreciably, but hardly measurably, above those of the diffraction disks. To measure a star's diameter, however, the stellar interferometer makes use of the very diffraction disk which is a hindrance to measuring it directly. For the purpose of measuring stellar diameters, the effective aperture of a telescope may be increased by a kind of double periscope arranged above the objective lens to reach out and reflect light on the lens from two more widely separated portions of the incoming cone of light from the star. Each of the periscopes is an aperture and gives rise to a diffraction disk according to the sizes of its mirrors. The light forming their two similar patterns is in a condition to *interfere.*

Light acts in many respects as if it were a series of radiating wavelets. The wavelets will reinforce or cancel one another, depending on the relative positions of the two sources in the intervening media. The interference of the two diffraction disks of the periscopes results in a single diffraction disk crossed by a series of alternating light and dark fringes. Such a pattern is formed by the interferometer for each star or point of light. Suppose, however, that our star is really double, the components being so close that the two fringed diffraction disks superpose. There will be a confusion of the fringes of the two disks, but for a certain separation of the two periscopes corresponding to the separation of the two components of the star, the dark fringes of the one disk will fall upon the bright fringes of the other disk and the fringes will disappear. The application to the measurement of the diameter of a single body is to consider the two halves of such a body as in effect the two components of a double body. Obviously, the method is useful for measuring separations of double stars, but particularly because bad seeing does not affect it as greatly as the more direct methods. The first successful application of the stellar interferometer was the measuring of the diameters of the moons of Jupiter. Later, the diameters of several giant stars were measured. The diameter of the red giant, Betelgeuse, for example, was found to be 270 million miles, three hundred times that of our sun, large enough to include the orbit of Mars. This figure can be verified by less direct calculations based upon the measured distance and radiation of this star.

MATHEMATICS AS AN AID TO VISION

We have now discussed some of the chief instruments by which man has extended his sense or power of vision or sight in the field of astronomy. It may be well to mention another tool or instrument which might be said to extend his power of insight; we refer to that tool of reasoning, the instrument of mathematical logic. A simple illustration from the field of astronomical statistics may be helpful. Suppose we take typical sample patches of the sky and count therein the numbers of stars of each magnitude visible through our largest telescope. Putting these data into our mathematical machine, we find that while at first the ratio of the number of stars of any magnitude to the number of the next brighter magnitude is fairly constant, the ratio gradually becomes smaller until, at the limit of the one-hundred-inch telescope, around the twentieth or twenty-first magnitude, the ratio is only half its value for the brighter stars. By mathematical extrapolation we infer or "see" that after about the thirtieth or thirty-first magnitude there would be no more stars, or in other words, the boundaries of our galaxy or Milky Way system of stars would have been reached. By similar methods we see the rotation of our galaxy, and looking into the interiors of stars, we take their internal temperatures and pressures. But it is to be emphasized that the acuteness and correctness of our insight depend very closely upon our sharpness and accuracy of sight, and that we can get out of our mathematical instrument only results in accord with what we put into it. Mathematics abstracts or idealizes from our experience and like it, therefore, is limited.

Through our various astronomical instruments we have greatly clarified many of our hazy or nebulous notions about the heavenly bodies, including the various celestial nebulosities. The word nebulous means hazy or misty, like a cloud of vapor or gas. That appearance is shared by a variety of astronomical phenomena which upon further resolution are found to be rather different. Some of the nebulous patches in the sky turn out to be really gaseous in nature, like the nebula of the constellation Orion, and those surrounding the bright stars of the Pleiades. But the Milky Way clouds, the cluster in Hercules and others like it, and the Andromeda nebula and other extragalactic nebulae, turn out to be not small gaseous particles relatively near, but actual systems of stars at tremendous distances. In a sense, however, the stars are gigantic particles of giant gases, so perhaps our original idea is not misleading after all. Giant gases at tremendous distances, or dwarf gases nearer by, have about the same appearance. And through the microscope the particles of an ordinary gas become indeed as stars, and through the instruments of mathematical physics we see those single and multiple stars, the atoms and molecules, each with its planets in their orbits, accompanied sometimes by their satellites or moons.

A HOMEMADE 16-INCH REFLECTOR

Mr. Preucil's astronomical photographs which are reproduced in this book were made with this telescope.

Courtesy Frank M. Preucil

GREAT AMATEURS AND THEIR WORK

An amateur is one who engages in a field of endeavor through sheer pleasure of achievement. The efforts of such amateurs have resulted in important contributions to almost all of the fields of knowledge, especially to that of astronomy. Even a brief consideration of the history of this old science reveals how enthusiastic amateurs, inspired by the majesty of their task, have co-operated unselfishly with professional astronomers.

The famous Huyghens was among the first of a noted host of amateur telescope makers. In 1659 he built a telescope with lenses more perfect than those of other astronomers, and was thus able to discover the true appearance of Saturn's rings.

About the time of the American revolution, astronomy was undergoing a change equally revolutionary. A church organist and music teacher by the name of William Herschel became interested in astronomy. This musician ushered in the new era of huge, powerful telescopes. He was dissatisfied with existing telescopes, and, unable to obtain one large enough to suit him, he decided to make his own. After several hundred attempts he mastered the art of grinding and polishing large disks of speculum metal which produced star images much brighter than those in any previous telescopes. His largest telescopes greatly exceeded in size all others of his time. With his powerful, home-made telescopes, Herschel won universal fame by his discoveries. One of the most important accomplishments of this amateur was the discovery of the planet Uranus. For this discovery King George III gave him a pension which enabled him to devote his entire time to astronomy.

There was once an astronomer who, having been assigned to observe and discover double stars with the great forty-inch Yerkes telescope, came to believe that practically everything within its range had been discovered. This complacent belief was effectively shattered by Burnham, a Chicago journalist who mounted a six-inch telescope on a clothes pole in his backyard. Looking up through the smoky air of south Chicago, he discovered several hundred more double stars. European astronomers familiar with his remarkable accomplishments were dumfounded when Burnham showed his visitors the small telescope with its homely mounting. There are amateurs today who in the future may take their places beside Huyghens, Herschel, Burnham, and others whose names are immortal in the annals of astronomy.

A wave of interest in telescope-making has swept the country in recent years. Thousands of people have learned to rub glass disks together with carborundum and water

Courtesy Bausch & Lomb Optical Co.

A COMMERCIAL TELESCOPE

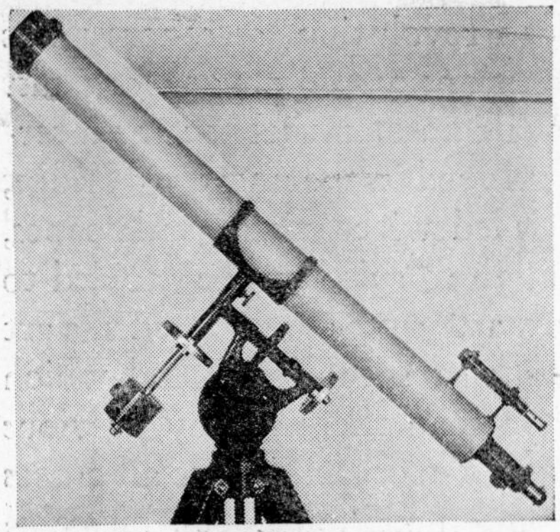

Courtesy Gaertner Scientific Corp.
ANOTHER TYPE OF COMMERCIAL TELESCOPE

through walking around a barrel. One disk is fixed on the barrel top, and the other is rubbed against it as the person walks around the barrel. This results in grinding a parabolic surface on the glass that will become the lens. Some of these people have become lens-grinders, and the difficult task of producing fine optical surfaces is in no danger of becoming a lost art. Amateur astronomy thus finds itself in a greatly strengthened position because of the increased number of excellent telescopes used by amateurs.

In what esteem are amateurs held by the professional astronomers? This question can be answered by mentioning a man who is called the father of the amateur telescope-making movement—Russel W. Porter. Part of his reputation has come about as a result of his ingenious designs for mounting telescopes. Hence, when the two-hundred-inch telescope of Mount Palomar, California, was decided upon, it was Porter whom the authorities asked to help design the world's most difficult mounting.

ASTRONOMY WITHOUT A TELESCOPE

When we compare the power of the one-hundred-inch and many other large telescopes with the seemingly puny six- to twelve-inch telescopes of the amateur astronomer, it appears futile to expect any serious consideration of his work. However, many types of observation are handled better with the smaller instrument. The professional is usually so preoccupied with his larger problems that he leaves some fields wide open for the amateur. As a matter of fact, a telescope is not at all necessary to do comprehensive work in methods of observation. Intelligent, carefully planned observation is winning significant recognition. The greatest volume of amateur work is being done in the fields of variable stars and meteors, both under the direction of, and for, professional astronomers.

Even the methods of reporting data on meteors have come in for their share of attention. Dr. Charles P. Oliver is responsible for the great advances that have been made in this work. He has devised standard ways of reporting meteor observations. This standardization makes possible the correlation of the results obtained from hundreds of individuals.

Photo by Clarence R. Smith

ASTRONOMY WITHOUT A TELESCOPE

Picture of a solar eclipse, from a photo made with an ordinary camera.

The simplest method of meteor observation consists of reclining comfortably in a folding lawn-chair in a spot where one has an unobstructed view of the sky, and then counting the meteors seen in an hour. This is known as a "solo count" and is the type reported by hundreds of persons on the nights when important meteor showers occur. But the lawn-chair doesn't insure a period of comfort and leisure. Amateurs remain at their posts in both warm and cold weather, at all hours of the night when "seeing" is good. When a meteor falls the observer must work swiftly and accurately. The more experienced observer draws the path of each meteor on a special star chart, and records the following data: time of appearance to the nearest second, class, color, magnitude, duration in tenths of a second, duration of train, and a rating of the accuracy of the mapping. Individual mapping can be done for determining the radiant of a meteor shower, but the most valuable mapping is obtained when two or more observers thirty to ninety miles apart plot the same meteors against their different backgrounds of stars. These are known as duplicate observations and are carried out for the purpose of determining the heights at which meteors first meet sufficient friction from the air to become incandescent, and also the altitudes at which they burn out. These heights have been found to vary with different conditions, and this type study is leading to a better understanding of the physical condition of our upper atmosphere.

Professor C. C. Wylie, of the University of Iowa, has directed amateur organizations in group meteor counts throughout the United States. This work has been carried on in order to determine a more reliable ratio of a solo count to the much larger number of meteors that actually would be visible at that point.

Much attention is given to determining the true paths of large fireballs and detonating meteors. In this work, amateur astronomers interview observers of these phenomena and carefully measure the altitude and azimuth of the spot first seen, and the end point. With measurements of the apparent path of the meteor as seen from several widely separated points, it becomes possible to determine the probable landing point of meteorites resulting from the explosion. This has all the fascination of a treasure hunt, and many amateurs have traveled hundreds of miles inter-

A HOMEMADE TELESCOPE AND ITS MAKERS

This small reflecting telescope was made by the young men standing beside it. Its construction required over a year, but their smiles say the labor was justified.

Photo by Frank M. Preucil

viewing farmers, night watchmen, truck-drivers, locomotive engineers, "spooners," newsboys, and frightened housewives, if they report having seen meteors as large as the full moon suddenly blaze across the sky, particularly if they produce a sound like thunder or an explosion. The amateur needs a sense of humor —at least there are occasions when smiles are in order. A few years ago the attention of the Joliet Astronomical Society was directed to an important "find" of what were supposed to be meteorites. Members of the Society soon discovered that the "meteorites" were cinders left by a coal-burning threshing engine!

The advanced amateur with a telescope also contributes to meteoric astronomy by recording the magnitude and direction of the very faint meteors which cross his telescopic field while he is doing other work.

WATCHING THE SKY FOR NOVAE AND COMETS

Most of the bright novae that have been discovered were first seen by amateurs. While no bright novae could long go unnoticed, those reaching only the fourth or fifth magnitude may escape our attention. Many extensive programs have been developed to keep the sky under a more detailed scrutiny. One such program, under the direction of Frank Preucil of Joliet, Illinois, involves the assigning of sky areas of five degrees square to a large number of observers. So far no discoveries have been made, but definite negative results are equally important to statistical studies.

Comet-finding represents another opportunity for the amateur who possesses a small telescope of wide field, plus perseverance. The professional astronomer has practically abandoned comet-finding in favor of observations producing definite results. New comets do not follow schedules, and an amateur might sweep the sky for a lifetime without becoming a discoverer. Nevertheless, the secret urge to immortalize one's name by having the word "comet" attached to it spurs most amateurs occasionally to try this field.

Unusually successful in this branch is Leslie Peltier, a well-known amateur astronomer of the present day. He has five comet discoveries to his credit. An examination of his telescope reveals the year of their discovery carved on its wooden tube, much as the

Photo by Frank M. Preucil

LESLIE PELTIER'S COMET-FINDING TELESCOPE
Note inscriptions on the tube.

Western "bad men" notched their guns to attest to their homicidal prowess. Peltier's telescope, which was lent to him by the Harvard Observatory, is a six-inch refractor especially designed for comet sweeping. Its large, clear field also makes it ideal for observations of the brighter variables, a field in which Peltier has excelled.

OBSERVING VARIABLE STARS AROUND THE WORLD

The Harvard College Observatory has for twenty-five years encouraged the co-operation of serious amateur astronomers. It has done this principally through the American Association of Variable Star Observers, familiarly known as the A.A.V.S.O. Leon Campbell, of Harvard, has been the principal director in this work. Because of the splendid work being done by this group, the professional astronomers have been glad to turn over to the amateurs most of the variable star observations; and thus the professionals are free to turn their attention to other problems.

The English boast that the sun never sets on the British Empire. The A.A.V.S.O. is proud that no variable star can escape its observation. A chain of observers in foreign countries has joined its forces, and although the sun may be shining in America, an observer in Greece or India may catch the sudden rise in brilliance of a variable which may have been at minimum when last observed here. The Association makes record of the changing brightness of some four hundred stars, and has made well over a half million observations in the past twenty-five years. In recent years, an average of over a thousand observations per month have been made.

Amateurs are assigned work in this group only after they have demonstrated their ability to estimate the brightness of variable stars satisfactorily. The active members are furnished with star charts having the variable star in the center of the map. In the surrounding area are the stars visible in the telescopic field, with a carefully selected series of comparison stars whose accurately measured brightness is marked beside them. After locating the variable's field, the observer proceeds to select a comparison star that is just brighter and another that is fainter. He then estimates between them to the tenth part of a magnitude.

There is a fascination in watching these stars. At their maximum they are easily recognized by their red color. One may be several hundred times brighter than when last observed, while another star of fair brilliance may have dropped below the power of the telescope to reveal it. Many of the variables have fairly regular periods ranging through several hundred days, but the ones that keep the amateur "on his toes" are the irregular variables. There are stars which unpredictably increase in brightness a hundredfold after long periods of inactivity. An opposite type remains bright for long periods and then suddenly decreases in brilliance. One star of this type kept the observers on edge for ten years before its fadeout. The amateurs are performing a valuable service in recording these variations, and full credit will be given to them when these recorded light curves aid in solving the mysteries of these stellar enigmas.

Amateur astronomical societies are now engaged in studying occultations and sunspots. They have undertaken an increasingly important photographic program of sky patrol, meteor trails and spectra, and variable star work with color filters.

Amateur astronomers are thrice blessed. They have the same sky to work in as the professionals; most of them have the ability to adapt their own instruments; and their work is desired and appreciated by their big brothers—the professional astronomers.

Photo by Frank M. Preucil

LESLIE PELTIER, ONE OF THE FOREMOST AMATEURS
Peltier has five comet discoveries to his credit.

GALAXIES AND SUPER-GALAXIES

STAR CLOUDS OF THE EVENING SKY

ON ALL SIDES OF THE EARTH, above and below, as far as the eye can see, are the stars—twinkling points of light sprinkled everywhere in the vault of the heavens. The appearance of the sky on a clear evening gives one the impression of infinite calm and peace; it seems almost incredible that each of these stars is in a state of chaos, rushing through space at a speed which startles the imagination.

The Milky Way, stretching across the sky like a great arch of light in an almost continuous band, comprises almost ninety per cent of the stars which can be seen with the unaided eye. As the glance travels away from this bright belt of the heavens, the number of visible stars diminishes gradually until in the region of the polestar, Polaris, few can be seen.

The Milky Way itself is believed by astronomers to be a tremendous number of distant stars distributed regularly in a disk-shaped universe. Imagine a greatly flattened, watch-shaped mass revolving about its own center, and you will have a picture of the Milky Way system, or galaxy; but the sun and its planets are inside this system—buried in the countless number of stars—so that from the earth only a portion of the galaxy is visible.

Between the sun and these stars are great clouds of obscuring matter which blot out many of the stars and cause the Milky Way

Courtesy Yerkes Observatory

A GROUP OF DISTANT GALAXIES

to be seen as an irregularly shaped border. When the Milky Way is observed with a telescope, the dark clouds can be seen against the brightness of the star belt. Great wisps of nebulosity stretch across the sky like filmy silk. These are clouds of meteoric matter which reflect the light of nearby stars. Other clouds completely blot out the light beyond. In the region of the Milky Way, comprising the constellation Sagittarius, they resemble the head of a gigantic horse.

Although these clouds have an appearance of solidity, they are, in reality, extremely tenuous. It has been possible, through the association of these nebulae with stars, to determine their distances from the sun, and from these distances, their diameters can be found. Like the stars, these nebulae show motion. Their velocities have been found comparable to those of average stars in that their speed does not exceed ten to fourteen miles per second. Some of the nebulae approach the earth, some recede. For instance, the sun and the great nebula in Orion are moving away from each other at the rate of 340 million miles per year. But, to show how distant the nebula is, there would be no appreciable change in its apparent diameter in ten thousand years.

Courtesy Yerkes Observatory

DARK AND BRIGHT AREAS IN THE MILKY WAY

The internal heat of some of the stars reaches an unbelievable intensity. The Milky Way is made up of objects ranging in surface temperatures from almost absolute zero to 50,000° Fahrenheit. Astronomers have explained this tremendous range in temperature by the difference in the development and age of the various members of the galaxy.

THE BIRTH OF A STAR

One of the most striking astronomical objects, seen in our galaxy and others, is the nova, or so-called new star: one which appears where no bright star was seen before. This phenomenon is so striking that it has greatly influenced the development of astronomy. Perhaps even the Star of Bethlehem was a nova.

On February 22, 1901, there first appeared the brilliant star, Nova Persei. Only three days earlier photographs had been taken of the region, and it had been inconspicuous in the field. Within three days it had blazed out with the suddenness of an explosion to a brightness one hundred thousand times its previous luminosity! As suddenly, too, it declined in brightness. In a single day

Courtesy Yerkes Observatory

NOVA HERCULIS BEFORE AND AFTER THE OUTBURST

it lost two-thirds of its brightness. At the end of little more than a year, it was again an inconspicuous object in the sky. Nova Herculis increased its brightness by one hundred and fifty thousand times within a day or two. About twenty novae have been seen with the unaided eye.

The outstanding features of these novae are their changes in luminosity. No forewarning is given. They suddenly blaze forth

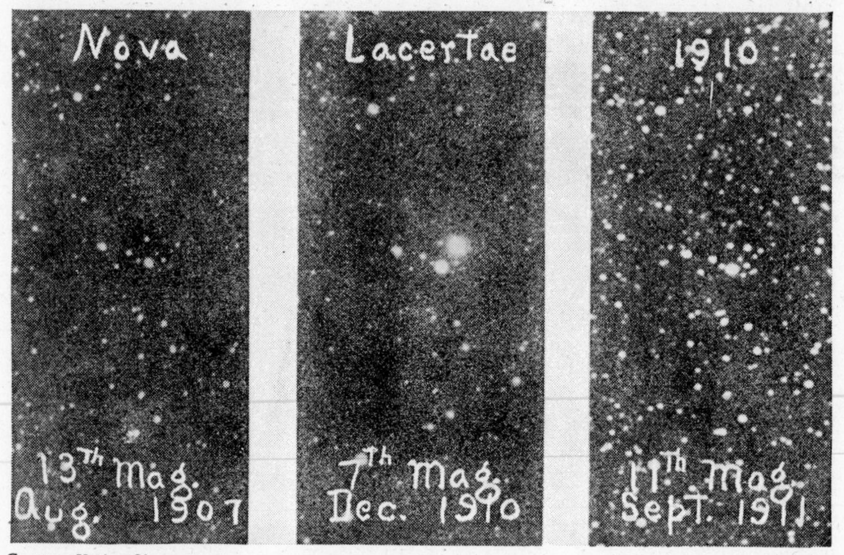

Courtesy Yerkes Observatory

ANOTHER STAR THAT BLAZED AND FADED

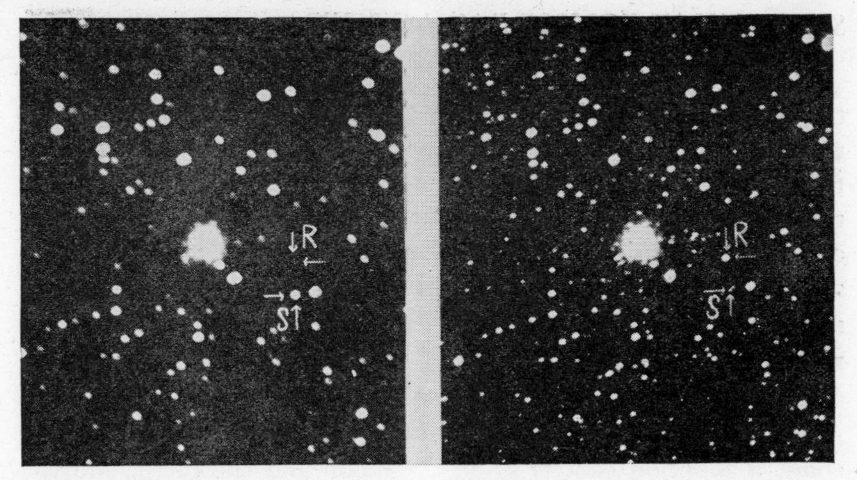

Courtesy Yerkes Observatory

PICTURES MADE AT DIFFERENT TIMES
The arrows point to stars that varied in brightness.

and as suddenly diminish. Between twenty and thirty novae are seen in our galaxy every year. At that rate, since the beginning of the geologic history of the earth, from twenty to thirty billions of novae have appeared. Astronomers have concluded that there are between twenty and thirty billion stars in the galaxy!

Two alternatives are apparent. Either each star, during its history, becomes a nova for a relatively short period of time, or certain stars become novae time after time. If the first view is correct, then the sun will some time blaze out as a nova, destroying all its planets. On the other hand, some novae have reappeared in the same place time after time. Thus, astronomers have taken the latter view—"once a nova, always a nova."

What causes novae? Astronomers cannot answer this question, because if they try to explain novae, they must explain the appearance of Cepheid variables. The Cepheid stars also vary in the amount of light which they radiate, but their variations are almost simple when compared with the changes in the luminosity of the novae: Cepheids pulsate; novae seem to explode. Astronomers have much to learn concerning the constitution of stars before they can find reasons for the existence of certain types of variable stars.

STARS THAT ECLIPSE EACH OTHER

Other types of variable stars to be found in the galaxy are the binaries. It has been known for centuries that certain stars revolve one about another, composing a gravitational system of two or more stars. The amount of light given off by certain types of these systems varies, but the variation of light in this case has its physical interpretation. The oldest known two-star systems are the eclipsing binary stars. If we were to imagine a solar eclipse in which the moon passes between the earth and the sun, we would have a picture of what occurs in the case of an eclipsing binary. The light of one star, as seen from the earth, is cut off by another passing before it. Since the two stars rotate about a common center, as do the moon and the earth, and the earth and the sun, each star eclipses the other over a given period of time. Now, if one star is larger than the other, the rotation is easily observable. The brightest star in the heavens, Sirius, was observed to have a faint companion which radiated very little light. The possibility that these binary and multiple stars may be a direct outgrowth of certain phenomena relating to the birth of stars is being investigated by astronomers at present.

PLANETARY NEBULAE

Another interesting object in the skies is the planetary nebula. The name of this object is quite misleading, because it is not related to a planet; it appears in the telescope as a faint star surrounded by one or more rings, or shells, of matter. These nebulae can be seen distributed over the entire sky. They rotate and have their own independent velocities. Astronomers have found it very difficult to determine the distances to these stars. It is suspected, however, that they are millions of times larger than our sun. Perhaps the planetary nebulae have developed from novae. Astronomers are not certain, however, and the nature of planetary nebulae remains an unsolved problem.

Different features of the sky have been described because astronomers perceive a definite relation between some of them.

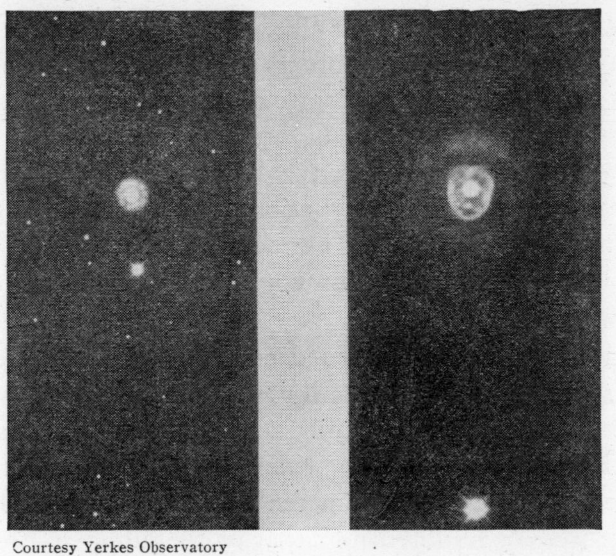

Courtesy Yerkes Observatory

PLANETARY NEBULAE, EACH "LIKE A DIAMOND IN THE SKY"

Courtesy Lick Observatory

THE RING NEBULA IN LYRA

Nebulae, that is, the filament-like nebulosities which stretch for millions of miles inside the borders of our galaxy and others, are thought to represent the first stage of development of stars. After the stars have developed, the binary and multiple stars appear—probably developed by fission, the dividing of single stars because of their instability. This designation of the different stages in the development of stars is only tentative, in the light of the additional knowledge which is constantly being garnered by astronomers.

Nothing has been mentioned concerning the different kinds of single stars found in the Milky Way. They are of every conceivable kind, temperature, and size, from those millions of times larger than the sun to those which are smaller than the earth. Their temperatures vary from ten times hotter than the sun to temperatures one hundredth of that of the sun.

Consideration will now be given to the other galaxies, their relation to the Milky Way systems, their distances, and their dimensions.

THE UNIVERSE

Universe means *everything*. It is at first difficult to see why the astronomers use the term to mean that which was once thought to exist instead of what is now known to exist. To the modern scientist, the term *universe* indicates that the general knowledge of present-day astronomy has far surpassed the original conception of the universe.

With a stroke of his pen, as it were, the astronomer has leaped into space. He has given his mind freedom and what has been thought of as *the* universe is now thought of as *a* universe. By the use of modern telescopes, the astronomer can look into the far reaches of space and by means of light rays which have come pulsating through space, for untold centuries, he can see the condition and growth of other island universes. The great boundary formed by the Milky Way is only a boundary for *our* star system and not for the upper realm of the universe.

MEASURING THE UNIVERSE

Courtesy Yerkes Observatory

DR. HARLOW SHAPLEY
Director of Harvard Observatory

According to Harlow Shapley, director of Harvard Observatory, man is "in the middle" in relation to the rest of the known physical universe, since the physical units range from protons and electrons to atoms, molecules, *man*, worlds, solar systems, and galaxies—each a small unit in itself when compared with the next higher unit. It is not strange that he seeks light on the mysteries of the largest and the smallest. His research has been tending toward a discovery of the secrets of the infinitely great and the infinitely small. In his study of the galaxies, he must use the smallest measuring units available in order to measure the spectrum of color range of those objects which are almost infinitely distant.

For many, many years the earth was thought to be the center of the universe. The sun, the moon, and the stars seemed to be moving around the earth. The great Galileo, who actually used the first telescope, was constantly obstructed by the Church and the secular government because of his insistence that the earth was not the center of the universe.

At present, the astronomer can utilize research of the infinitesimally small and correlate it with his study of the infinitely large. The astronomer uses such units as electrons and protons, and quadrillionths of an inch (10^{-15}) to analyze the light which he receives from the stars and galaxies.

In the laboratory, special units are used to measure the smallest lengths, such as angstroms, which measure to one-billionth of an inch. The immense size of the cosmos forces the astronomer to assume longer units, because the lengths are too great to be measured. He first adopted the distance to the sun—ninety-three million miles—and called it an astronomical unit, but as his research continued, and as he took longer and surer steps into space, he found this unit too small.

At present, the astronomer uses a measuring-stick which is about six trillion miles long. This unit is the light-year, and is the distance which light, traveling at about 186 thousand miles per second, traverses in one year. The star Proxima Centauri is the closest to the sun. A ray of light leaving that star would have to travel for about four and one-half years before it would reach the sun, and for each of those years that light would be speeding through space at a velocity of 186 thousand miles per second. In one year it would go six trillion miles! The unaided human eye can see stars which are about one thousand light-years away. In other words, the light gathered by the eye focused on one of

THE GREAT GALAXY IN ANDROMEDA

Compare the upper lefthand part of the picture with the enlarged view on the next page.

Courtesy Yerkes Observatory

THE GREAT GALAXY IN ANDROMEDA
Magnification of the upper left corner of the view on the preceding page shows the white patches to be "clouds" of stars.

Courtesy Yerkes Observatory

those distant points of illumination, started on its journey one thousand years ago. Such a star could be obscured from view and man would not be aware of the event until centuries had passed.

THE ISLAND UNIVERSE IN ANDROMEDA

Seen high in the sky, during the winter months in the northern hemisphere, directly on the opposite side of the polestar from the Big Dipper, is the constellation Andromeda. Hidden almost from view because of its smallness to the eye, a tiny patch of light can be seen in that constellation. That patch of light is the great nebula, or galaxy, in Andromeda—one of the giants of the heavens. This galaxy or, as it is now called, island universe, is a thing so large that light, traveling at the rate of 186 thousand miles per second, takes fifty thousand years to cross it. It is so distant that we are seeing it as it appeared almost a million years ago! To the eye it appears as a nebulous patch of light; thus the ancients called it a nebula.

The Andromeda nebula was one of the most interesting of the objects in the sky to the early astronomers, because it was the only galaxy which could be seen by the unaided eye. From the quality of its light, it used to be called a "white nebula." When Lord Rosse's six-foot telescope was used to examine this object, it was found to be of spiral structure; it was therefore called a spiral nebula. Marius, examining Andromeda telescopically in 1612, described it as looking like a "candle light seen through a horn."

A nova, or new star, which appeared almost in the heart of the nebula in 1885, directed so much attention to this object that it was photographed in 1887 by Isaac Roberts. Even then, and for many years afterward, its true nature was not realized. It was thought to be partially condensed nebulous matter surrounded by gases, existing inside or near the boundaries of the Milky Way.

When astronomers began to determine the velocities of stars in the line of sight by the measurements of the displacements of their spectral lines, they applied this method to the Andromeda galaxy. They were astonished to find that it is approaching our galaxy with a velocity of about two hundred miles per second! This speed was so much greater than that of average stars that it was obvious that the nebula was not a member of our Milky Way system, but an external object which was approaching at a great speed. Only when many more novae were discovered, and after years of research, which included Edwin Hubble's outstanding studies, was it conceded that the Andromeda galaxy was a true star system.

The history of the investigations of the Andromeda galaxy has been sketched in order to show how rapidly progress has been made in recent years. Within a few short years, this insignificant and gaseous star grew in the minds of astronomers from a condensation of nebulous material, hidden deeply in our galaxy, to a spiral galaxy, containing billions of stars, and located at a tremendous distance from the sun. When the galaxy is resolved by the modern telescope, it is seen to be composed of stars as large as, and larger than, our sun—stars which distance has smoothed out to the vision so that they cannot be seen individually.

The Andromeda is in every way comparable to the Milky Way galaxy and is only a representative of the millions of island universes, each a system in itself, pulsating their stories to the eye by means of light rays.

CLUSTERS OF STARS

Just outside of the borders of the Andromeda galaxy there are over one hundred globular clusters, similar to the globular clusters seen relatively near to the Milky Way galaxy. It will be best at this point to examine the relation of globular clusters to the galaxy, since they appear to be an ever-present part of the island universe system.

A GLOBULAR CLUSTER OF STARS

Globular clusters are condensed regions of stars.

Courtesy Lick Observatory

THE PLEIADES CLUSTER

White masses which appear as single stars in the picture consist of probably millions of separate stars.

Courtesy Lick Observatory

Globular clusters are very remarkable features of the sky when seen through the telescope. They are condensed regions of stars; that is, a great number of stars seem to be clustered about one point. So far as the Milky Way system is concerned, there are two types of clusters: the galactic cluster, which is scattered throughout the galaxy, and the exterior or globular cluster, which is generally exterior to it. Even the sun is a part of a galactic cluster, and there are many suns with approximately the same speeds and motions in each galaxy.

Astronomers disagree as to the physical relation of globular clusters to the galaxy proper. Some claim that the clusters are a framework for the entire star system of island universes, while others contend that the exterior clusters, at least, are independent systems, probably older—older, perhaps by billions of years—than the spiral system with which they are connected. Whether they are related is immaterial to the general observation that they do seem to be near all spiral galaxies which can be resolved into star systems by the human eye.

Some of the clusters are so far away that they cannot be seen with the unaided eye; but when seen with the telescope, they are overwhelmingly magnificent astronomical objects—with innumerable stars seeming to branch or flow out in all directions. Their centers are so thickly crowded with stars that, when a photographic plate is exposed to the globular cluster for a long period of time, a solid white mass is seen.

From the astronomer's point of view, the globular cluster is important because it is helpful in determining distances to the exterior galaxies. The light of most stars is steady, but there are a few whose light fluctuates from bright to faint and then bright again, as though someone were regularly decreasing and then increasing the current in an electric lamp. Delta Cephei is such a star; its cycle is repeated regularly every five days. This star is inside our galaxy and is relatively close. Its distance has been measured by ordinary surveyor's methods, and its candle power was similarly determined.

FLICKERING LIGHTHOUSES OF THE SKY

The globular clusters contain many of such Cepheid variables; it is found that they all appear equally bright. As they are approximately at the same distance, they must all actually have the same candle power. After much astronomical research, it has been found that all those stars which behave like Delta Cephei have exactly the same candle power as Delta Cephei. Other stars were found which varied in the amount of light which they radiated, but their periods of radiation were different from that of Delta Cephei. Again, all those which had the same time of fluctuation were found to have the same brightness, which was originally found by calculating the distance of a star close to the earth.

Thus the candle power of a Cepheid can be found by noting the period, or cycle, of its light variation, and then its distance

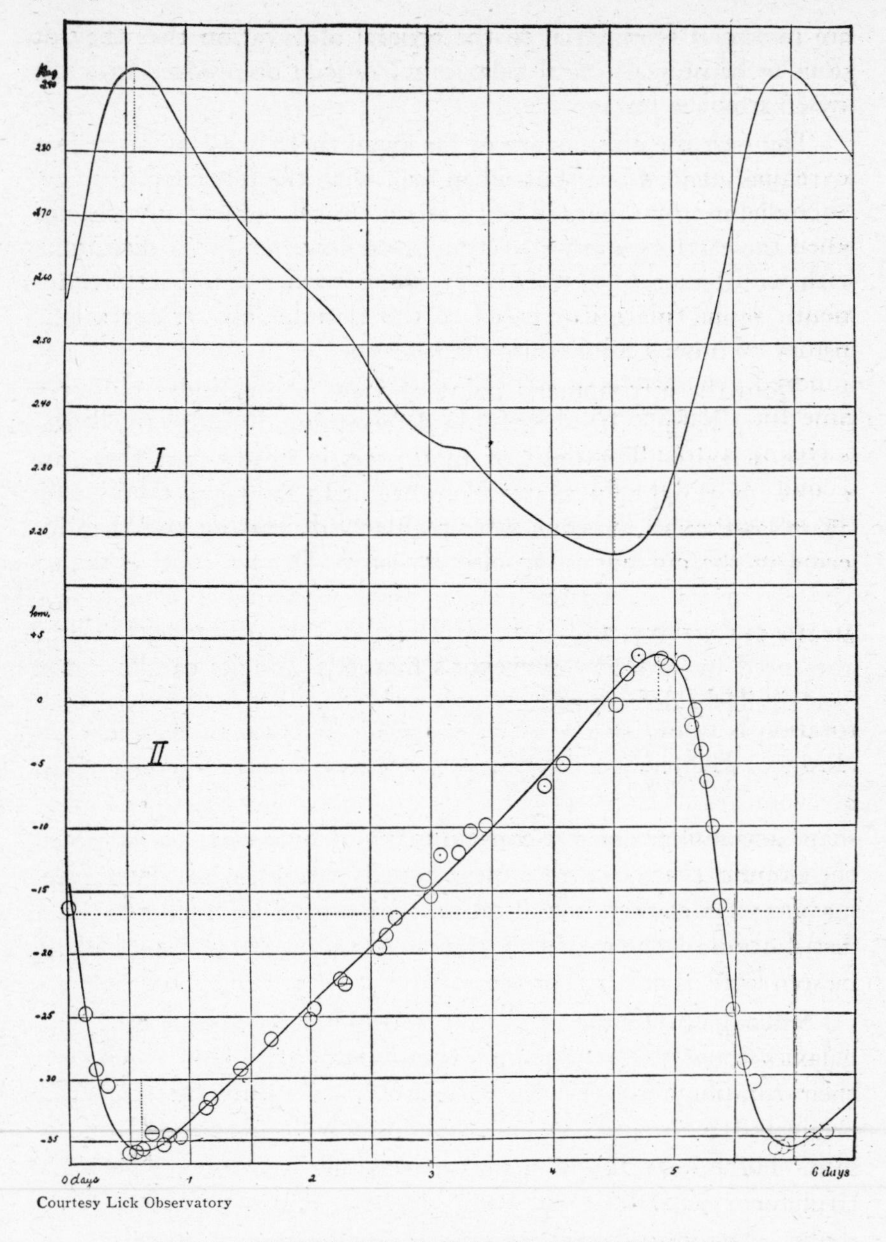

Courtesy Lick Observatory

LIGHT AND VELOCITY CURVES OF A VARIABLE STAR

The upper curve shows how the star Delta Cephei wanes and waxes every five days. The lower curve shows how the velocity changes with respect to the observer.

can be found from its apparent brightness. The distances to the globular clusters have been accurately determined by means of these variable stars.

The nearest of the exterior, or globular, clusters proves to be so remote that its light takes about eighteen thousand years to reach the earth. The light of this cluster started on its journey when the earth was covered with primeval forests and populated with wild beasts, and when man was just beginning his development. While this light journeyed to the earth, all of the recorded history of man took place; empires rose, fell, and decayed; six hundred generations of man lived and died. It has taken all this time for the light from the nearest globular cluster to reach us, traveling through space at the rate of 186 thousand miles per second. The farthest globular cluster is ten times farther than the nearest—that is, 186 thousand light years—while the nearest island universe is four times that distance from the earth.

MOVEMENT OF THE STARS

It should be noted here that it is a generally accepted fact that rotation is found in the island universes, but not in the globular clusters. The lack of rotation in the clusters is due to their stage of evolution. This is the impressive fact that scientists see in the shape and dimensions of these clusters. The symmetrical shape of the globular cluster indicates that it has reached a stage of dynamic maturity. Although their member stars also move in and out, the distribution of the mass is not essentially disturbed. This, as will be seen later, is not true of the galaxy.

Since galaxies and certain clouds of stars found near the galaxies show the effects of unequal distribution of masses in their rotation, it is improbable that the globular clusters have originated as the beautifully symmetrical systems which are now seen. The possibility of the cluster's disintegrating from its beautiful form because of the motion of the individual stars is very slight. Astronomers have figured that a given star will have a close approach with another—in a globular cluster—once in a hundred billion years! And perhaps thousands of these near ap-

Courtesy Lick Observatory

A SYMMETRICAL STAR CLUSTER

proaches among the stars are necessary to cause any marked difference in the shape of the system as it now appears.

It was remarked in passing that there was a controversy among astronomers concerning the possible relation, from a physical and gravitational point of view, of the globular cluster to the island universe. Some astronomers have explained the presence of the galactic clusters, mentioned earlier, by assuming close approach of a globular cluster with the galaxy—hence an intermingling of stars. This might well be true. At one time or another, in its flight through the space of the intergalactic regions, it may approach another, or perhaps greater cluster. Then, perhaps, because of the mutual attractions of the two systems, it may rush into the other and intermingle with it. Thus, a system such as our galaxy may be formed. After a long period of time, the globular cluster will again result because of the dynamical evolution of the galaxy.

About thirty years ago, astronomers, ever wakeful to the possibilities of the secrets to be found in the motions of stars, noted that many of the interior groups, or galactic clusters, exhibited motions which were both alike and parallel. This type of research was necessary in order to determine the dimensions and general properties of our own Milky Way galaxy, or island universe, so that these results might be used in turn to find the properties of other greatly distant island universes.

By noting the positions of these stars with precise measurements, and then after a lapse of a considerable number of years again measuring the positions of the same stars, their displacements are determined. Astronomers have found that these stars are moving across the sky as a family. The motions of these stars are found to converge; that is, it seems as though they are all rushing through space toward a certain point.

Astronomers realize, however, that they are dealing with perspective; that is, they are situated at the side of a family of stars which are actually speeding along in parallel directions. If a person were to stand about twenty or thirty feet away from the straightaway of a railroad track, he would see the rails seemingly converge at a distant point. This is exactly the explanation which astronomers give to the apparent motions of galactic clusters.

One family of stars, known as the Taurus cluster, has been examined very thoroughly. The results of the investigation follow: The group is made up of about seventy-five stars, similar in size. They are moving in parallel lines at a speed relative to the sun of about thirty miles per second. These stars are over 780 trillion miles away from the earth! From the determination, not only of their speed but of the *direction* of their speed, it is known that almost a million years ago this cluster was exactly half its present distance away from the solar system. Fifty million years hence they will be at a distance so remote that they will be seen as a compact group of stars, occupying half the field of a large telescope. The direction of this cluster is toward a distant point of the galaxy, and eventually it will no longer be seen.

Courtesy Yerkes Observatory

THE CONSTELLATION COMA BERENICES
Some of these stars are moving together through space.

If the distance between the earth and a galaxy—in this case we are speaking only of the arms of the galaxy—decreases, all of the spectrum lines are increased in pitch, that is, shifted toward the violet. If the distance between the two objects is increased, all of the spectrum lines are decreased in pitch or shifted toward the red.

In the discussion of motions, the use of the "shift" of spectral lines is very important. A shift toward the red indicates an increase in the distance between the light-giving object and the earth; a shift toward the violet indicates that the distance between the object and the earth is decreasing. It can be seen now how important is the use of the spectroscope in finding the rotations, distances, and observable speeds of all of the exterior island universes.

The Taurus group occupies space in the form of a sphere, the

Courtesy Lick Observatory

THE PLEIADES REGION IN THE NIGHT SKY

diameter of which is thirty-five light-years—two hundred trillion miles. Although the stars of this group are separated by tremendous distances—on an average of fifty trillion miles apart—they are very definitely a family, because they speed through space together, in parallel paths. This family will probably remain related for millions of years; just as will the larger system of which it is a member—the Milky Way. As was mentioned earlier, groups of stars such as these must have had a common origin, although at present it is not known. Some time, far in the future, however, this cluster and all like it are doomed to disintegrate. This is understood to be true because of the disturbing forces to which they are subjected as they pass through space.

Many other families of clusters are known, such as the Pleiades and the Perseus groups. Some of these clusters, such as the Pleiades, are at present so far away that they cover only a small area of the sky.

Courtesy Yerkes Observatory

J. C. KAPTEYN

THE MOTIONS OF STARS IN CLUSTERS

As important as these investigations of the families or clusters of stars have been, certain associated studies have cast more light on the understanding of this and other galaxies of stars. J. C. Kapteyn discovered in 1901 that the stars belong to one of two classes, or streams, which move in opposite directions. These streams are not related in precisely the same manner as the Taurus or Perseus clusters, since they do not move with the relative speeds or in exactly parallel paths. These two star streams, as Kapteyn discovered, present a phenomenon which shows strikingly the organization and motions of a typical island universe.

It has been found that the sun is speeding through the sky at different velocities with relation to different stars; that is, with respect to stars of low velocity the speed of the sun is low, but with respect to stars of much higher velocity the speed of the sun is much greater. This means only that different classes of stars are moving with different speeds in relation to one another. Probably each class of stars is a great star cloud like those seen in distant parts of the galaxy. That there are two star streams means that these great clouds of stars are intermingling and passing through each other.

This passage of star clouds through one another is simpler than might at first be imagined. The distances between stars are so great that there is little, if any, chance for even *one* of the stars to encounter another, even though there are millions of stars in each stream! If one could imagine two particles of dust separated by a distance of four miles, one would have an approximate picture of the average distance between two stars in these two star streams.

What are the chances for these stars to make close approaches, if given random motions? They are very slight.

For many years after the discovery of the two star streams, astronomers decided to accept the phenomenon as it stood, with little or no explanation for it. In late years, however, explanations of the two-star-stream hypothesis have been numerous and varied, but one explanation stands out above all others: two star streams signify galactic rotation. If the stars of certain types are held together by the unseen but strong bonds of gravity, they will move more or less as a stream. If the galaxy is rotating, then these streams will not describe a purely circular motion about its center. Instead, they will pass around the center by speeding toward one edge of the galaxy, then changing their direction and speeding toward another edge in the path of an ellipse.

MEASURING THE ROTATION OF GALAXIES

We see then the first picture of rotation of these galaxies, which we have been pleased to call island universes. Each of these universes is rotating about its center, making these rotations in periods ranging from millions to billions of years. A galaxy then cannot be thought of as only an immense aggregation of stars, but rather as a dynamic organism, with each of its units dependent upon another for its life. The disk-like shape of the distant island universe implies its rotation. The study of its spectra substantiates this. It is, however, more difficult to determine the period of rotation for our galaxy than it is for exterior galaxies.

THE PERIOD OF ROTATION

The method of determining the period of rotation of other island universes is comparatively simple. By means of the spectroscope the velocities of the opposite sides of the distant universes can be found. It has been discovered that when one side of the galaxy shows approach, the other shows the opposite effect. Therefore, the only conclusion which can logically be reached is that the galaxy is rotating. With the spectroscope this rotation can be measured quite accurately. The Doppler effect can be illustrated as follows:

While people stand near the tracks of a railroad, they notice that, as a train is approaching, the pitch of the whistle noticeably increases, and, as it rushes away, its pitch decreases. As the distance increases, the pitch is lowered, and when the distance decreases, the pitch is raised. This same effect is true in the case of light. A luminous body approaching the earth has its color pitch raised, so to speak; and as it recedes from the earth its color pitch decreases. Lines on the spectrum are more or less equivalent to notes on a musical scale, because a spectrum is merely a light scale. The highest notes of the musical scale correspond to the violet light, while the lowest notes correspond to the red light.

Courtesy Yerkes Observatory

THIS GALAXY APPEARS TO BE ROTATING

If the distance between the earth and a galaxy—in this case we are speaking only of the arms of the galaxy—decreases, all of the spectrum lines are increased in pitch, that is, shifted toward the violet. If the distance between the two objects is increased, all of the spectrum lines are decreased in pitch or shifted toward the red.

In the discussion of motions, the use of the "shift" or spectral lines is very important. When a shift toward the red is spoken of, it will mean an increase in the distance between the object and the earth; when the shift is toward the violet, the distance between the object and the earth is decreasing. It can be seen now how important is the use of the spectroscope in finding the rotations, distances, and observable speeds of all of the exterior island universes.

UNSTABLE UNIVERSES

As for our own galaxy, it is accepted as a fact that it is in a state of rotation. Recent research shows that its theoretical rotation agrees very well with the observable motions of its component parts. The motions of the star streams indicate that the entire galaxy is rotating about its center with a period of about 350 million years. What if the gravitational attraction of the island universe should disappear? In the study of the stars, such as the sun, it has been found that they are throwing off tremendous quantities of matter in the form of radiation. The sun loses 131 trillion tons of matter per year! Since gravitation depends upon mass, it is not at all impossible that, as time goes on, the stars of the island universes will lose their attraction for one another.

THE LAWS OF GRAVITATION

If the mutual gravitational attraction of stars were suddenly lost, the curved paths of the stars would become straight lines along which they would travel with their present speeds. Their paths would be unaffected by the gravitational pull of any other

Courtesy Yerkes Observatory

A GALAXY APTLY CALLED THE "WHIRLPOOL"

Each island universe is rotating about its center, the stars being held in their positions by gravitational attraction.

stars, and they would continue on their journey, scattering throughout space. Although a sudden loss of gravitational attraction is practically impossible, a gradual loss of gravitational pull is occurring. It is calculated that the size of the Andromeda nebula will double in about thirty-five million million years from the loss of mutual attraction of its individual members.

It has been shown how the motion of the island universe affects its shape. Nearly all of the watch-shaped, or very oblate, exterior galaxies are spiral in form with two arms coiling outward from a center or nucleus, which is thickly crowded with stars. These spirals are of various types: some have almost all of their mass concentrated at the center; in others much of the mass is found in the arms. It is these arms which are actually measured by the spectroscope for rotation.

EDGEWISE VIEW OF A SPIRAL NEBULA

Courtesy Yerkes Observatory

THE GREATER MAGELLANIC CLOUD
This group of stars is actually a great cloud scattered over a large area.

Courtesy Lick Observatory

It was mentioned that the Andromeda galaxy is a spiral. Astronomers are agreed that the Milky Way galaxy, like Andromeda, also is a spiral. This is important because it will lead to a better understanding of the evolution of the island universes.

One of the closest of the celestial conglomerations is the vast Greater Magellanic Cloud, which was first seen by Magellan on his famous trip around the world. This object is neither a globular cluster nor a rotating galaxy. It is larger than the average globular cluster, but is smaller than either the Andromeda or Milky Way galaxy. This group of stars is actually a great cloud which is scattered over a large area. These star clouds are considered by astronomers to be an intermediate development between the older globular cluster and the very young spiral.

THE MILKY WAY AND ITS NEIGHBORS

In order to define the subject of island universes more clearly, astronomers have assumed that the Milky Way galaxy is a typical island universe. It is a relatively thin disk of stars, similar in shape to thousands of other known galaxies, with a thickness of about six thousand light-years and a diameter of about one hundred thousand light-years. It contains between twenty and thirty billion stars. Some estimates have set the number at fifty billion! The local cluster of stars to which the sun belongs is speeding about the center of the galaxy at the rate of 250 miles per second. The path of this cloud has been shown to be not a simple circular path, but a more or less closed path by which it makes a circuit of this gigantic galaxy once in about fifty million years.

There are many of these clouds, all revolving about the galactic plane in periods averaging about 150 million years. This shows that the sun is relatively close to the center of the galaxy. Among these star clouds are the more intimately related star families such as the Taurus cluster, but there are many more single unrelated stars. The irregularities of the Milky Way system, as seen in the difference of the paths of the individual clusters, the sprinkling of nebulae throughout the galaxy, the different types, sizes, and temperatures of the individual stars—all these show that this galaxy is relatively immature.

Distributed outside the borders of the Milky Way are the globular clusters, much more regular in form than the island universe with which it seems to be related. Farther off can be seen the Magellanic Cloud. With this picture of an isolated galaxy and its immediate surroundings in mind, it will be possible to fathom the depths of space and look into the distances and velocities of the other island universes.

Five galaxies are within one million light-years of the position which we now occupy in the heavens. Many thousands of these galaxies, however, are within reach of the greatest telescopes. None can be seen through or near the Milky Way belt itself. The lack of visible galaxies near this region is accounted for by the great masses of black or obscuring matter found near that great belt of stars. The same obscuring matter can also be seen in the dis-

Courtesy Lick Observatory

VIEWS OF DISTANT GALAXIES SHOWING SIMILAR OBSCURING MATTER

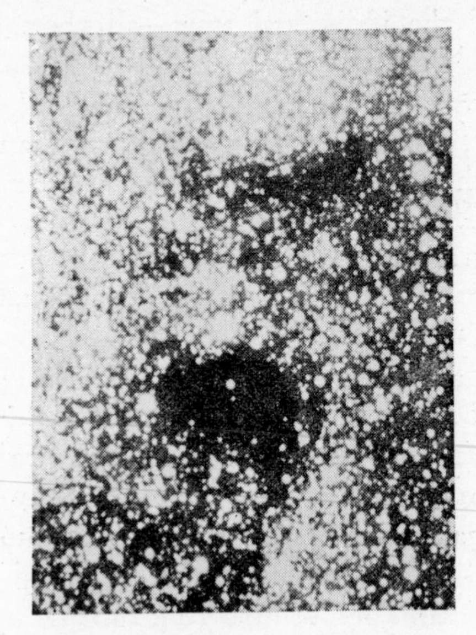

A DARK SPOT IN THE MILKY WAY

Courtesy Yerkes Observatory

tant island universes which present their sides to the observers; so it is accepted that the apparent absence of the galaxies near the galactic center is due only to a physical obstruction.

It has been mentioned that the Magellanic Clouds are the nearest of the distant island universes. Only thirty-five years ago it was thought that these clouds were but detached fragments of our system. However, it has been found that the larger of these clouds is almost ninety thousand light-years from the solar system. Its speed is 175 miles per second and is one of recession, as found by the spectroscope. To show the immensity of this distance in relation to its velocity, it may be stated that the distance of this cloud from the solar system will not increase more than ten per cent in the next ten million years!

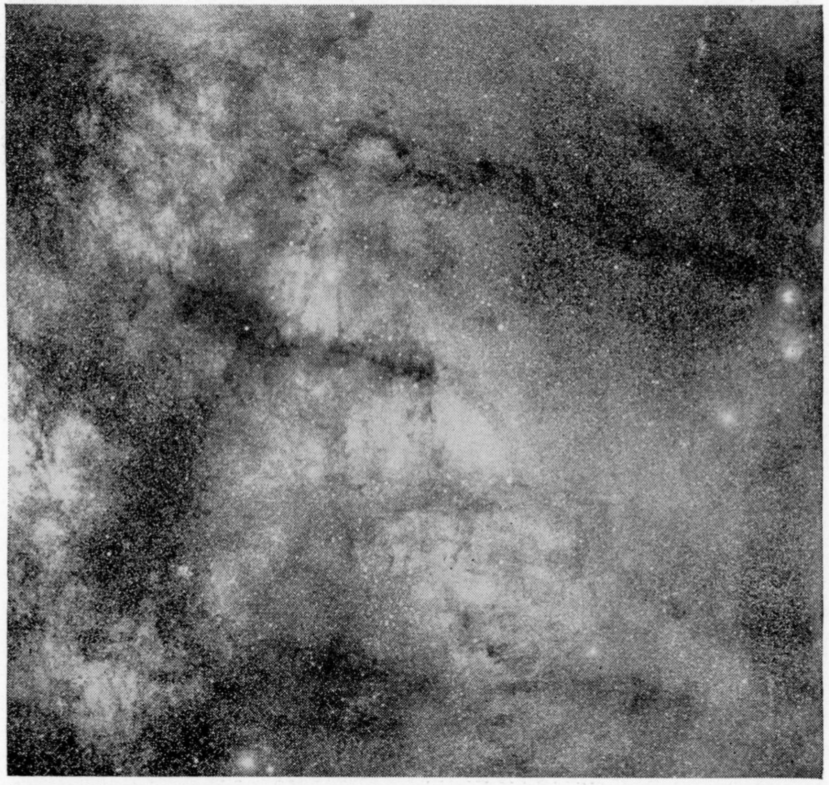

Courtesy Yerkes Observatory

THE MILKY WAY IN SAGITTARIUS, OPHIUCHUS, AND SCORPIUS

The larger cloud is about twenty thousand light-years in diameter; hence it is one-fifth smaller than the Milky Way system, and about one-half the size of an average globular cluster.

The smaller of the clouds, called the Lesser Magellanic Cloud, is more remote. It is at a distance of about one hundred thousand light-years, and is receding from our solar system at the rate of 110 miles per second. Its diameter is ten thousand light-years.

It was only a few years ago that astronomers measured the distances to these clouds and thought them to be exceedingly remote. Now they are considered our immediate neighbors, because there is a space of almost seven hundred light-years between these clouds and the next distant galaxy. At that distance we observe a very small galaxy which astronomers call by number, N. G. C. 6822. This greatly remote island universe can be seen far beyond the stars located in the region of Sagittarius.

At a distance of almost nine hundred thousand light-years, seen in the direction of the constellation Triangulum, is another spiral galaxy. Then, almost one million light-years distant is the great Andromeda nebula, which has already been described. By means of the spectroscope, the Andromeda galaxy is found to be approaching the earth with a velocity of about 190 miles per second.

THE UNIVERSE ON A SMALL SCALE

Thus the great island universes seen in a sphere the radius of which is one million light-years have been pictured. But man has not been satisfied with the knowledge of these five island universes. He has actually gone out to distances five hundred times as great! Several thousands of island universes within ten million light-years have been observed and charted. Not only have these galaxies been noted, but their diameters, distances, and shapes have been calculated. Within a radius of five hundred million light-years there are almost one hundred million galaxies!

But what, actually, is the meaning of a distance such as five hundred million light-years? To the average mind, a tremendous measurement of space is involved. The immensity of this distance, however, challenges the most vivid imagination. It will be best to

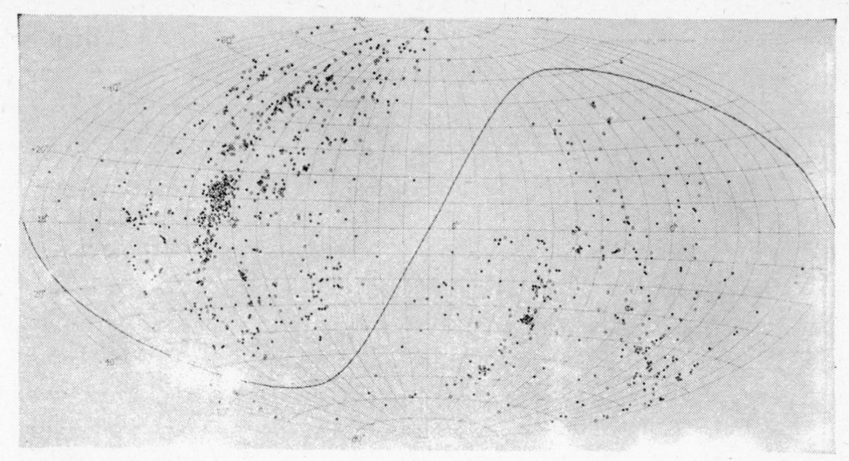

Courtesy Yerkes Observatory

THE DISTRIBUTION OF EXTRA-GALACTIC NEBULAE IN THE SKY

illustrate here how a scale of the distances mentioned can be shown to match the scope of human experience with the inch and the miles.

Starting with a scale which will place the sun at a distance of one-half inch from the earth, let us see how the other objects which we have described will be placed with relation to that distance. On this scale one inch equals two hundred million miles. The nearest star in the sky, Proxima Centauri, must be placed at a distance of two miles! With this very small scale, the size of the sun will have shrunk to microscopic size, and therefore we can disregard the diameters of the stars. To include a hundred of the nearest stars, the model of this universe will be a cube each side of which would be sixteen miles long. Near the sun, the microscopic specks which represent stars will be placed at a distance of four miles from each other. In other regions of space, these particles will be even farther distant from one another.

This model must be built out several thousand miles in each direction in order to include the limits of the galaxy, and the stars must be placed farther and farther apart as the outside of the galaxy is reached. If the outside of the galaxy is to be reached, the distance to the farthest point will be more than one hundred thousand miles.

Courtesy Carl Zeiss, Inc.

WITH TELESCOPES SUCH AS THIS ASTRONOMERS ARE PEERING BEYOND THE MILKY WAY

The Zeiss Refractor in the Tokyo, Japan, Observatory.

After traveling the length of the galactic system, a distance of more than 450 thousand miles must be traversed in order to reach the closest exterior object, which is the Magellanic Cloud. To reach the Andromeda galaxy, a distance of nearly three million miles must be traveled! The model now stretches three million miles in each direction, and we have gone out only to the distance of the five closest island universes! The model will continue to be built out until a distance of sixty-four million miles is reached. Then our model will comprise over three million of these island universes.

This is the picture which astronomers now have of the known physical universe. That there are other universes farther and farther out is accepted, but how far do they reach? It is understood now that all of the space so far measured by man is only a mere fraction—an infinitesimal part—of the greater system. Each of the universes included in this model contains millions upon millions of stars, or gaseous clouds which are destined to form

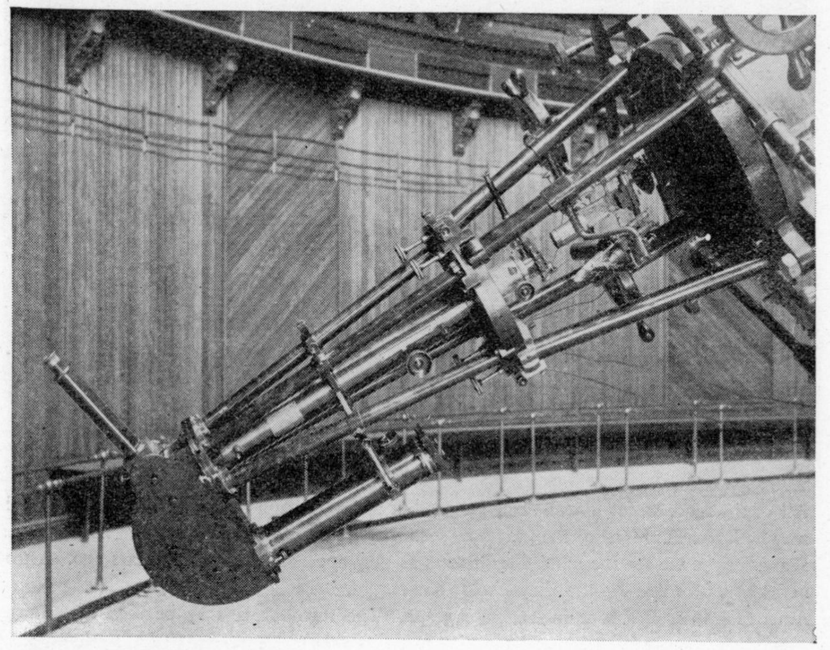

Courtesy Lick Observatory

THE SPECTROGRAPH, AN INSTRUMENT THAT READS LIGHT'S MESSAGE

Courtesy Yerkes Observatory

RARE SPECKS IN EMPTINESS

All of the space so far measured by man is but a tiny fraction of the greater system, which may be limitless. Many of the stars now seen may have been transformed, and new galaxies shaped, since we see the more distant stars as they appeared millions of years ago. Astronomical figures relating to distance and time stagger the imagination of man. (The North America nebula is shown in the photograph. The resemblance may be seen by turning the picture on its side.)

stars. Perhaps perspective has been lost because of the tremendous distances. These galaxies of stars are seen now as they were millions and millions of years ago. Perhaps now these stars have been transformed, and new galaxies have taken shape. There are, then, millions of millions of stars which can be seen with the most powerful telescopes.

The number of specks of dust to be found in the air over a large city might well represent the tremendous number of stars found in the heavens. The distances between these specks of dust are very small fractions of an inch. If that distance is increased to four miles, we obtain a correct picture of a crowded space near the sun. But it has been shown that there are none of these specks in a distance of more than two million miles of our scale galaxy!

A remarkable conclusion can be reached regarding the vastness of space. Even with the tremendous number of stars in the heavens, space is so vast that it is, to all appearance, very empty. In our model, the *average* distance between specks of dust is not four miles but rather one thousand miles. The universe, then, is not filled with stars. Rather, stars are rare specks found in the great desolation of emptiness.

If space were crowded with stars, collisions would often occur; but there is so little crowding that most of the stars must move for millions of years before colliding. Observers on the earth have never even seen two stars in close proximity.

The different objects in the heavens have different speeds, some of which are so tremendous that they startle the imagination. The sun is moving through space with a velocity of from twelve to fifteen miles per second, or four hundred million miles per year. The smaller Magellanic Cloud is receding from our galaxy with a velocity of one hundred and ten miles per second, or over three billion miles per year.

THE EXPANDING UNIVERSE?

It has been noted previously that some of the conglomerations of stars approach our galaxy; for instance, the Andromeda nebula, which is approaching the Milky Way with the terrific velocity of about 190 miles per second, or over five billion miles per year.

ARE GALAXIES SUCH AS THIS RUSHING AWAY FROM THE EARTH?

Courtesy Lick Observatory

But most of the distant galaxies, instead of approaching the Milky Way, seem to be "running away" from it. This apparent tendency toward large recessional velocities is especially noticeable when measured by displacements of the spectrum lines: the lines almost always show a large shift toward the red.

All of the remote galaxies may be receding from our galaxy with high velocities, and these velocities increase as the distance increases! The velocities of the distant island universes range from minus three hundred (the negative sign represents recession) to minus seventeen thousand miles per second.

According to Edwin P. Hubble and William LaSalle Humason of Mount Wilson Observatory, the galaxies which are one million light-years distant have a velocity averaging about three hundred miles per second. As the distance increases, the velocities increase; that is, for every one million additional light-years' distance, the velocities increase three hundred miles per second. For the very distant galaxies, the velocities cannot be determined accurately, but the galaxy having the greatest velocity of recession—seventeen thousand miles per second—has a distance known to be greater than eighty million light-years. If the relation between velocity and distance is true for distances of half a billion light-years, the remote galaxies have a velocity of recession almost equal to that of the speed of light.

When astronomers state that the island universes are receding with great velocities, they are stating it on a relative basis; that is, no fixed point has been chosen as a basis for comparison with the motions of these objects. The actual motion is not directly toward, or away from, the solar system. An observer on the earth sees only a component of the velocity. For instance, if an object is far enough away and has a rather large recessional velocity at an angle of forty-five degrees from the line of sight of the observer, all of the motion which can actually be observed is a component velocity which will be smaller than the actual velocity. Now, with the spectroscope, all that can be seen of a given motion is directly in the line of sight. When it is said that a galaxy is receding, what is really meant is that the component in the line of sight is receding, but not necessarily in a direct line from the earth.

The only clue to recessional velocities is found by means of the spectroscope. When the light rays from vastly distant stars traveling for millions of years strike the spectroscope, a shift toward the red is seen. It is then assumed that the objects are "running away" from the earth.

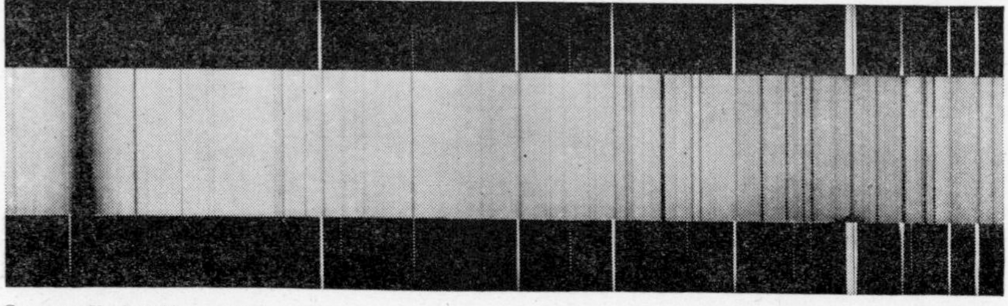

Courtesy Yerkes Observatory

SPECTRUM OF ETA LEONIS, VERTICALLY ENLARGED

The outer bands are for comparison, and the amount by which the lines fail to correspond indicates that the star is moving away from the earth at an estimated speed of two miles per second.

According to the theory of the renowned physicist, Planck, light is cast off in the form of quantum, which is a form of energy depending on the length of the light wave. It has been definitely proved that violet light has a very energetic quantum, while red light has a very feeble quantum. Light waves, as they traverse space, may lose some of their energy, but it has been assumed that light waves remain unchanged from the time they leave a distant galaxy to the time they reach the earth.

With the assumption that light waves do not change in length from loss of energy, several theories have been advanced. The most notable and interesting theory is that of an expanding universe, the expansion being like that of a small soap bubble. Internal pressure causes the bubble to expand until equilibrium between the outside and inside pressures is reached. The same principle may hold true for the apparent recession of the galaxies.

If this theory is accepted, then two alternatives must be considered. First, all of the galaxies must have begun billions of years ago as one gigantic conglomeration of stars. As time went on expansion occurred, and as they were speeding outward toward the depths of space, they formed into local condensations which are now called island universes. Second, it might be true that the universe is alternately contracting and expanding. From our present position, we are merely seeing an expansion. Perhaps, during a long period of time in the past, the universe was contracting.

The first theory has an important point in its favor in that it tries to explain the original formation of the island universes. Like most theories, it starts with chaos. Equilibrium is a tendency which is constantly being sought in nature. If this is true, the expansion at one time or another will lead to an explosion as in the case of the soap bubble. From a consideration of its expansion and its loss of heat, scientists are convinced that this universe is a dying one. The second theory can be called optimistic. It would make the universe ageless. The picture would be one of eternal expansion and contraction. Nevertheless, both of these theories merit consideration.

Courtesy Lick Observatory

ARE THESE TWO GALAXIES BOUND TOGETHER?

THEN, GALAXIES—NOW, SUPER-GALAXIES

The galaxies have been referred to as independent universes, but the modern telescope has found even greater secrets in the heavens. Astronomers have stepped farther into space and have found super-galaxies. Forty or fifty super-galaxies are already known. Thus astronomers have added another unit to their list. Enumerated earlier were the seven—proton, atom, molecule, man, earth, solar system, galaxy, and now super-galaxies. It is known at present that galaxies are not uniformly distributed. Rather, they, like the stars, tend to cluster near one another. Consider the enormous extent of space which these units occupy. In the direction of the Como-Virgo constellations the nearest super-galaxies are found. One is at a distance of over ten million light-years, and another is more than four times that distance.

Courtesy Yerkes Observatory

THE SPIRAL IN TRIANGULUM, A MEMBER OF OUR SUPER-GALAXY
Super-galaxies are made up of galaxies, and are held in their positions by gravitation.

The diameters of these systems as a whole are about two million light-years, and the systems are separated by distances averaging one million light-years. The dimensions of other super-galaxies, even larger than these, are now being investigated. Naturally, the distances of these and other large systems are so great that accurate measurement is impossible, but distances of the right order of magnitude can be ascertained.

Our galactic system is also a member of a super-galaxy. Earlier, the five island universes within a distance of a million light-years were named—these are the two Magellanic Clouds, N. B. C. 6822, the spiral in the constellation Triangulum, and the great spiral in Andromeda. It must be remembered that many galaxies cannot be seen because of the great obscuring belt of matter in and near the Milky Way. Astronomers are agreed that ours is a rather medium-sized super-galaxy, composed of perhaps fifty to one hundred island universes, and being about two million light-years in diameter.

Super-galaxies are made up of galaxies; they are dynamic systems, since their constituent members, the galaxies, are dynamic systems. The super-galaxies seem to be unaffected by age. Gravitation holds the members of the super-systems together, just as gravitation holds members of a local star-cloud in a rather compact group. Regardless of the distance at which these super-galaxies are found, they all seem to be in approximately the same stage of development. This further substantiates the assertion that they are bound together by the bands of their mutual gravitational attraction. Thus it can be seen that these great super-systems are also revolving about some common center, probably with motions which are similar to those of the streams of stars in an island universe. The circuit of the individual galaxy about the center of the gigantic super-galaxy would take from hundreds of millions to billions of years.

A more correct picture of the formation of the individual island universes can now be obtained. Just as the stars have a probability—though slight—of passing one near another, so have the galaxies. The galaxies can be considered single members of a gigantic island universe. Like the stars, they will at one time or another tend to make a close approach with a member galaxy.

These close approaches will cause new conglomerations of stars to be formed. We see in our own super-galaxy examples of these island universes in different ages of development, probably after close approaches. Our spiral galaxy and the Andromeda galaxy may have formed as a result of a close approach of two clusters, as was mentioned earlier. Super-galaxies, then, represent dynamic systems containing island universes of all ages.

WHAT LIES OUTSIDE SPACE?

Are there any limits to the extent of space? Years ago scientists would have answered this question in the negative. The human mind, it was thought, could only conceive of an end of space by imagining something present which was not space. But even this conception is difficult. It is much harder to conceive of a barrier which is not space that could prevent the mind from traveling on

Courtesy Lick Observatory

WHAT LIES BEYOND?

and passing into further space beyond that barrier, than merely to imagine endless space.

It is true that a sphere is unlimited in curvature but finite in extent, since one can travel endlessly over its surface without ever reaching a barrier. Albert Einstein, the great physicist, claims that space, too, is finite in extent, yet unlimited. This means that space, at some points, bends back on itself.

Einstein also says that the volume of space is determined only by the amount of matter which it contains; thus, space which is empty is infinite. The problem of finding the extent of space becomes one of finding the amount of matter contained in space. The diameter of space, according to Edwin Hubble, is 168 trillion light years. We know, if this figure is accepted, that even with our largest telescopes we are seeing only a tiny portion of the gigantic reaches of space. But man has far to go. He has had the telescope only a short while in relation to the length of his stay on the face of the earth. Who can tell what he will discover in the next thousand years!

Another theory, advanced by de Sitter, deserves consideration. De Sitter's cosmology accounts for many of the observed phenomena of the entire cosmos for which Einstein has not accounted.

DR. ALBERT EINSTEIN

Paul's Photos, Chicago

Courtesy Yerkes Observatory

WILLEM DE SITTER

For instance, de Sitter predicts that the spectra will be displaced to the red as a direct function of distance. That an explanation of a cosmos should introduce a consideration of an observed phenomenon which has been so puzzling, shows that this explanation is important. The spectrum shift toward the red is to be expected with de Sitter's cosmos.

Using the velocities of recession, the diameter of the universe is found to be four trillion light years, according to de Sitter. De Sitter claims that light would take an infinite time to travel the circumference of his finite universe, instead of the finite time given by Einstein. De Sitter, however, begins his theory with the assumption that space is void of matter. We would expect that his theory would be in accord with Einstein's to the extent that light would bend back upon itself in the presence of matter.

The discussions of the structure of space are, of course, highly speculative. If it were said that space is finite, it would be logical to ask what lies beyond the boundaries which have been set for this cosmos. The question is unanswerable. Whether the life of a single island universe, a super-galaxy, or the entire cosmos is or is not infinite is not known. The second law of thermo-dynamics

—energy is continually changing in form, and is going from a higher to a lower level, with the impossibility of that energy returning to a higher level—gives the cosmos a death sentence.

Other consideration must be made of the birth of matter—cosmic rays. Is the great cosmos undying? Are cosmic rays really the birth pangs of matter? Many years of research may discover the answer.

In the meantime man will continue on his journey through space. With the same perseverance which he showed in his exploration of the face of this earth, he can go on to the greater things which are to be found in the unknown depths of space.

Courtesy Yerkes Observatory

ANOTHER UNIVERSE OF STARS AND WORLDS

Courtesy Yerkes Observatory

STARS OF OUR OWN GALAXY

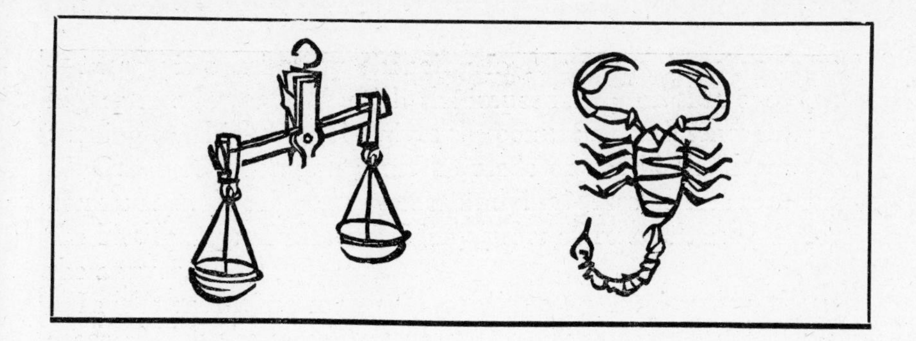

THE TITANS OF OUTER SPACE

ASTRONOMERS FIND THE STARS

UNTIL THE BEGINNING of the nineteenth century, astronomers devoted most of their time to the study of the solar system and its near neighborhood. The sun, the moon, the planets, and the comets were objects of the closest study. Mathematicians proved that the motions of these objects obeyed definite physical laws.

In the nineteenth century, however, the astronomer widened his scope. The stars, once merely points of reference in the study of the earth and the solar system, were seen as individual members of a great system, each with its particular size and motion.

Increasing attention was given to the study of far-distant stars, and a system of brain-defying complexity was discovered. No two stars, it was seen, are exactly alike. For instance, they vary in brightness, ranging from seven thousand times brighter than the sun to one-thousandth of that body's light emission.

Stars have been divided into classes according to their temperature. According to the popular belief of an earlier time, based on knowledge assumed without sufficient evidence, it was thought that stars could be classified according to the number of their points. This fallacy was soon made apparent by the increasing use of more sensitive equipment. With the help of an instrument called the thermocouple, scientists found that the temperatures of stars ranged from about 5,400° to about 54,000° Fahrenheit. The

Courtesy Yerkes Observatory

BETWEEN THE POINTERS IS A RED STAR
The view at left is from an ordinary photograph, while that on the right was made with a red-sensitive plate.

spectroscope was also used. It was seen that the temperature of stars had an influence on the spectrum, determining the relative brightness of otherwise inconspicuous lines. Therefore, it was by such means that astronomers put the stars into ten categories: O, B, A, F, G, K, M, R, N, and S, the letters indicating the position of lines on the spectrum.

The class O stars are the hottest. They achieve a temperature as high as 54,000° Fahrenheit. Predominantly blue on the spectrum, these stars are many times hotter than the electric arc or spark. Class B stars exist in an atmosphere similar in density and elemental make-up to that of the Class O stars, although that atmosphere appears to have assumed a state of somewhat less excitation. The temperature in class B stars does not exceed 36,000° Fahrenheit. Class A stars have surface temperatures of about 18,000° and are analyzable into parts of iron, magnesium, and calcium. The surface temperature of class F stars is not less than 14,000°. The sun around which our earth rotates is a class G star. The approximate surface temperature is 10,000° Fahrenheit. Seven thousand degrees Fahrenheit is the temperature of class K stars, and classes M, N, R, and S do not realize an intensity of light higher than 5,400° Fahrenheit. Stars in the R and S classifications cannot be seen without a telescope, and only a few M and N stars can be seen with the unaided eye.

These classes contain the individual members of the galaxy.

Indeed, the sun and the stars belong to a celestial organization of more than three billion members. In it each star is a globe; some are larger, some smaller than the sun. Densities vary greatly as to the quantity, kind, and state of excitation of the elements in the atmosphere of each star. Stars that have a great density, like Krueger 60, are called dwarf stars, and those that are highly tenuous are called giant stars.

THE DOG STAR

Sirius, the Dog Star, is the brightest of all the stars. In times past it was used with other bright stars to determine time, but it soon was found untrustworthy as a timekeeper. Now it would gain; then it would lose. Sirius was not describing a perfect circle in the sky; instead, it was pursuing an

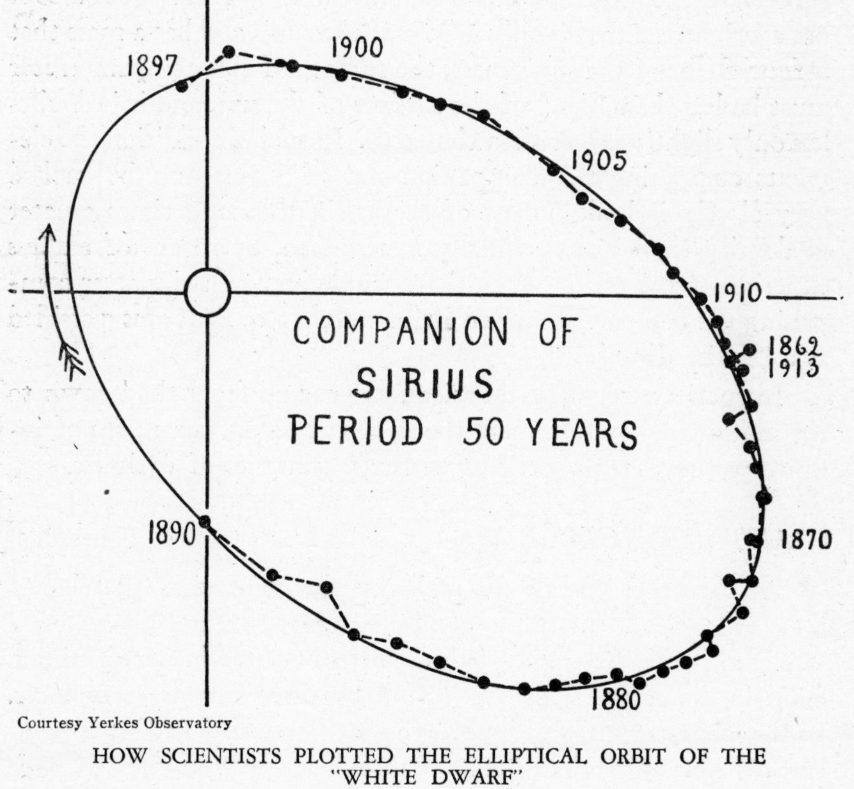

Courtesy Yerkes Observatory

HOW SCIENTISTS PLOTTED THE ELLIPTICAL ORBIT OF THE "WHITE DWARF" elliptical orbit. This led to the conclusion that since the earth describes an elliptical orbit around the sun—a star—Sirius must also do so. It was soon recognized that Sirius has a companion which for the moment had to be described as dark. It was not until 1862 that Alvin Clark found this companion, perceiving as he did an infinitesimal point of light near Sirius. Later determinations led to the conclusion that this companion star is not much less massive than the sun and that its matter is packed together with indescribable intensity. All that matter, however, is in a gaseous state.

In 1914 Adams discovered that the companion star of Sirius is a white star—white hot, not much less massive than the sun, though giving off only about 1/350 of the sun's light. It had been originally thought that because of the meager amount of light it emitted, this companion could be only a red hot star; but since it has a brightness that is only 1/350 of the sun's and has a mass that is four-fifths of the sun's mass, the surface of this companion star must be less than 1/360 of the surface of the sun, and it is doubtless only slightly larger than the earth. In such a condition the elements composing this companion star of Sirius must be packed very closely indeed, a mass of atoms six thousand times greater in density than water. Finally it was seen, by means of endless experiment and observation, that a cubic inch of the matter comprising the companion star to Sirius weighs a ton! It was classified as a "white dwarf."

In such a way, then, do scientists proceed from the known to the unknown. By observing the habits of Sirius, these men of infinite patience acquainted us with the contents of darkness.

GIANT BETELGEUSE

At the other end of the scale are the giant stars. Betelgeuse is a good example of this type. It has great size and low density. A class M star, Betelgeuse is known to be three hundred million miles in diameter. This was found by using an interferometer. In the laboratory it was discovered that Betelgeuse had a temperature of not more than 5,400° Fahrenheit, putting the star into

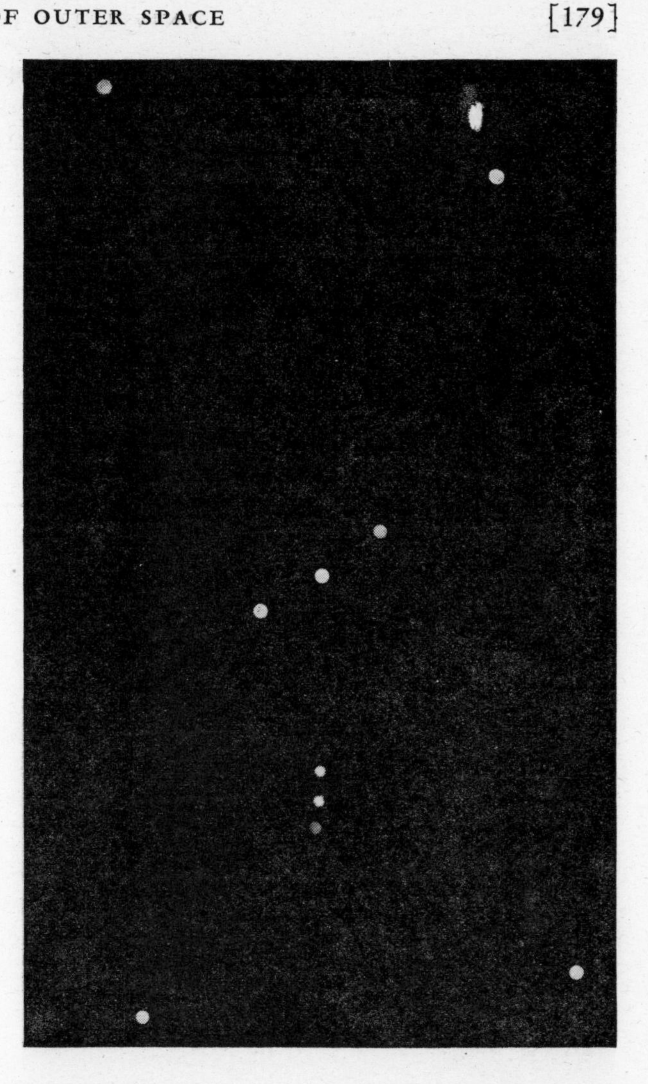

EXTRA-FOCAL IMAGE OF THE BRIGHTEST STARS IN THE CONSTELLATION ORION
The one in the upper left hand corner is Betelgeuse.
Courtesy Yerkes Observatory

class M. This temperature means that the density of Betelgeuse is one-millionth of the density of water. Indeed it is much less dense than air.

The question occurs at this point as to the relation between size and heat. Betelgeuse is tremendously large, yet it gives off relatively little heat. The companion of Sirius is exceedingly small, yet it is two and a half times hotter than Betelgeuse. The missing link is density. The companion is packed so tightly as to defy the imagination. Iron is as light as a feather compared to the compact mass of this star. Betelgeuse, on the other hand, is truly lighter than air.

STARS DIE

Present-day astronomers explain the changes of stars on the basis of radiation of substance. Stars give off not light as we generally think of it, but actual matter. As time passes the star grows smaller. With the contraction of diameter the temperature increases. After an interval of time a point is reached at which contraction fails to bring a corresponding increase in temperature, and the star cools through successive stages. By this theory the sun is said to be radiating its substance into space. It is steadily progressing on its way to extinction. According to this theory, the sun will some day become a small, red, dim star, and will give

WILL THESE STARS DIE?

Some day, millions upon millions of years hence, the sun may become but a small red star, giving out no heat.

Courtesy Yerkes Observatory

out no heat, perhaps arriving at a density comparable to that of the companion of Sirius.

Astronomers are able to describe the life of stars in definite numbers of years. Eddington, the distinguished English scientist, has stated the principle simply and adequately. He points out that the rate of evolution of a star can be found by observing the rate at which a star loses mass. Since the rate of loss of mass by radiation is known, the time needed for passage of a star from one type to another can be found. On this basis astronomers have determined that the sun is between five billion and five billion, five hundred million years old.

DOUBLE STARS

It has been mentioned in the chapter that concerns itself with galaxies that among the most interesting objects of astronomical study are the double stars. The amateur astronomer will experience real pleasure in observing the double star. The best known double stars in the northern hemisphere are Castor and Pollux; the most familiar ones in the southern hemisphere are Alpha and Beta Centauri.

Two stars which exhibit attracting traits, one for the other, make up what is called a binary system. Castor and Pollux are such stars. They revolve about one another about once every ten thousand years.

In recent years it has been found that each of the stars in this binary system is in reality but one of a pair of stars. In other words, the star Castor as seen by the unaided eye is actually, along with Pollux, a member of a quadruple system of stars.

Double stars are held together by the force of gravitation. Indeed, it must be emphasized that gravitation is a universal force, responsible for the paths the stars follow and for all their peculiar motions.

It should be noted that a binary system is composed of two stars revolving about one another. It was originally assumed that double stars were physically related. This is not true. They may differ greatly in physical constitution; but must lie closely

Courtesy Yerkes Observatory

THE ARROW POINTS TO BARNARD'S STAR. NOTE HOW FAR IT MOVED IN 22 YEARS

together. Because of our observing position, these stars appear to lie on a straight line projected from the earth. This is not a true observation, as later astronomers have shown. Visual double stars are numerous. Indeed, it is said that one star in every nine is actually a double star.

DOES LIFE EXIST IN BINARY SYSTEMS?

Many astronomers have considered the possibility of life on planets similar to those known in the solar system. In the case of double or binary stars it is only natural to ask whether life of some sort can spring up. Since double stars are mutually attractive, tides would certainly form, matter would be thrown off, and perhaps planets would come into being. Indeed, the possibility does truly exist that planets may attend the stars in binary systems. Of course, the paths of such planets in the binary system would differ from those of the planets in the solar system, for it must be plain that two or more stars will exert a force on the tiny planets much different from that which is exerted by a single star. It is difficult to determine at the present time whether or not planets do exist in the binary systems, for such planets would cast not direct light but reflected light.

HOW BINARIES ARE STUDIED

The difference between visual binary stars and eclipsing variable stars—those stars that pass before each other when seen from the earth—can be readily realized when it is pointed out that eclipsing binaries achieve complete revolution, or whole round of orbit, in terms of days, while visual binaries require periods of thousands of years to complete their orbits. Indeed few of the actual masses of visual double stars can be determined. The members of their unit are so far apart that determinations of their periods of rotation will require many years.

Binary stars are seen from the earth in various positions: now in edgewise position, now in flatwise, or in degrees between these two extremes. Regardless of position, these binary stars must be

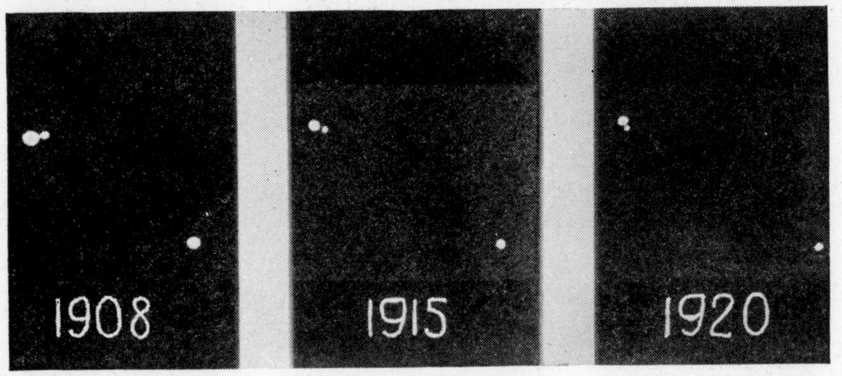

Courtesy Yerkes Observatory

THREE PICTURES OF THE DOUBLE STAR KRUEGER 60, SHOWING ITS REVOLVING MOTION

determined by astronomers in respect to their orbits. When binaries present themselves edgewise, the spectroscope is used. If two stars cannot be seen as casting the same vibration of light, or color, on the spectroscope, because of their distance apart, they will not be noticed. Stars that do cast identical vibrations on the spectroscope are called spectroscopic binaries.

The original studies of spectroscopic binaries was made by Professor E. C. Pickering in 1889 on the visual double star, Mizar. He found that one of the two stars in the double star system was in itself a binary system. The astronomer sees this through his observation that the lines of the spectrum were periodically doubled. The reader will remember that in the discussion of galaxies a shift in the lines of the spectrum shows either the approach or the running away of a star. If the approach and the running away are periodic, one conclusion only can be reached: two stars must be revolving about each other. By noting the results of such observation, astronomers are able to assume that out in the incalculable depths of space the star that they see as a pin point of light through their telescopes is actually a complex system of at least two and perhaps many stars very close together. Indeed, so closely do the color vibrations of some systems come together on the spectroscope that astronomers assume that the surfaces of many stars are in contact. These close stars have particular significance when the beginnings and endings of stars are discussed.

It is unusual for the two or more members of a binary system to be equally bright. Stars that cast identical light vibrations on the spectroscope, in brief, spectroscopic binaries, are in many cases only approximate. Indeed, in many cases the lines on the spectroscope represent a shift rather than a doubling of the lines. The lines of the spectrum of the bright star vary as the star completes its periodic orbit about its fainter companion, shifting toward red on the spectrum when the star is running away and shifting in the opposite direction, toward violet, when the star is approaching. By means of this method—use of the spectroscope—an amazing fact has been discovered: the greater number of spectroscopic binaries have masses much greater than that of the sun.

Let us for a moment pause and consider the significance of all this. Technicalities have their place; but we poor harassed mortals, who wander with apparent aimlessness this dark and subsidiary planet following the flaming sun, demand much more. Look tonight into the heavens. See that needle of light? It is not merely a distant star; this one is a universe. It is a measureless space profoundly more vast than all the stars we see in our own system.

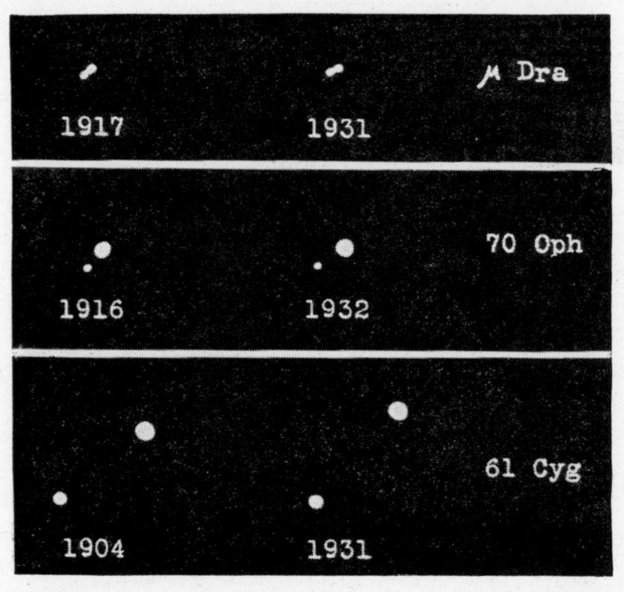

THREE MORE REVOLVING DOUBLE STARS

61 Cygni was the first star whose distance from earth was measured.

Courtesy Yerkes Observatory

Look at our moon; within that needle of light there are many moons. Look at our sun; within that infinitesimal speck of light there are a thousand suns. There within that speck which our most powerful telescopes bring to imperfect view it requires ten thousands of years to make one year. Our earth completes its round of the sun in 365 days. Those stars up there, those flaming balls of gas, require 3,650,000 days and more to come to an end of their ethereal seasons.

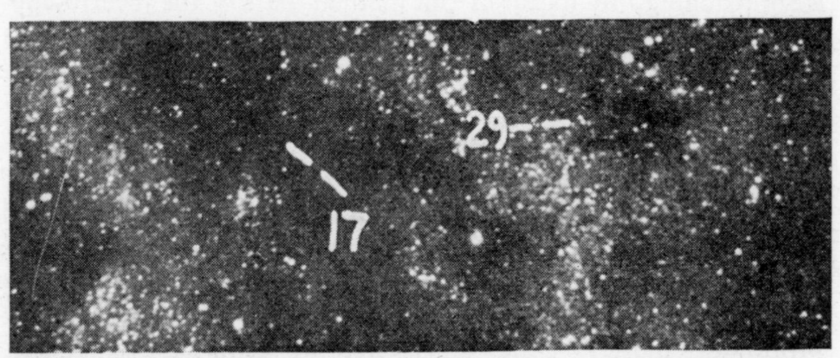

Courtesy Mt. Wilson Observatory

POINTERS INDICATE STARS THAT VARIED IN BRIGHTNESS

ECLIPSING BINARIES

Eclipsing binaries are those star systems that have the plane of their motion through or near the earth. They are farther apart than spectroscopic binaries, though this does not mean that they are actually widely separated. They are observed from the earth as passing before each other, one blotting out the other's light. There are fewer eclipsing than spectroscopic binaries; but stars of all classes—O, B, A, F, G, K, M, R, N, and the giants and the dwarfs—may be binaries.

HOW BINARIES ORIGINATE

Astronomers have been eager to find a theory for the origin of binaries, for certainly if they could find the action behind the first formation of these relatively primitive bodies, they could see farther into the origin of our own universe and into, at last, the origin of our own planet. Scientists have theorized variously and, of course, have come to no final conclusion. But the theory is interesting and certainly the observed facts in a certain measure back it up. It has been assumed that originally the binaries which now are observable as separate bodies were at first but one large body. It was seen that if this large body revolved slowly only one star would be formed. But it had to be assumed as the facts indicated that this large body revolved at a tremendous velocity. Because it was impossible for such an unimaginably great body to hold together at such velocity, it divided into two parts, sometimes more, thereupon creating a double star or binary system. This original body was an egg-shaped mass. Velocity and various other forces caused it to contract and to become more elongated, almost cigar-shaped, and therefore unstable. At this point division took place. On the divided parts great tides arose, caused by attraction one for the other. During the period of the original forming of the tides, a conflict between the bodies is observable, and the parts are driven farther apart. But then the tides subside, and the parts, or stars as they now are, exert a gravitational force upon each other. These stars are constantly radiating away their masses. Consequently, since the gravitational force exerted is dependent on the mass, and since (because of radiation) the stars tend to shrink appreciably, the distance between the stars grows steadily greater. This could be an explanation of those double stars that, though millions of miles apart, exert considerable gravitational force upon each other.

Paul's Photos, Chicago

SIR JAMES JEANS

One may be inclined to question this theory and ask what happens to those stars that are so widely separated that no appreciable attractive force could be expected to exist between them. Sir James Jeans answers this question by saying that neighboring stars exerting their respective forces tend to establish and maintain a pattern of forces that holds the stars in their places, thus counteracting their inclination to wander off aimlessly into space. According to Jeans' reasoning, the stars separated by large distances have developed from the division of a single star, while those rather close together became related after they became stars.

This theory of Jeans introduces another attack on the problem. Perhaps double stars of all types and masses have originated from the close approach of two stars? Physical laws state that if two stars do not collide, but merely approach one another, they will separate to the original distance from which they came. It has been suggested that under special conditions the two stars may capture one another and form a binary system. Of course, two stars may collide or scrape each other; but it is doubtful if even an occurrence such as this would cause the formation of a binary system.

PLANETARY STAR HYPOTHESIS

A more satisfactory explanation for the formation of binaries is found in the planetary star hypothesis. This hypothesis assumes that a planet revolves about a star, just as the earth revolves about the sun. In its passage through space, the planet sweeps up all of the material which lies in its path. As is true in the case of the moon or the earth, the mass of the planet will become larger as time passes.

It is not fantastic to think that deep in the future—a future measured in millions or billions of years—the planet we now know as Jupiter will rival the sun in size. As the star rushes through space, sweeping up meteoric dust, both itself and its companions take on additional mass. To some astronomers this seems the most acceptable theory that has been advanced in recent years. A binary star will not begin in chaos or end as a single star. Instead, it is assumed that in its endless path through the depths of space, at one time or another a strange star will approach. Great tides will form on the surfaces of both stars, causing tremendous amounts of material to be ejected. As the stars pass away from one another and continue on their endless journey, planets form and pursue their paths about the parent star. The planets sweep up more and more of the material which was originally ejected as they grow older—an age representing billions of years—and finally approach the parent star in size. Perhaps two or three of the planets form stars. This would account for the existence of the multiple binary systems, such as Mizar and Alcor. Furthermore, this theory is acceptable on the grounds of the observed action of the earth and its related planets. The earth is slowly moving away from the sun—only a yard a year. Multiply this yard a billion times, and the distance becomes more significant. The earth will have enlarged its orbit by a half million miles in the next billion years.

THE NEBULAE

Since the beginning of astronomical observations, little cloudy patches of light have been observed in the sky. Sometimes these nebulae, or clouds, seem to be related to single stars or groups of stars, and sometimes they seem to be independent masses of dust.

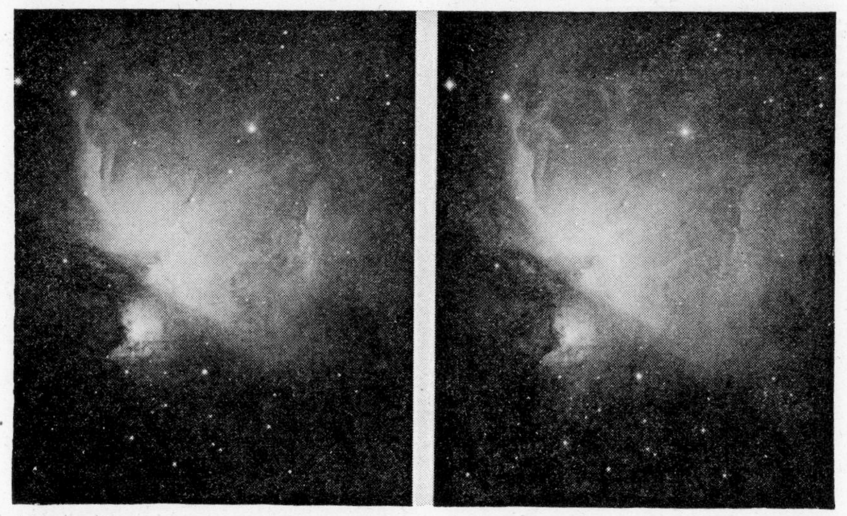

Courtesy Lick Observatory

THE GREAT NEBULA IN ORION

The bright nebula in Orion, which is the constellation seen directly overhead during the winter months in the Northern Hemisphere, is a good example of cloud matter almost entirely enveloping the stars in this section of the sky. There is little doubt in the minds of astronomers that there must be some relation between the stars in Orion and this cloudiness or nebulousness.

Other sections in the sky, especially in the Milky Way region, are rich in nebulae. Indeed, the most famous example of a dark nebula is found in the Horse's Head, located in the Sagittarius region of the Milky Way. It is obvious that this region is made up of dark clouds.

Astronomers were long puzzled by the brightness of some nebulae and the complete absence of light in others. These clouds have too little density to sustain high temperatures. It was fairly certain that the light seen in these clouds was reflected light. When the brightness of the stars with which the nebula was associated was measured, and the amount of light reflected was found, the agreement was obvious. With few exceptions, when a cloud of matter is close to a group of bright stars, it will be a bright nebula.

The densities of some of the nebulae are exceedingly slight. Equal volumes of water and the particles found in the Orion Nebula would disclose the fact that this nebula is between one fifty-thousandth and one-millionth as dense as the earth. For example, a sphere with the diameter of the earth which would contain the matter occupying an equivalent space in the Orion Nebula would weigh between one hundred and two hundred tons, or less than the weight of an average locomotive.

DARK AND LUMINOUS NEBULA

When astronomers found that both light and dark clouds of matter exist side by side, so to say, they felt that their explanation of the cause of light in the luminous nebulae was substantiated. Many dark spots and dark strips in the Milky Way have for centuries been known to exist. At first astronomers thought that these blank spots were narrow lanes through which they could see

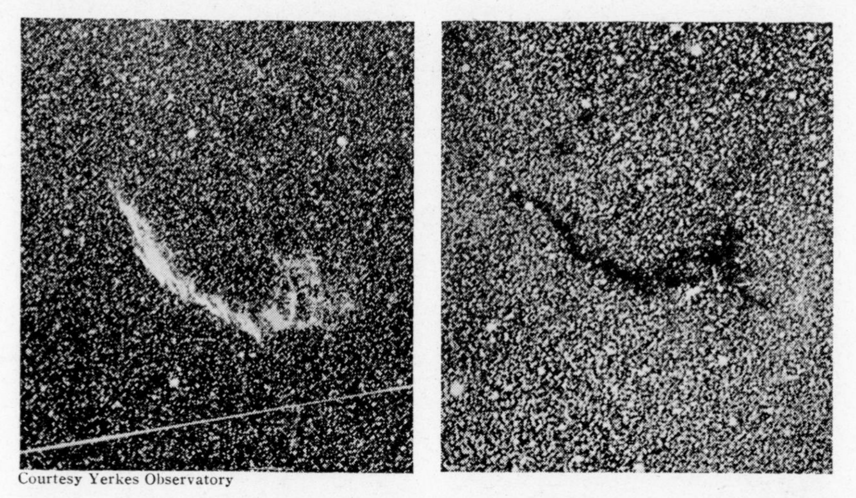
Courtesy Yerkes Observatory

A COINCIDENCE OF THE MILKY WAY
Bright and dark patches that seem to be of the same shape. A meteor trail crosses the former.

farther into space. When their great telescopes were perfected and trained on these "open" spots, it was found that they were in reality great areas filled with obscuring matter. Part of the conclusion which astronomers reached was due to their knowledge of probability. What are the chances that the earth would be in such an enviable position for observing the skies that, with stars moving at random, a tunnel-shaped opening would point exactly toward the earth, especially at a distance of thousands of light-years? It would be very remarkable if even one opening like this could be found. It has been decided that these dark clouds are essentially of the same type as clouds which, if in the neighborhood of a luminous body, would reflect light.

Much research has been based on the discovery that some parts of the cloud-matter are brighter than others. Naturally, this would show that the clouds are distributed irregularly through space and receive varying amounts of light. Many thousands of nebulae, both bright and dark, and of varying dimensions, are known to astronomers. Much of the study of nebulae has been greatly helped by the use of the spectroscope. Some of the clouds are so faint that they cannot be seen with either the eye or the telescope. Nevertheless, the photographic plate and the spectroscope do help in discovering their presence in the stellar atmos-

Courtesy Yerkes Observatory

A NEBULOUS REGION IN THE MILKY WAY

The dark nebulae which produce the dark areas in the Milky Way are of inconceivable size, stretching almost entirely across the borders of the galaxy. This opaque, non-luminous mass obscures the stars which lie in it, as well as a large number of island universes located nearby.

phere. Photography is important because a definite record is procured of the exact size and shape of the nebula, whereas the eye would not be able to delineate the exact beginnings and endings of the clouds.

NEBULAE FOUND THROUGHOUT ALL SPACE

Nebulae seem to be common to all galaxies, or island universes. For instance, astronomers have noted the existence of nebulae in the closest of these cosmic islands, the Magellanic Clouds. These nebulae are seen in all sections of our galaxies, and vary in shape from small, circular, and rather compact masses to great wisps stretching across vast local clusters of stars.

The Orion Nebula is about six hundred light years from the solar system and the great nebular cloud is at least ten light-years in diameter, or more than sixty trillion miles.

The vast dark nebulae which produce the dark lanes in the Milky Way have the greatest size, because they stretch almost entirely across the borders of the galaxy. This opaque, non-luminous mass obscures not only the stars which lie in it, but also completely shields from view the large number of exterior island universes located near this section.

These dark nebulae are by no means extraordinary, since all universes which are viewed edgewise present the same type of dark band lying across their middle. Even the Andromeda Galaxy, which is not seen edgewise, but rather at a three-quarter view, definitely shows the presence of this dark material. It is seen that this dark obscuring matter stretches across the entire length of the galaxy.

VARIABLE NEBULAE

More astonishing than variable stars are the variable nebulae. The astronomer has explained the brightness of the nebula as a result of the reflection of starlight. But he does not explain the peculiar variation of light coming from a nebula that does not show the presence of a variable star. In the constellation Monoceros there is a star that astronomers call an irregular vari-

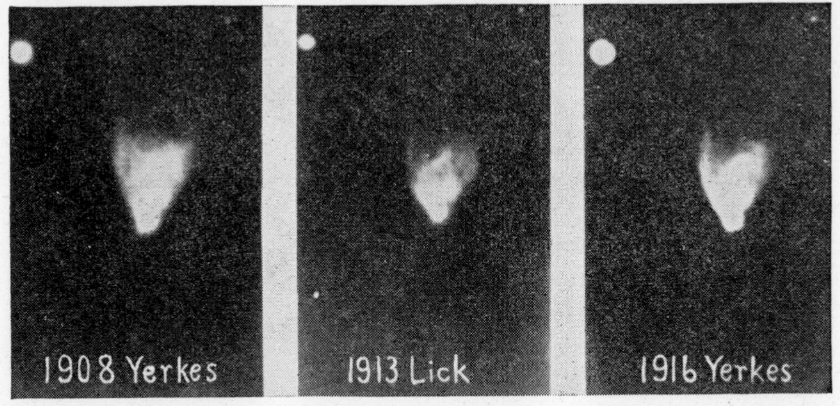

Courtesy Yerkes Observatory

A NEBULA IN MONOCEROS THAT VARIES IN BRIGHTNESS FROM TIME TO TIME

able. That is, this star does not vary regularly, like the periodic brightening and dimming of an electric light bulb. Instead, this star seems to have been a nova at some time in the past and has a nebulousness or cloudiness of matter that is shaped like a comet and spreads away from the star. This star varies as to the amount of light it radiates at rather long and irregular intervals. The brightness of its nebula, on the other hand, varies quite frequently and has a wide range between its brightest and dimmest points. In addition, the shape of its nebula seems to change quite radically. From the calculation of the distance of this star and the size of the nebulae, the brightness appears to sweep over the surface at a speed greater than light.

This star and nebula are not the only examples of this rather peculiar and inexplicable occurrence. Corona Austrina, a star of the giant type, is associated with a nebula which shows almost the same characteristics as the nebula in Monoceros. If it is argued that perhaps these stars are not physically related with their nebulae, the spectrum shows very conclusively that they are, because the reflected light of the cloudy matter shows the same type of light as that of the star with which it is related. We must, therefore, accept the theory that the nebula shines with reflected light. The variation of the light cast, however, remains a mystery

MASSES, DISTANCES, AND DIMENSIONS OF NEBULAE

Are nebulae gases or solids? Since they can cut off the light of stars, it is highly probable that they are made up of very fine particles. Recently, Harvard Observatory has advanced the theory that the nebulae seem to be composed of the same material which is found in the meteorite, or "shooting star." This conclusion is based on the observation that most of the meteorites seem to be wandering members of the universe, and not permanent members of any system.

It has been suggested that at the present time the earth is passing through a cloud that has an exceedingly low density. In fact, if the source of the meteorites is actually nebular, then it must be recognized that this nebula is much rarer than any that has yet been found.

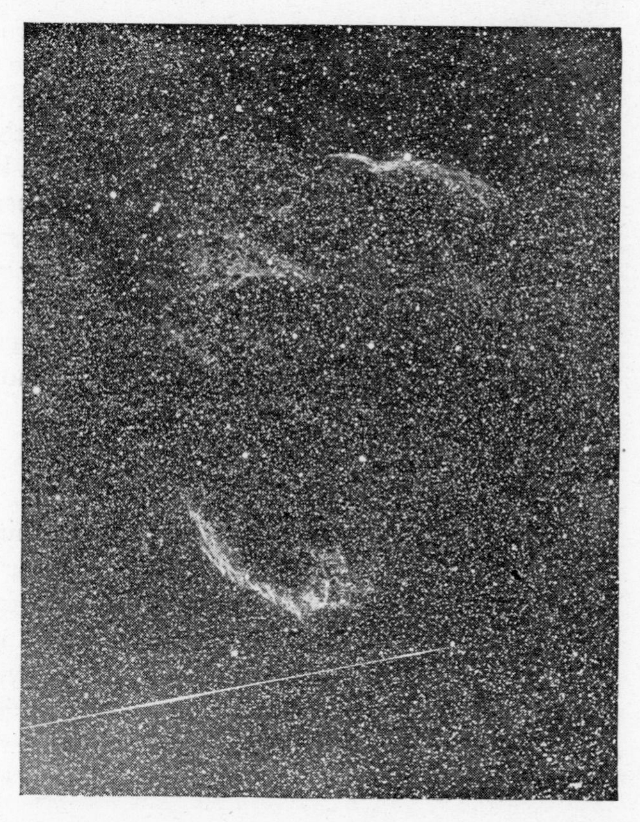

BRIGHT NEBULOUS WISPS AND A METEOR TRAIL
Are both composed of the same material?

Courtesy Yerkes Observatory

Because many of the nebulae are associated with stars, their distances are not difficult to determine. The Pleiades are more than two hundred light-years, or a quadrillion miles distant. The nebulae associated with this group of stars have been measured and are found to be more than thirty light-years in diameter.

Because the defining limits of the nebulae are very difficult to determine, the surveyor's method has failed to result in definite approximations of distance. The spectroscope has again proved of much help in this instance, especially in connection with the luminous nebulae. Although results are only approximately accurate, this spectroscopic method permits us to assume that the speed of most of the clouds varies between ten and twenty miles per second.

Similar to the stars, the nebulae show that some are approaching and some receding from the solar system. In addition to their motion with respect to the sun, the nebulae also exhibit internal motions. The motion of the inside of the nebulae can be compared to the motions of clouds in the sky during a storm. Some of the clouds scud across the sky more quickly than others. In the same manner the motion of the clouds of matter can be visualized. At one time one part may move faster, and at another time a different section of the cloud will plunge ahead through space. Their relative motions are not great, however, since they seem to be fairly permanent parts of our galaxy. Perhaps they act like a heavy cloud of cigar smoke that has been blown out into the center of a room; it slowly changes in volume, but is not subject to disintegrating forces.

INTERSTELLAR MATTER

For many years scientists were content to think that the space between stars was a vacuum, containing little or no matter. This theory was held until it was found, by the use of the ever-useful spectroscope, that space does actually contain matter. Granted that this matter is less dense than anything which can be imagined, it nevertheless has a very important bearing on the discussion of the actual existence of matter in space. Sir James Jeans avers that stars are a rarity in the great depths of space.

The infinitesimal amount of matter which exists between stars must also be appreciated. One of the components of interstellar matter is calcium, one and one-half times the weight of water. Yet this matter has a density which is one-billionth the density of the Orion Nebula, which in turn is much less dense than the greatest vacuum which it has been possible to produce in a laboratory.

As the years go on, more and more will be discovered by the astronomer. The mystery of the formation of the binary stars, the existence of the great tenuous nebulae that stretch for many millions of miles across the sky, and the complete explanation of the physical composition of interstellar matter will receive the attention of the scientist. To him these are the mysteries that ultimately will give him the answer to his enduring search for truth.

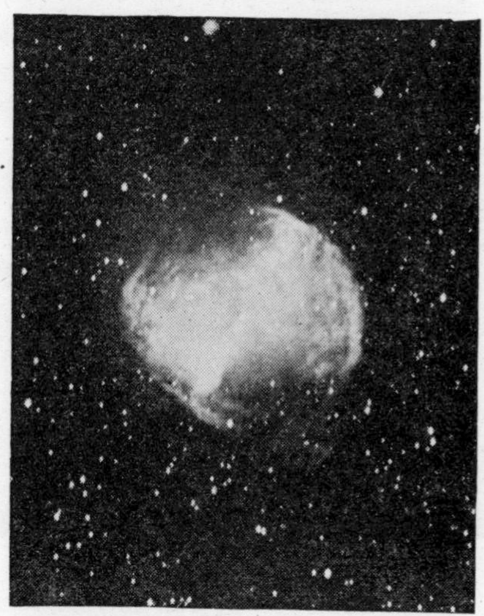

Courtesy Lick Observatory

IS THIS A CLOUD OF METEORIC MATERIAL?

Courtesy Lick Observatory

A CLOSE-UP OF THE MOON

This view shows the moon as it appears through the 36-inch refractor at Lick Observatory.

THE SOLAR SYSTEM

THE THIRD-RATE STAR

NEAR THE CENTER of one of the innumerable galaxies of the heavens is a small star. Viewed from outside the galaxy, and judged by its size and its comparative brightness, this star appears to be distinctly third-rate. By another standard, however, it is unique. This small star has a system of planets revolving about it. Most of those planets, too, have bodies which are known as moons, revolving about them. On one of the planets, one that has only one moon, live men who can look out into space and comprehend something of what is happening in what appears to be a boundless universe.

This small star, the sun, is almost lost in the vast space of the galaxy in which it is located. Indeed, some astronomers have said it is but a microscopic speck of dust in an ocean of space. This speck, the sun, is nevertheless 864 thousand miles in diameter! At its tremendous distance from the earth it appears to have the same size as does a ten-cent piece held at arm's length.

Like all other stars, it is moving. The measure of movement, however, must be in relation to some second object. In astronomy it is customary to compare the speed of movement of distant stars with reference to the sun, which is considered as stationary. But when the speed of movement of the sun is determined, it is necessary to adopt a new point of reference. By so doing,

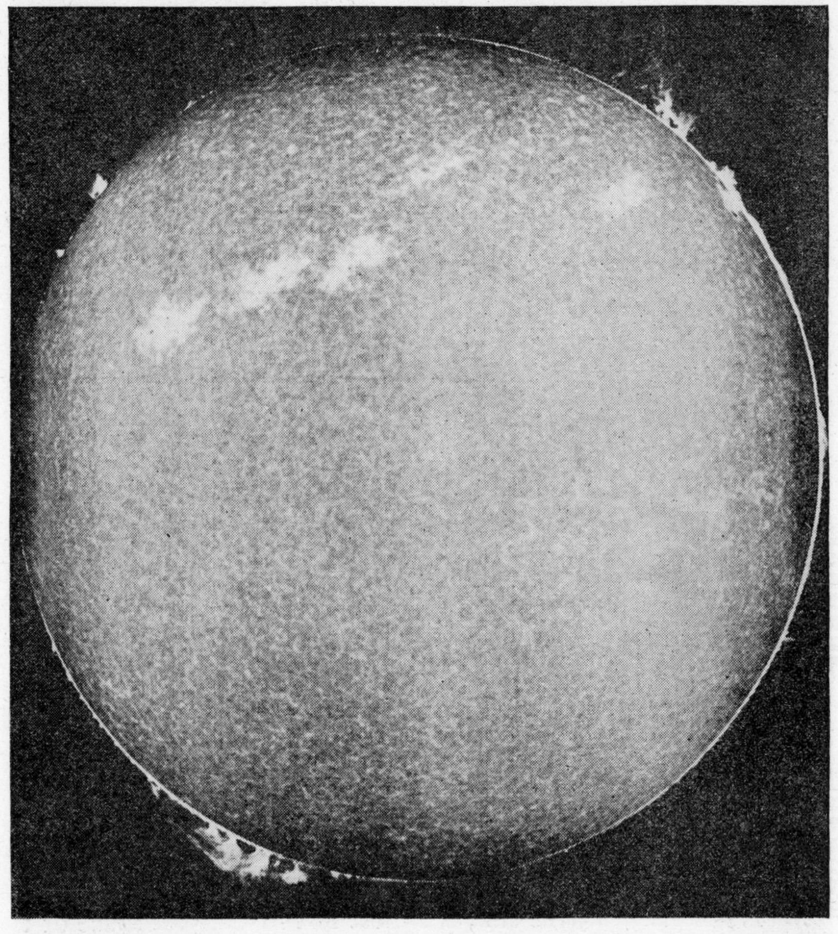

Courtesy Yerkes Observatory

CALCIUM SPECTROHELIOGRAM

astronomers have calculated that the sun is moving toward the constellation of Hercules at a rate of about thirteen miles each second.

Like all other stars, the sun also rotates about its own axis. Were it not for some distinguishable marks on the sun, it would be impossible to determine how rapidly it turns on its axis. By noticing the movement of sunspots, it has been possible to observe that the sun completes a rotation in about twenty-five days. However, it has been found that some of the landmarks on the polar regions of the sun do not complete a revolution in twenty-five days. Near the poles of the sun the period of rotation is lengthened to about thirty-five days. If the countries of the earth could be moved to their similar positions on the surface of the sun, a complete rotation in Brazil would be twenty-five days long, but in Iceland it would be thirty-five days long! The obvious conclusion is that the polar regions of the sun's surface are being literally dragged along by the fast moving equatorial region. This is possible only if the sun's surface is plastic or liquid. In a plastic or liquid state the matter of the sun must be intensely hot. We know this to be true.

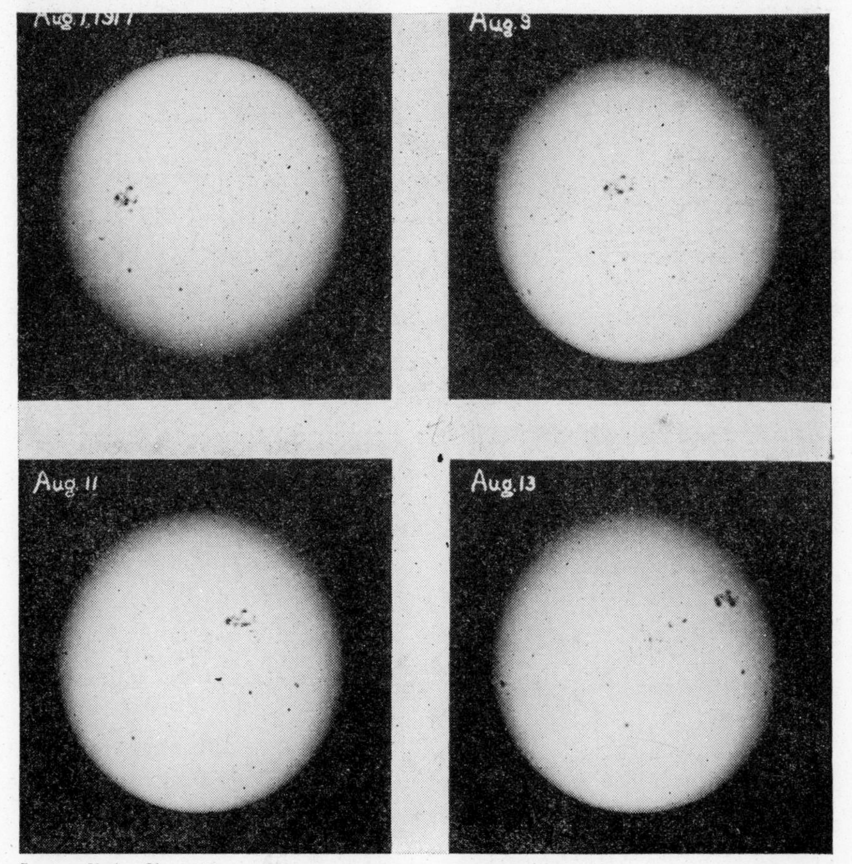

Courtesy Yerkes Observatory

THE PERIOD OF THE SUN'S ROTATION WAS DETERMINED BY WATCHING THE MOVEMENT OF SUN SPOTS

Our sun, being the central body in the solar system, is not only the largest body in the system but also the most important. Even the system derives its name from the Latin word *sol,* meaning sun. Though astronomers are accustomed to think of the sun as a rather ordinary star in respect to its size and temperature, it nevertheless is so large that the distance from the earth to the moon is only a little more than half the distance from the center to the outside of the sun! It is so hot that man has only with great difficulty produced temperatures exceeding its surface temperature—about ten thousand degrees Fahrenheit—and has never even hoped to produce temperatures approaching those of its interior—probably twenty to seventy million degrees Fahrenheit. In no sense can the sun be said to be *burning*—it is too hot to burn. Burning involves chemical union with oxygen, and although the materials comprising the sun are essentially the same materials we know on earth, they are all in a gaseous form and at a temperature at which combustion cannot take place.

At the surface of the sun gravitational pull is far greater than on earth—about twenty-seven times as great—so that a barrel of sugar weighing three hundred pounds, if it could be transported to the sun, would weigh about four and one-eighth tons. A man would weigh over two tons.

Its density is about one and a half times that of water and, as observations have shown that various parts of the sun rotate at different speeds, it cannot be a solid body.

A "CLOSE-UP" OF THE SUN

As observed on photographic plates the disk of the sun shows a granular appearance. On photographs taken in rapid succession these granules prove to exist for only a short time, and as they are hundreds of miles in diameter, their rapid formation and disappearance show an intensively active change of conditions at or near the surface of the sun. These markings appear to be similar to water waves which alternately raise themselves higher than the earth's highest mountains and sink to depths lower than the floor of the earth's seas—all within half a minute of time!

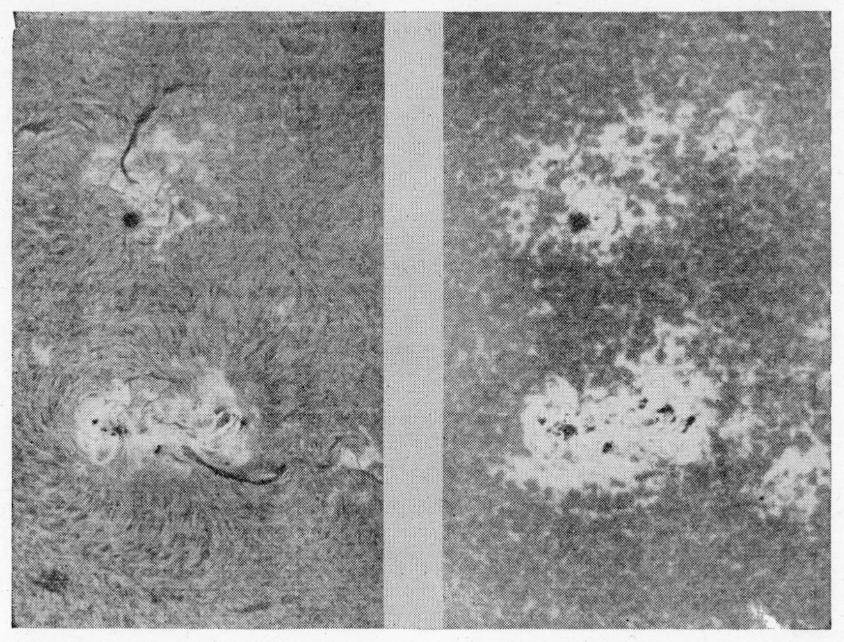

Courtesy Yerkes Observatory

A CLOSE-UP OF THE SUN
The granular appearance and sun spots are easily recognizable.

The disk also shows unusually bright areas of irregular shape and enormous size. These bright areas, called *faculae,* are usually seen near the limb or outer parts of the disk. There is some evidence that they are at higher temperatures than the surrounding areas, and possibly somewhat elevated above those areas. This is quite possibly due to a "boiling" effect of gases of high temperature coming to or near the surface.

THE SUNSPOTS

Of all the phenomena we observe in the sun, the feature which most readily lends itself to imaginative speculation is that of the sunspots. The average period of greatest activity of sunspots is about eleven years. These spots appear in pairs so frequently as to eliminate the possibility of mere chance. One spot of a pair is usually much larger than the other, and they appear most frequently in definite zones from ten to thirty degrees on either side of the sun's equator. The generally accepted conclusion concerning the nature of these phenomena is that the sunspot is a solar storm closely resembling an earthly tornado, but of such tremendous size and velocity as to be beyond the scope of human imagination. Spots of such size that the earth might easily be dropped into them are quite common during the periods of greatest activity.

These fierce solar storms are known to affect the magnetism of the earth. The increased activity of the Northern Lights when sunspots are observed, and the increase in static on the radio are only two noticeable proofs of this phenomenon. Attempts have been made to establish a connection between sunspots and terrestrial business cycles, as well as with the physical well-being of man himself. Impressive evidence has been presented that tree-ring growth in the giant redwoods of the West has been affected by the recurring sunspot cycles in the past, and the argument is, if these cycles affect vegetable life noticeably, why not also animal life, including man and his activities? These, however, are matters for speculation, and are presented here merely for what they may or may not be worth, without favor or prejudice.

We do know that radio reception is very noticeably affected by those cycles, and it is quite possible that extended observations will

Courtesy Yerkes Observatory

THE GREAT HEIGHT OF SOLAR PROMINENCES
The white dot indicates the size of the earth in comparison.

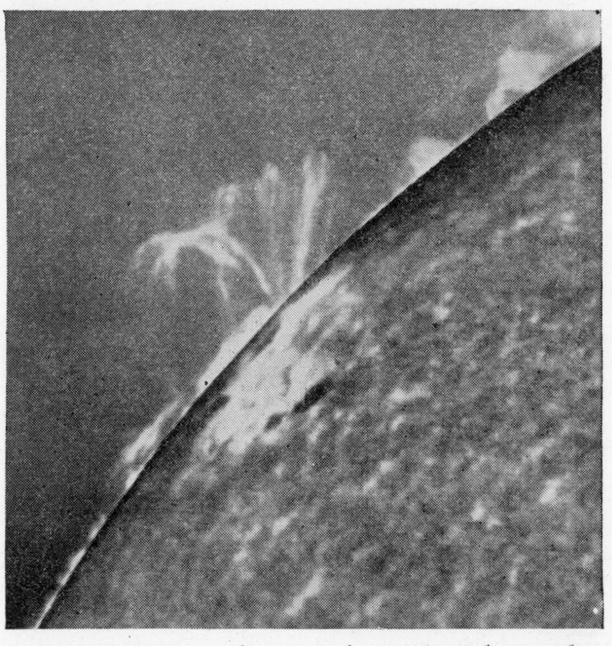

SUNSPOTS AND PROMINENCES ARE RELATED

This picture shows that prominences rise above the spots.

Courtesy Yerkes Observatory

show direct connection between them and terrestrial weather conditions.

At the outer edges of the sun are observed vast eruptions which at times rise to heights exceeding sixty times the diameter of the earth, or one-half the diameter of the sun itself. These are called solar prominences. Some of these remain almost stationary, like great clouds over the surface of the sun, for periods extending several days at a time, while others move with great velocities so that they change form within a few minutes. Those of the stationary type are known as quiescent prominences, and the others, which sometimes develop velocities as high as two hundred miles a second, are called eruptive prominences. These prominences are observed most frequently in the sunspot zones, but are also observed in other regions, sometimes even at the poles. Prominences of eruptive type are frequently found above sunspots.

THE ENERGY PRODUCED BY THE SUN

Sir Arthur Eddington, a noted British astronomer, estimates that the surface temperature of the sun approximates ten thousand degrees Fahrenheit, and that this temperature increases in

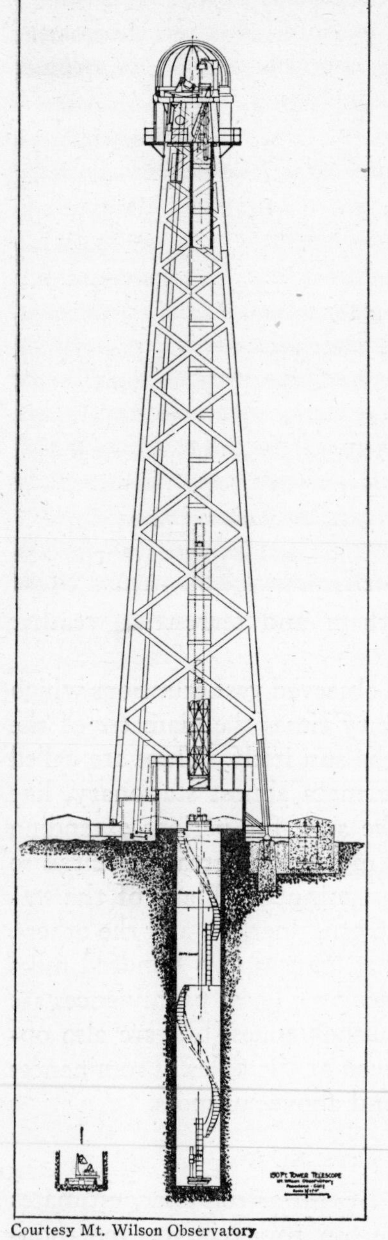

Courtesy Mt. Wilson Observatory

THE 150-FOOT TOWER TELESCOPE
In daily use at Mt. Wilson observatory.

the solar depths to something near eighty million degrees at the center. As stated before, such temperatures are totally beyond human comprehension, but they serve to impress upon us the fact that there is absolutely no comparison between these temperatures and those we know and understand upon the face of the earth. We know and understand, too, the heat produced by the friction of atoms and molecules brustled together, but such temperatures as the foregoing must be produced by the actual disintegration of the atoms themselves.

The atom, according to the modern conception, is a minute planetary system, with a central nucleus of protons surrounded by rapidly revolving electrons, roughly comparable to the solar system. There is, however, this difference: there is no likelihood of any force appearing which would drive the planets from their courses about the sun. While the electrons in the atom are as definitely fixed in their courses —under normal conditions—as are the planets in their orbits, the electrons may be, and are, driven out of their courses through collision or impact with other atomic systems. If the collisions be not too forceful these electrons eventually fall back to their given courses about the nucleus, and in this process give out the equivalent of the energy they have acquired through the collision or impact. This amount of energy, determined by the orbit to which the electron falls, is released as radiant energy.

Formerly this energy was considered to manifest itself as "ether waves." In the modern conception the energy-discharge is not visualized as a continuous stream, but goes out as a successive bombardment of bullet-like particles which are known as *quanta.*

The foregoing, in brief, is a rough statement of the "quantum theory" of Planck. It was once considered quite revolutionary and it changed many of the existing ideas of the physical world. The Rutherford-Bohr atom, in a general way, conforms to this depiction, but it was considered, earlier, to be deficient in its explications. The foregoing roughly described atom, however, with its preponderance of mass in the central proton, and with its electrons comparable to planets in the solar system, is the best picture we can now conceive to explain the internal structure of the sun and its almost incomprehensible output of energy. The sum of all knowledge on this subject contemplates not merely the frictional contact of atoms, but the very disintegration of systems of atoms, even though such a conception would have been considered rank heresy a generation ago.

THE COMPOSITION OF THE SUN

It is assumed that under conditions of enormous pressure atoms are stripped of their electrons, and protons and electrons are squeezed together without regard to atomic systems. Possibly protons and electrons come together in pairs forming hydrogen atoms when the condition of pressure changes. The hydrogen atom is the simplest of the atomic structures of the ninety-two elements, having, according to Bohr's theory, one positive charge of electricity forming a nucleus about which a single electron revolves. These simple hydrogen atoms are assumed to join together in groups of four, forming helium atoms. The more complicated forms of matter, then, are assumed to be built of these helium atoms in combination with sufficient hydrogen atoms to fill

Courtesy Mt. Wilson Observatory

MIRRORS OF THE SNOW COELOSTAT

The Snow Coelostat is a horizontal telescope which does the same work as the tower telescope.

in the odd numbers, but with no atom of these more complex elements ever containing more than three of the hydrogen atoms.

It has been demonstrated that the helium atom does not weigh precisely four times as much as the hydrogen atom, though made up of four electrons and four protons, which leads to the conclusion that there is an actual loss of mass in the combining process. There is no apparent way to account for this loss of mass except that it is transformed directly into energy, and using one of Einstein's formulas as a basis for calculation it appears that the volume of energy thus liberated is tremendous. It has been estimated that the amount of energy so released in transforming the hydrogen in a teaspoonful of water would be sufficient to drive the largest ocean liner across the Atlantic Ocean.

Large as is the amount of energy emitted by the sun, the earth receives only an infinitesimal fraction of the whole amount. Yet this fractional amount is sufficient to sustain all the life on the earth. If, by some chance, the sun should cease its beneficent radiation of energy for even a week, all the fresh water, and eventually the salt oceans, would be congealed in ice so that no water would be available, and within a very short time all the plant and animal life on earth would perish from the intense cold. Man, himself, might survive a little longer than the other forms of life because he knows how to store his food for future consumption, but the lack of water and the increasing cold would certainly limit his existence to a very short time.

WHAT CAUSED THE SUN TO HAVE PLANETS?

What was the origination of the solar system? How were all the planets formed? Naturally, we have no positive explanation, but theories, or hypotheses, have been propounded from time to time. Some have gained recognition and some have remained obscure. Others have collapsed upon exposure of their weaknesses, and still others have withstood cross-examination. For a hundred years the theory propounded by Laplace, called the nebular hypothesis, was generally accepted by astronomers. It stated that the solar system originated from an intensely hot gaseous globe which contracted in cooling, and in this process occasionally threw off rings of substance from its equatorial region. These rings were supposed to have eventually formed the planets. Such, roughly, was the accepted theory, but like many theories which have been accepted and discarded in turn, there were difficulties. Why, once the process of leaving residual matter behind was established, did not this process continue unbroken—why the intermittent ring effect? Again what would prevent a hot gaseous ring from disintegrating? Why would this ring contract into a more or less spherical ball of matter? These and other objections to the theory remained unanswered, or at least unsatisfactorily answered.

The planetesimal hypothesis of Chamberlin and Moulton takes a different view of the whole question. According to this theory,

Courtesy Yerkes Observatory

ORIGIN OF THE EARTH?

According to one theory the earth may have been formed of sun prominences larger than these. The white dot in upper right part of picture indicates the relative size of the earth.

two stars, one of which is now the sun, swept close to each other at a terrific speed. Their association was short, but eventful. The exertion of gravitational force of the other star resulted in great tides upon the sun, one toward the other star and one directly opposite. These tides, or prominences, were wholly or in part ejected from the sun's mass. There may have been a quantity of scattered material in the vicinity of the sun before this happened. Materials ejected from the surface of the sun perpendicularly would fall directly back to it were there no other force exerted, but the motion through space of the visiting star would impart to this scattered material and to the material ejected from the sun an angular motion which accounts for the planetary orbits about the sun. These masses of material are supposed to have assumed globular form, and to have swept up the debris of the cataclysm to a great extent in the course of time. They are assumed to have cooled rapidly, to become the system of nine planets with their twenty-six satellites, comets, meteors, and more than a thousand planetoids, all revolving about the sun in approximately the same plane. The "sweeping up" of debris by the planets still continues, though at a very greatly diminished rate, as demonstrated by the meteors that continually enter into the the earth's atmosphere.

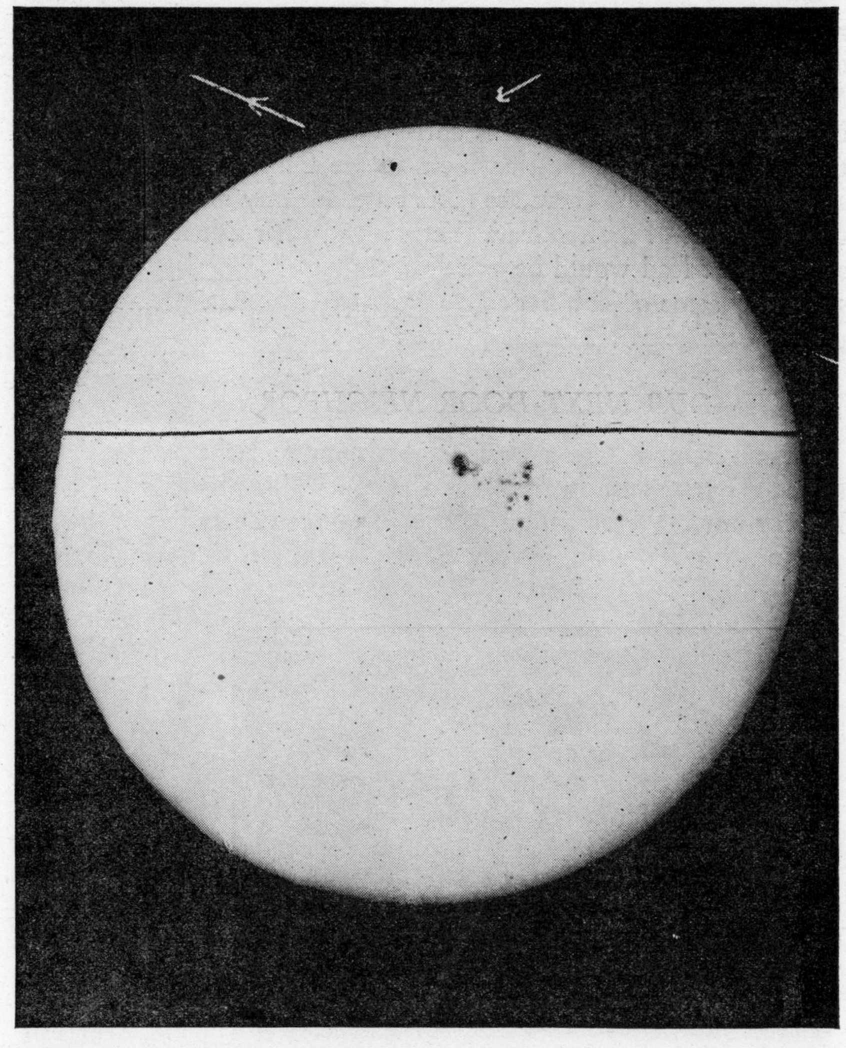

Courtesy Yerkes Observatory

A TRANSIT OF MERCURY

The small black dot indicated by arrows, near the top of the sun's disk, is Mercury.

MERCURY—A YEAR IN EIGHTY-EIGHT DAYS

Mercury, the closest planet to the sun, is only thirty-six million miles from it. Because of this comparative proximity, it has the swiftest motion of all of the planets, completing its orbit in about eighty-eight days, and receives the greatest intensity of radiation. Its diameter is only three thousand miles—about the distance from New York to San Francisco. To all appearances, Mercury does not rotate. The surface facing the sun is intensely hot, while the opposite side is correspondingly cold. It is certain that life in any form with which we are familiar could not possibly exist there. If there are lakes on the sunny side of Mercury, they could be of molten lead. Yet, on the other side it seems to be so cold that lead would be brittle and shatter like glass if it were struck by some object. Mercury apparently has the greatest temperature range of all of the planets.

VENUS—OUR NEXT-DOOR NEIGHBOR

In an orbit between those of Mercury and the earth, Venus serenely pursues her way about the sun. This planet appears to be very much brighter than Mercury, and can easily be seen in the daytime when the sky is very clear. It is often seen long before

THE CRESCENT VENUS

When Venus is closest to the earth it appears as a crescent. We see only a portion of it because we look upon its night.

Courtesy Yerkes Observatory

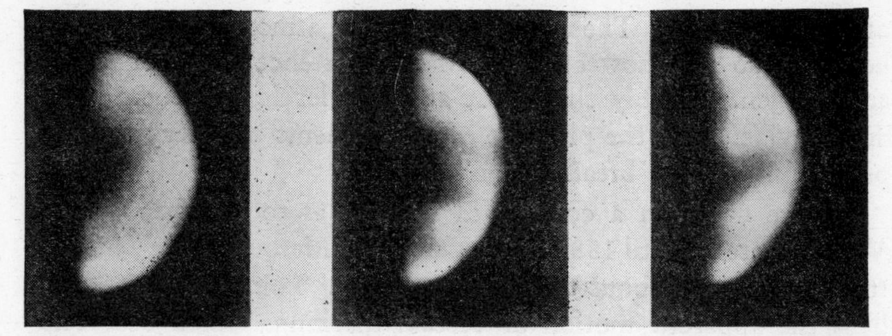

Courtesy Yerkes Observatory

THREE PICTURES OF VENUS SHOWING THE EFFECT OF ITS HEAVY ATMOSPHERE

sunset and long after sunrise. With a fairly good telescope phases like those of the moon are distinctly visible. Its distance from the earth is approximately twenty-six million miles.

The planet Venus undoubtedly has a very dense atmosphere, for astronomers have never seen its surface, even with the most powerful instruments. Quite possibly, sunlight itself does not penetrate the dense atmosphere to the surface. However, Venus receives almost twice as much solar radiation as the earth, and it is not difficult to imagine that the surface is bathed in a pearly, opalescent glow of light which would be pleasing to the human eye. To the annoyance of observers, this dense atmosphere makes it impossible to obtain any information of the planetary surface. Some astronomers have suggested that it is much like the surface of the earth.

Studies of the atmosphere of Venus indicate a temperature of about ten degrees below zero Fahrenheit on the dark side, with the bright side only a few degrees warmer. This temperature can be compared with that of our own stratosphere, which seems to remain fairly uniform at about sixty degrees below zero. Carrying the comparison through, one would be led to believe that the surface of the planet itself is much warmer than that of the earth, and any form of life which might possibly exist there would probably be ponderous and sluggish, somewhat comparable to the great prehistoric dinosaurs of our own planet. These creatures would probably be unaware of the existence of the sun and other bodies exterior to their own sphere because of the visual impenetrability of the atmosphere. The upper layers of the atmosphere of Venus, however, do not show evidence of the existence of water vapor and oxygen. Possibly these exist at lower levels, but there is no direct evidence of the presence of the elements necessary to support the life of air-breathing animals.

There has been a conflict of opinion as to whether or not Venus rotates. Until 1880, both Venus and Mercury were believed to rotate once in about twenty-four hours. This belief had as its basis the apparent motion of certain markings which observers believed they had detected. Schiaparelli, however, observing under favorable conditions in Italy, found periods of rotation of these two planets to be identical with their respective periods of revolution, so that they would always present the same face to the sun. Some other observers confirmed, and still others disputed the results. The markings on these planets are too vague to give reliable results as to rotation periods from direct observation, but with all the evidence taken into consideration, probably a rotation period of about thirty days for Venus, and for Mercury a period that is identical with its period of revolution.

MARS—THE RUDDY PLANET

Now we come to the red planet next beyond the earth, over which there has been, and still is, probably more controversy than over any other astronomical body; the controversy over the habitability of Mars with the intensive study incident thereto has resulted in a certain amount of knowledge concerning it, and almost unlimited speculation.

Mars is a little over one and a half times as far from the sun as is the earth, which, of course, decreases the amount of radiation it receives to about one-half as much as received by the earth. Its sidereal period—the time it takes for the planet to complete one revolution about the sun—is one and four-fifths of our years. Thus the Martian year is approximately 687 of our days in length. However, its rotation period is twenty-four hours, thirty-seven minutes, and twenty-three seconds of our time, so that the Martian year is about 670 Martian days long.

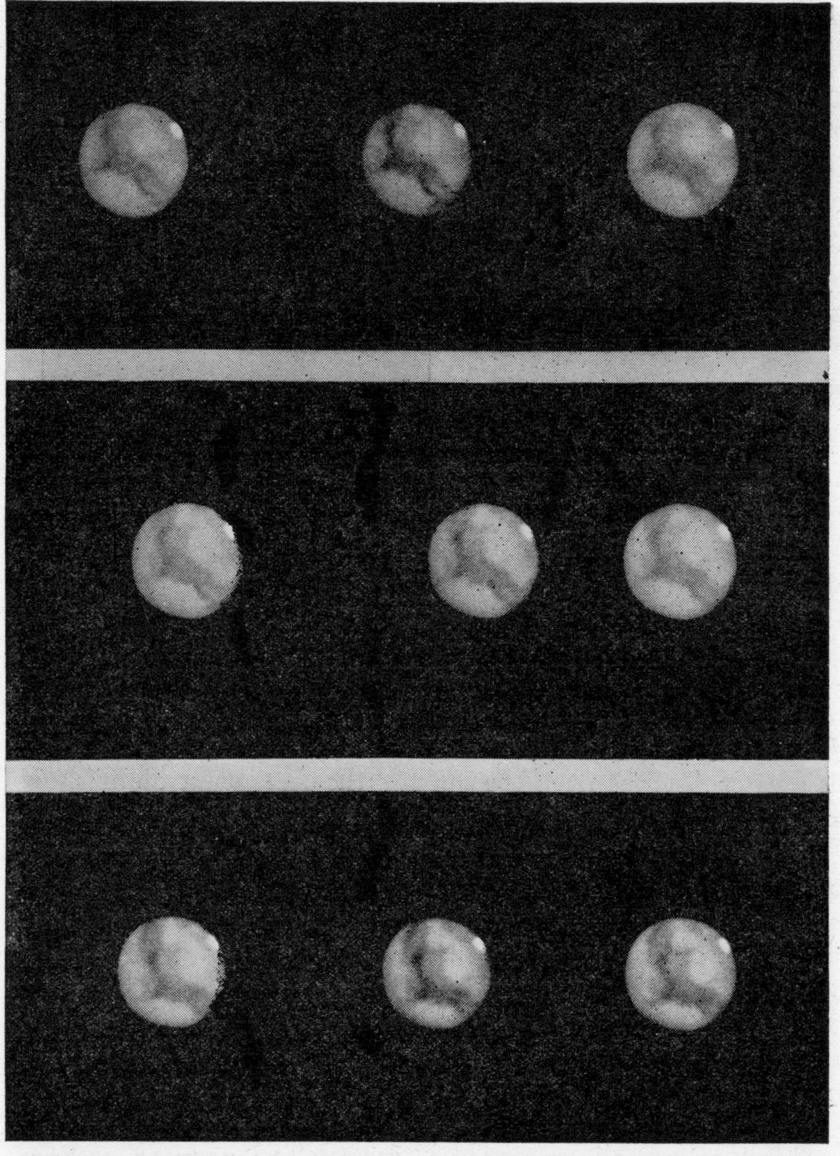

Courtesy Yerkes Observatory

NINE VIEWS OF MARS

Pictures such as these have led to wide speculation concerning the surface of the red planet. If life as we understand it exists on Mars, it must be of a totally different form because of the lack of moisture there.

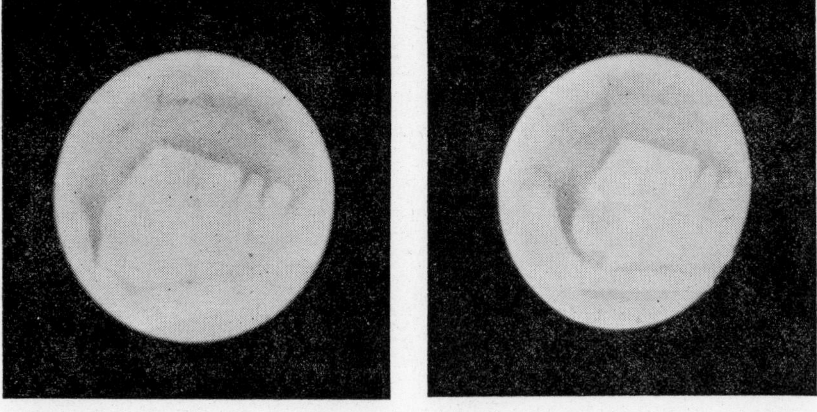

Courtesy Lick Observatory

TWO DRAWINGS OF MARS BY J. E. KEELER

Its closest approach to the earth is thirty-five million miles; its mass is a little over one-tenth that of the earth, and its density about four times that of water.

The inclination of the axis of Mars is just about the same as that of the earth, hence, its seasons are comparable to ours, except that each is almost twice as long because of the length of the Martian year. They must be, however, less pronounced because of the greater distance from the sun and the consequent diminished intensity of radiation received.

The changes in the surface appearance are significant in that about three-fifths of the surface is reddish-brown at times, with darker regions of a constant nature. When summer comes, the white polar cap is observed to shrink, and these dark regions seem to take on a decidedly greenish appearance. The observation of these phenomena has led to the belief that the melting of the polar cap supplies moisture from which some forms of vegetation derive nourishment.

In 1877, Schiaparelli discovered what he called the *canali*; the word was mistakenly translated as *canals*. This network of fine lines in the "continents" of the planet is difficult to distinguish, and there is still controversy as to whether they exist as such or as broad shadings of more or less indefinite character. If the "canals" really exist, they show considerable evidence of being artificially constructed, and those who support the theory of the existence of intelligent life on the planet hold up this fact as evidence. It is certain that there is very little water on the planet, and what were formerly called "seas" cannot possibly be bodies of water.

Various estimates as to the amount of oxygen in the Martian atmosphere range from sixteen per cent to fifty per cent as high as that in the earth's, and the amount of water vapor is generally considered to be about six per cent as much as in the earth's atmosphere. The occasional presence of floating clouds and the periodic shrinking and growing of the polar caps indicates conclusively that there is an atmosphere, but the difficulty of observation due to our own atmosphere makes determinations of its density unreliable.

Extreme desert conditions probably prevail because of the dearth of water, and if intelligent beings do exist on this interesting sphere they must find the conditions of life difficult. What forms of life these severe conditions would induce we can only guess, but who can say that other intelligent creatures cannot have their being in forms of which we know nothing and under conditions which we would find impossible?

MOONS OF MARS

This planet has two tiny moons, Deimos and Phobos, which are each probably less than twenty miles in diameter. These satellites revolve about Mars in the plane of its equator, and the nearer one, Phobos, is interesting in that its period of revolution is only a little more than seven and one-half hours, moving faster than the surface of the planet so that from Mars it would appear to be rising in the west and setting in the east. Phobos is less than four thousand miles from the surface of the planet. The period of revolution of the other, Deimos, is a little over thirty hours—so little greater than the rotation period of the planet that at a given point on the Martian surface it would remain above the horizon more than sixty hours, and go through all its changes of phases twice between moonrise and moonset.

Courtesy Yerkes Observatory

THE TRAIL OF THE PLANETOID EROS

THE ASTEROIDS OR PLANETOIDS

Although astronomers found no planet between the orbits of Mars and Jupiter, they long suspected that there was one. This gap was unexplainable; their calculations told them that there should be a planet having such an orbit between Mars and Jupiter. For years they examined the sky most carefully. They found no planet, but were surprised to find many little bodies revolving in the orbit in which they had expected the larger body. Because these bodies were small, and yet exhibited all the necessary qualifications of a planet, they were called planetoids or asteroids, the name indicating that they are small planets.

These little planets are still being discovered, the modern method being to expose a photographic plate over a period of time on the region where they are most generally found. A clock mechanism is adjusted to counteract the rotation of the earth so that the stars are recorded on the plate as points of light, but due to the planetary motion of the asteroids, if one is present in the field, it leaves a record of itself on the plate by causing a trail or short streak of light to appear on the photographic plate.

Vesta, though not the largest of these, is the brightest, and is sometimes visible to the naked eye. Its diameter has been computed at 248 miles. The diameters of Ceres, Pallas, and Juno have been computed as being 488, 304 and 118 miles respectively. The diameters of the others are, with comparatively few exceptions, probably less than fifty miles. Their average distances range from that of Eros, the nearest, one hundred and fifty million miles, to more than five hundred million miles, and their periods of revolu-

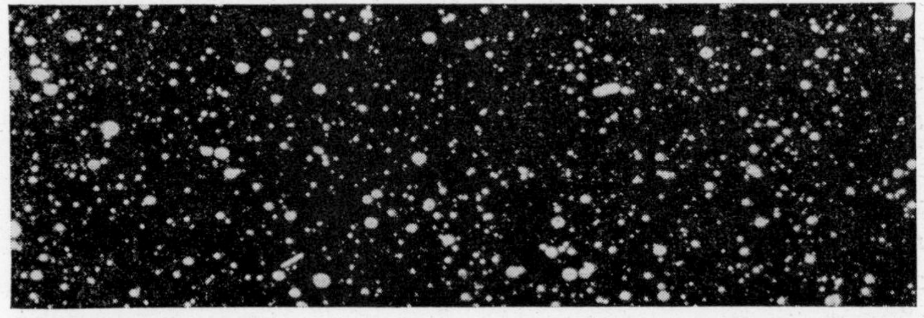

Courtesy Yerkes Observatory

THE TWO SHORT OBLIQUE LINES ARE ASTEROID TRAILS

Paul's Photos, Chicago

RELATIVE SIZES OF THE SUN AND PLANETS
Left to right: Mercury, Venus, Earth and Moon, Mars, Jupiter.

tion from two to more than twelve years. It is interesting to note the discovery by Kirkwood in 1866. He observed that the periods of none of them are simple fractions (such as one-half, one-fourth, or three-fourths of the period of the planet Jupiter). At that time there were only eighty-eight asteroids known, but the subsequent discovery of literally hundreds more has confirmed that discovery.

A very interesting aggregation of names was selected from Greek mythology for the first of these tiny bodies discovered, and later when these names ran out, other mythologies were drawn upon, and the works of classical writers such as Shakespeare and many more were consulted. With the exception of a few of these minor planetoids, the names selected were all feminine. More lately the custom has been to enumerate them by serial numbers combined with literal designations, as, for example, 1920 JA—the figures denoting the year of discovery. This has become necessary because, unlike the case with human beings, to duplicate names would be hopelessly confusing.

THE SUN AND PLANETS COMPARED
Left to right: Saturn, Uranus, Neptune, Pluto. Large disk at the top represents the sun.

Eros, coming close to the earth, has lent itself to the solution of the problem of redetermining the distance to the sun. It was used in 1900, and again in 1931, when a number of observatories participated in a concerted attack upon the problem of the distance between the earth and the sun.

THE FOUR GIANTS

Next, in order of distance from the sun, are four giant planets, Jupiter, Saturn, Uranus, and Neptune. These four have several features in common, although in other ways they distinctly differ from each other. Their distances from the sun are five hundred million, nine hundred million, one billion eight hundred million, and two billion eight hundred million miles, respectively. Neptune requires nearly 165 of our years to complete one revolution about the sun, or, to state it in still another manner, the Neptunian year is 165 times as long as ours. Jupiter's year is twelve times that of the earth; Saturn's, twenty-nine; and Uranus', eighty-four times that of the earth.

All four show evidence of very dense atmospheres, but curiously the order of density is exactly the reverse of their order of distance from the sun; that is, Neptune, the farthest out from the sun has the densest atmosphere of the four.

Each of these four giants is revealed through the telescope to have light and dark belts. Contrary to the order of indicated density of atmosphere, these belts seem more conspicuous in the order of their distance from the sun. Determinations of temperature made in 1924 resulted in mean surface temperatures for the inner three of the four, that is, Jupiter, Saturn, and Uranus respectively, of −270°, −306°, and −340° below zero Fahrenheit. From this point on it is best to consider other features of these massive planets individually.

JUPITER

The giant planet is larger than all the others combined, having a diameter eleven times that of the earth, and thirteen hundred times the volume. It rotates so rapidly that there is a pronounced equatorial bulge. This astonishing rate of rotation—once in ten hours—means that a given point on its equator travels at the rate of 27,850 miles per hour. Compare this with the fastest-flying creature on earth, the deer fly, which travels at only eight hundred miles per hour.

Jupiter shows a variety of beautiful colors, but excellent atmospheric conditions are necessary to observe them, for the slightest atmospheric disturbance blurs the detail. Rapid and frequent changes in the surface markings give proof of atmospheric disturbances on this planet compared with which our worst tornadoes and typhoons are mere "tempests in a tea cup."

Such a wealth of unusual and intriguing surface markings have been observed on this planet that it would be impossible to enumerate them here, but probably the best known of these was the "Great Red Spot" of 1878. For about three years this spot was very conspicuous, and indeed parts of its outline are still faintly visible, although it seems intermittently to disappear and recur. During periods of its absence, however, the place is marked by what appears to be a hollow.

Courtesy Lick Observatory

SIX VIEWS OF THE PLANET JUPITER

Quantities of ammonia and methane are now known to exist in the atmosphere of Jupiter. Methane is also known as "marsh gas" or that dread enemy of coal miners, "fire damp." Coal gas contains about twenty-nine per cent of methane.

As in the case of Venus, we cannot penetrate the dense atmosphere to see the actual surface of the planet, and there is some possibility that the dense gases of its atmosphere become increasingly dense as penetration is made farther into the planet itself, without any definite line of demarcation between gases and solids.

JUPITER'S SATELLITES

Jupiter has a system of nine moons, the two outermost of which revolve about the planet in a retrogressive direction. The periods of rotation of these satellites vary from forty-two hours to 758 days, and their distances from the planet range from 112 thousand to about fifteen million miles. The order of their distances is not, however, directly in order of their periods of revolution, because their masses are irregular in relation to both distances and periods.

THREE VIEWS OF JUPITER AND ITS SATELLITES, OR MOONS

Jupiter is eleven times the size of the Earth, and its volume is 1300 times that of our planet.

Courtesy Yerkes Observatory

Four of these, known as the Galilean Satellites, revolve in almost the plane of the earth, so that they always appear in a nearly straight line. This, however, does not hold for the remaining five satellites.

SATURN AND ITS RINGS

Saturn is the only planet with a system of rings and in this respect it is, so far as we know, unique among all the objects in the universe. This great planet, next in size to giant Jupiter, with its shining rings, is a beautiful object. Saturn's equatorial bulge is conspicuous—more so than that of any of the other planets—but its diameter is smaller and its rotation period slightly longer than that of Jupiter. This naturally leads to the conclusion, without further evidence, that its density is less, and such is actually the case, it being less than that of water. Saturn, like Jupiter, shows evidence of methane and ammonia in its atmosphere.

The outer diameter of the ring system is about 172,500 miles, while the diameter of the planet itself is 75,060 miles. The ring

Courtesy Lick Observatory

SATURN AND ITS RINGS, AFTER A DRAWING BY J. E. KEELER

Courtesy Yerkes Observatory

THE PLANET SATURN WITH ITS ENCIRCLING GASEOUS RINGS
(Photograph.)

system, consisting of two outer bright rings and one inner ring which is darker, is probably not more than one hundred miles thick, and all the evidence leads to a belief that these rings are made up of small particles of matter, probably not larger than a walnut and grading from that size to dust grains. There have been various conjectures as to their actual composition, including the suggestion that they may be ice or snow. The middle ring is far the widest and the brightest. Cassini's division, the space between the outer and middle rings, lies in a position similar to that occupied by the planetoids in the solar system. Other observers have reported various other divisions of the rings that seem to be analogous to the spacing of the orbits of the planets about the sun, which would indicate the possibility that such spaces are constant in all comparable systems.

URANUS

Uranus, because of its small apparent diameter and indefinite outline, is not as well known as the nearer planets. Its diameter is reckoned at 30,900 miles. It has a volume of about sixty times that of the earth. Its mass or weight is fifteen times that of the earth, and its density is a little greater than that of water. Its period of rotation is not definitely known, but V. M. Slipher determined that it must be about eleven hours by the spectroscopic method. If the figure is correct, and the value given for its diameter is also accurate, a given point on the equator must travel ninety-seven thousand miles in eleven hours, or at the rate of almost nine thousand miles per hour.

There are four satellites revolving about this planet with periods ranging from 2.5 to 13.5 days. Their diameters range probably from five hundred to one thousand miles.

URANUS AND TWO OF ITS SATELLITES

Uranus, because of its apparently small diameter and vague outline, is not as well known as nearer planets.

Courtesy Yerkes Observatory

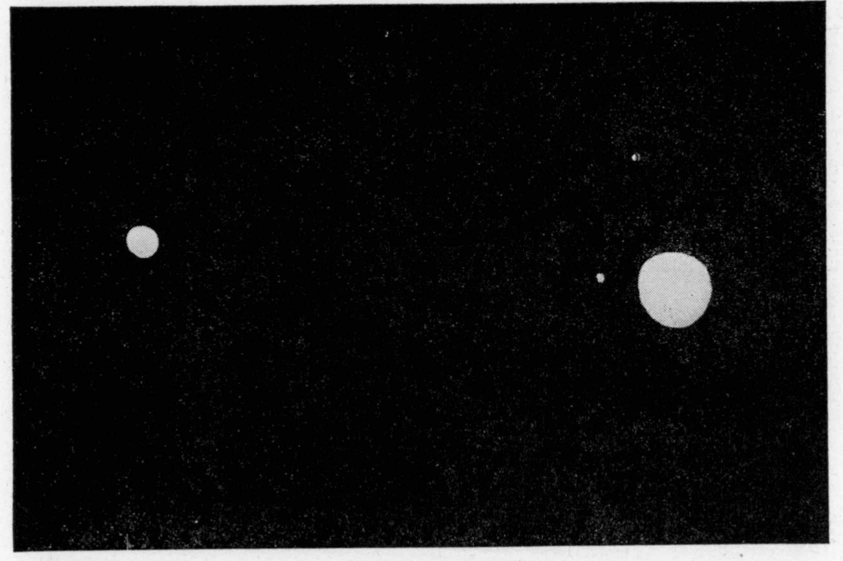

Courtesy Yerkes Observatory

NEPTUNE AND ITS SATELLITE

NEPTUNE AND ITS SATELLITE

Unique among the giant planets is Neptune, in that we find for it only one moon. Neptune's period of rotation is about sixteen hours. It is invisible to the naked eye. In the telescope it shows a faint greenish disk, and under exceptionally fine observing conditions there is about it a vague suggestion of belts. A little over one-third the diameter of Jupiter, it is so distant—almost seven times as far as Jupiter—that detailed study of its surface features is practically impossible with present methods and equipment.

The one moon of Neptune has a diameter estimated at two thousand miles, and revolves around the planet in a period of five days and twenty-one hours, at a distance of 222 thousand miles, in the retrogressive direction.

PLUTO

The recently discovered planet in our solar system, and the farthest out in the cold, dark regions of space, is most appropriately named after the god of the regions of darkness. It is probably

Courtesy Yerkes Observatory

TWO VIEWS OF PLUTO
The change in position among the stars in one day is apparent.

four billion miles distant from the sun and its period of revolution, or its "year," is estimated at two hundred and fifty of our years. Its orbit is the least regular of the planetary orbits. It even rotates about the sun in a different plane from that of the other planets. At times it is even closer to the sun than is Neptune, and at other times it travels half again farther than Neptune from the sun. In 1989 it will be at its closest approach to the sun, and in the most favorable position for observation. In size it is probably much smaller than the other four outer planets—possibly as small as the earth, Venus, or even little Mercury, the diameter of which is but three thousand miles. At its distance from the sun its surface temperature must be so low that any nitrogen or oxygen in its atmosphere would exist not in a gaseous but in a solid state.

The possibility of the existence of life on any of the outer planets, in any form which we know, is extremely slight if not, indeed, inconceivable. Conditions of temperature, atmosphere, surface disturbances, and even the stability of the planetary surfaces themselves, in some cases, would preclude the possibility of any human existence, and probably any vegetable growth as we understand the term.

The orbits of all the planets are elliptical, and all revolve in the counter-clockwise direction around the sun. The discovery of Pluto has increased the bounds of our solar system to the point where it takes light, at a velocity of about 186 thousand miles per second, some eleven hours to transverse the distance from one extreme to the other. Will further discoveries of even more outlying members of the system extend our horizons still farther? We can only say that the most unique and interesting phenomenon in the universe, the mind of man, will never lie quiescent as long as it exists, and no one now can tell what future accomplishments it may achieve.

WANDERERS THROUGH THE DEPTHS OF SPACE

Like some other celestial bodies, comets have been observed for hundreds of years. Among early peoples they were regarded as harbingers of disaster or evil. Unhappy indeed was the prince whose reign was begun under the malign influence of so strange a visitor. Today a bright comet would be regarded scientifically and popularly with great interest and, perhaps something of awe. Of all the attendants of the sun, the comets are perhaps the most curious. The very bright ones are, of course, the most spectacular.

When a comet is first discovered it is usually quite faint. It is then seen as a point of light, called the nucleus, surrounded by a small fuzzy patch of light, called the coma. As the comet moves nearer the sun, its brightness increases and the coma becomes larger. At the same time the characteristic fan-like tail begins to develop. The comet becomes continually brighter and the tail longer until the object reaches its shortest distance from the sun, after which it begins to recede from the sun and its light fades. This order of events is characteristic of all comets, though the fainter one may not show a perceptible tail. This need not necessarily mean that it does not have one, but simply that it is too faint to be seen.

Up to the present time several hundred comets have been observed and their orbits computed. The orbits of most comets are elliptical. This means, in effect, that those with such orbits belong to the solar system. Indeed, there is no certain evidence that any comets have come from the voids of interstellar space. Most of the comets revolve about the sun in less than one hundred

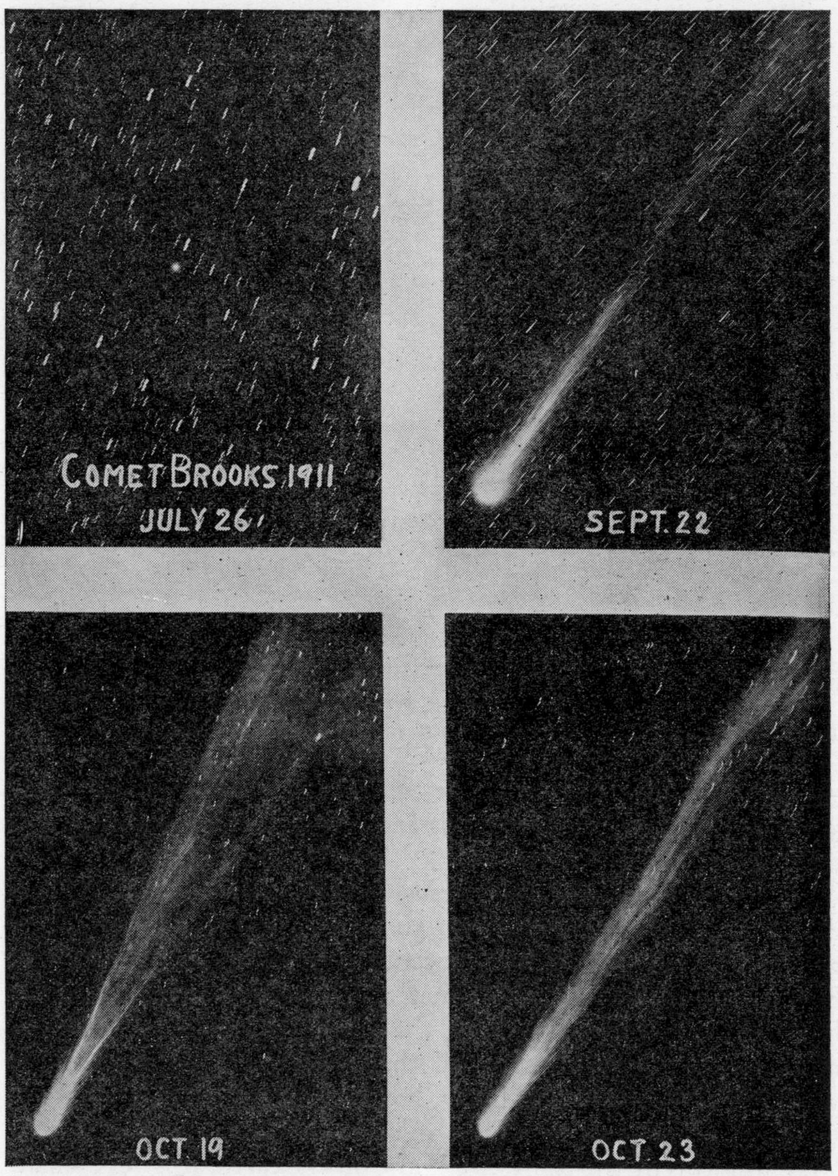

Courtesy Yerkes Observatory

A SERIES OF PICTURES SHOWING THE CHANGING APPEARANCE OF A COMET AS IT APPROACHES THE EARTH

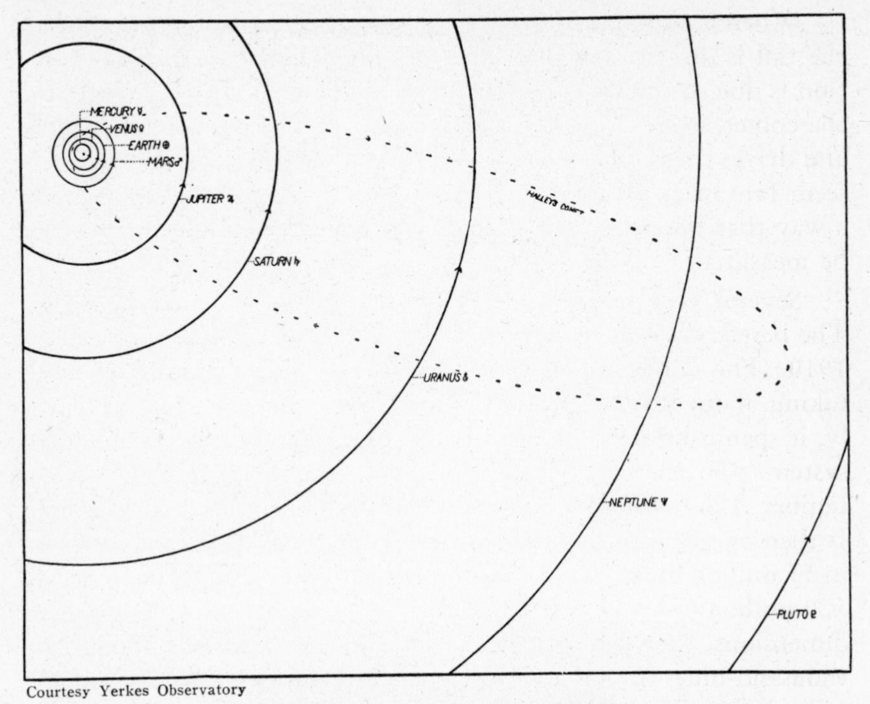

Courtesy Yerkes Observatory

DIAGRAM OF THE SOLAR SYSTEM

This diagram shows the orbits of the planets and that of Halley's Comet. The sun is represented by the small dot within the orbits.

years; there are, however, some with periods up to a thousand years, and for a few the periods are nearly ten times as large as that.

Comets are usually very large in size. In fact, very few indeed have heads as small as ten thousand miles in diameter. In general the head ranges from twenty-five thousand miles to one hundred thousand miles in diameter, and a few have even larger heads. But though the heads of the comets are large, the amount of material in them is so small that there is no direct way of weighing them. It is very likely, however, that they weigh only a few millions of tons, even for the largest. While such a weight is large in terms of the things we know on the earth, it is very small when we consider the weights of such astronomical bodies as the earth, moon, or sun. The tails of these objects are of prodigious extent, ranging from a few million miles to well over one hundred million miles in length.

When a comet with a tail is observed, it is always found that the tail is directed away from the sun. This characteristic position is due to the fact that the light of the sun, which illuminates the comet, exerts a pressure on the particles in the coma and tail, and drives them off—away from the sun. While such an idea may seem fantastic, it can actually be tested in the laboratory in such a way that the pressure of light—which is exceedingly small—can be measured.

Several very bright comets have been visible from the earth. The best known of these is Halley's comet which last appeared in 1910. This comet moves in a long, narrow ellipse around the sun, taking about seventy-seven years to make the trip. Consequently, it spends most of its time in the outermost reaches of the solar system. On the last return, the comet was first sighted in September, 1909, when it was about 310 million miles from the sun. It then moved into the vicinity of the sun, approaching it to within 55 million miles. Then on its way out it was studied until it was 520 million miles away. When the comet had attained its greatest dimensions, then being close to the sun, its head was about 220 thousand miles in diameter while the tail was over twenty million miles long! Though it is not certain, the earth probably passed through the tail of Halley's comet in May, 1910.

There have been many other bright comets. There was Donati's comet of 1858 which was exceedingly bright. The Great Comet of 1882 was one of the very largest. Holmes's comet of 1892 was so large that the diameter of the outer portion of the coma was nearly the size of the sun! Many have been bright enough so that they could be faintly seen during the day. Every return of Halley's comet from 87 B.C. to 1910 A.D., has been recorded.

Sometimes a comet breaks in two, as did Biela's comet of 1846. Two smaller comets were formed that actually traveled together for three months. Six years later the pair returned, but were separated by a million miles. They have never been seen since.

For the most part, however, comets are very faint, so that they can be observed only with large telescopes. It is a rare one that

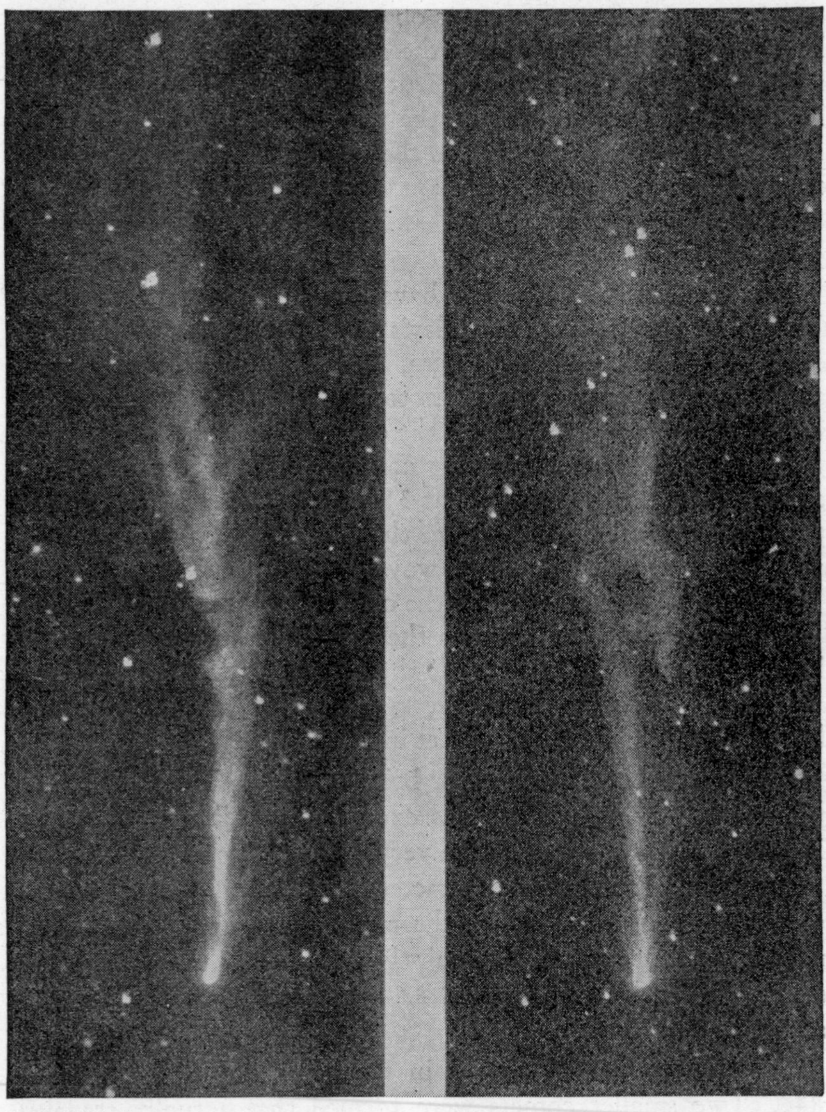

Courtesy Lick Observatory

A COMET AS WE MIGHT SEE IT

Brooks' Comet as it appeared October 21 and 22, 1893. The long tail of a comet always points away from the sun.

can be seen with the unaided eye. About six to ten are seen each year, about a quarter of which are known, and the rest are new. It has been estimated that there are about one hundred thousand comets in the solar system.

There is usually quite an exciting time at an observatory when a bright comet is discovered. All sorts of observational methods are used to determine its orbit, changes in brightness and appearance, and the analysis of the light of the comet itself. The reason why a comet is so interesting is the fact that its physical characteristics change. These changes are often extremely rapid and of great complexity.

FLASHY VISITORS FROM EVERYWHERE

The comets appear to be closely related to another group of bodies in the solar system—the meteors. Though their relation to the comets is not apparent at first, we will see that there is such a relationship.

If we were to watch the sky on a clear night for a half-hour or so we should probably see during that time a dozen bright objects flash across the sky and disappear. These transient objects are called meteors. Usually they seem to dart here and there in the sky at random. They can never be seen very long—a second or so at the most. Much more rarely we see an extremely bright meteor that is so brilliant that it lights up the whole landscape for miles around. While there is no essential difference between the faint objects and the brighter ones, the latter are usually called "bolides" or "fireballs." Often a bright meteor will leave a shining trail or train that persists for several minutes or even for as long as a half-hour. Exactly how or why this happens is not at all understood.

Occasionally one of the meteors reaches the ground and is called a "meteorite." Many of them have been recovered and may be seen in the various museums. The name "meteorite" is used to distinguish them from those that are seen in the sky, but do not reach the ground.

On close examination, a meteorite is found to be either metallic or stony in substance. They usually show definite signs of having

Photo by Frank M. Preucil

TWO COMMON TYPES OF METEORITES: THE STONY AND THE FUSED IRON

been exposed to very high temperatures. This fact constitutes the secret of their brightness when they appear in the sky. A meteor is usually, but not always, a small particle of matter that travels at a high rate of speed through space. The average speed is about 25 miles a second, though it varies greatly. Now, when one of these objects runs into the earth's atmosphere, the friction between the meteor and the gas is sufficient to raise the outer portion of the particle to a very high temperature. As a result it glows brightly. Usually meteors are completely "burned up" after having traveled a few miles in the upper atmosphere of the earth. It is only the larger ones that ever get to the ground at all.

The meteors that are commonly seen are the so-called "sporadic" meteors, that is, they appear haphazardly. But occasionally meteors will appear in great swarms. At such a time they appear to radiate from a single point called the "radiant." Such a demonstration is called a meteor shower. There are several swarms that reappear each year: the best known are those that come from the constellation Leo in November, and those that come from Perseus in August. The most famous shower of history is the one that took place in 1866. We are told that the meteors entered the earth's atmosphere on an average of two hundred thousand per hour for five hours or more. Another brilliant shower occurred in 1933, though it was not seen in America, when over a hundred meteors appeared per minute. The shower seems to have been observed before 1841, 1900, and 1926.

The explanation of a meteor shower is that the meteors themselves are moving in an orbit around the sun. And every year, at a given date, the earth cuts their orbit. At this time hundreds collide with the earth's atmosphere and we have a shower. In many cases it is found that their orbits are identical with those of known comets. For example, the August meteors or Perseids have an orbit identical with that of Tuttle's comet of 1862. Temple's comet of 1868 is associated with the November meteors or Leonids. Another group of meteors is closely associated with Biela's comet. The shower of 1933 is connected with Giacobini's comet of 1900.

So it appears that either the heads of comets are made up of meteors, or that comets and meteors have similar origins. In some cases, though, it seems that the meteor swarms are the result of the disintegration of comets.

There are a few instances known where huge meteors have hit the earth's surface with an impact so hard that great craters

Photo by Frank M. Preucil

POLISHED CROSS SECTION OF A METEORITE

Courtesy Field Museum of Natural History, Chicago

METEOR CRATER . . .

Photo by Raeburn Rohrbach

METEORITES FOUND IN METEOR CRATER IN ARIZONA

. . . NEAR WINSLOW, ARIZONA

have been thrown up. The most famous of these is the meteor crater in Arizona. This pit is about four thousand feet in diameter, and has walls 150 feet above the surrounding plain. Its floor is about seven hundred feet below the rim. Large numbers of meteorites have been found in the neighborhood of the crater so that there is no doubt as to its origin. These craters resemble, on a small scale, those on the moon.

On June 30, 1908, some natives of upper Siberia reported having seen a blinding flash of light and heard a thunderous noise. Years later an exploring party reported having found an area where great trees had been blown over as if by a great wind. All pointing in a uniform direction, some of these trees showed evidence of scars from burning. While there have been no accurate reports of the nature of the crater, it is probable that a great meteorite lies buried there. This meteorite apparently approached the earth at an oblique angle, brushing over trees for a distance of a hundred miles, and then buried itself in the ground or exploded.

Recently it has been found that the number of meteors that enter the earth's atmosphere is about ten billion per day. Some of them come from within the solar system, the rest come from interstellar space. But the great majority are very tiny, much smaller than a grain of sand, so that only a very small amount of matter is added to the earth's surface in this way. It is estimated that the earth gains weight in this way at the rate of a small fraction of an ounce per square mile per year. Fortunately for us, the earth has a thick atmosphere; otherwise we might not survive this hail of pellets from space.

THE EARTH

From the most ancient times man has speculated about the nature of the earth. Until the last few centuries, he thought the earth to be flat, fixed and immovable, and of limited extent. These beliefs were held for the simple reason that the earth looked that way in all his experience. His ideas of nature were simple because of his simple experiences with it. Nor was it strange that he believed the earth to be the center of the whole universe.

While these notions may seem fantastic to us of the present day, we should not be too critical of the folk of older times. Let us remember that there are still a few "flat-earthers." We should remember that the people of a more innocent time had not inherited so great a wealth of scientific ideas and facts as have now come to us. The ancients were right in thinking that the earth was limited in size, but they were wrong in believing it flat. That it is not flat may most easily be seen by noticing that the shadow of the earth on the moon (at the time of an eclipse of the moon) is always round, no matter when the eclipse takes place.

As a result of the great pains taken by scientists in making precise observations, we now know the earth to be a large globe, very nearly spherical. Its diameter is found to be 7,920 miles. The meaning of this figure may better be understood if we realize that an airplane, speeding at two hundred miles per hour along the equator, would take five and a quarter days, without a stop, to complete the round trip. About four hundred years ago the Magellan expedition took three years to circumnavigate the earth.

TONS ON TONS

But how much does this huge globe—the earth—weigh? We know its size and shape, but how much material—or "stuff"—is there in it? Now, even though we cannot put the earth on the

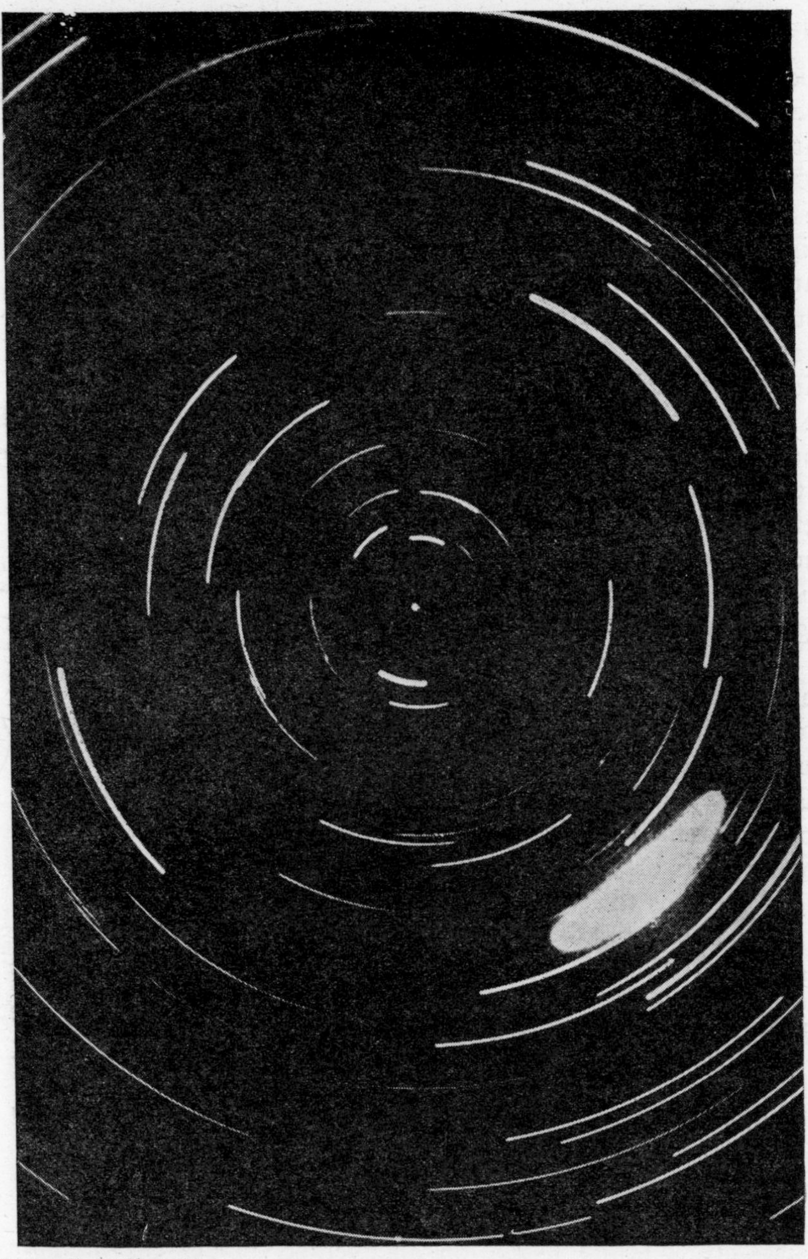

Courtesy Yerkes Observatory

PHOTOGRAPHIC PROOF OF THE EARTH'S ROTATION

If the earth rotates on its axis, the stars seen at the poles should have circular courses. The camera shows that they do.

scales of a grocer, we can still devise ingenious methods that will give the answer. To express the weight, of the earth, it is suggested that the reader write down the number "66" followed by twenty ciphers, and he will have the weight of the earth in tons. To find the result in pounds, multiply by two thousand. The stupendous weight of the earth staggers the imagination. Everyone knows that the earth turns on its axis in twenty-four hours else how would we account for the daily rising and setting of the sun, moon, and stars? With a diameter of about eight thousand miles, a little arithmetic shows that a point on the equator is moving at the rate of over a thousand miles per hour. This is a little more than seventeen times faster than the speed of an automobile being driven at a mile a minute. Although the earth is spinning at this dizzy speed, there is no possibility that we will be flung off into space, since the gravitational force that the earth exerts on us is much greater than is just necessary to hold us down. In fact, it might be well to remember that man has thus far not been able by any device to get far enough away from the earth to escape the gravitational pull which ultimately means his return.

In addition, our huge earth, a globe eight thousand miles in diameter and weighing six sextillion tons, spinning daily on its axis—very much like an enormous top—is rushing around the sun at a tremendous rate. The earth, along with the moon, is moving in its orbit about the sun at the speed of 18½ miles per second. This is the same as one hundred thousand feet a second, or about eleven hundred times the speed of a car doing a mile a minute.

FIFTY-THREE YEARS FROM EARTH TO SUN

The size of the earth's orbit is of the greatest importance to astronomers, and is used as the base line for the measurement of all other distances. Although the measuring of the distance from the earth to the sun is an extremely difficult problem, it can be done with an error not greater than one part in ten thousand. The result is found to be, on an average, ninety-two million eight hundred and seventy thousand miles. This distance is so great that light, traveling at the speed of one hundred and eighty-six thousand miles a second, takes eight and one-third minutes to

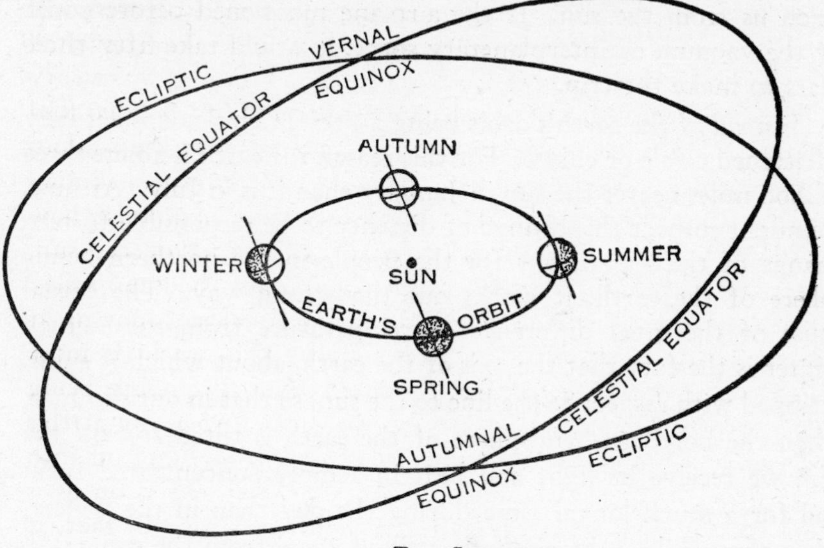

THE SEASONS

Courtesy Yerkes Observatory

THE REASON FOR THE SEASONS OF THE YEAR

Diagram of the earth in various positions in its orbit, illustrating the cause of the seasons.

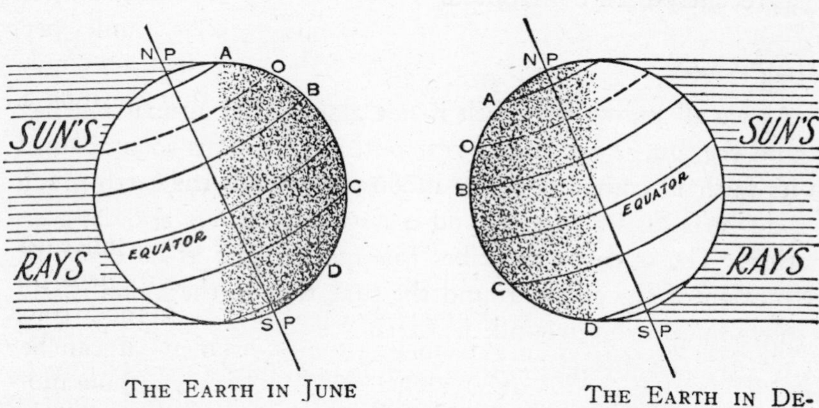

THE EARTH IN JUNE

Courtesy Yerkes Observatory

THE EARTH IN DECEMBER

THE EARTH'S POSITION IN JUNE AND DECEMBER

Diagram showing the cause of the reversal of the seasons between northern and southern hemispheres. That portion is warmest which receives the sun's rays in a most direct line.

reach us from the sun. If the airplane mentioned before could fly the vacuum of interplanetary space, it would take fifty-three years to make the trip.

Instead of the earth's orbit being a perfect circle, it is actually a flattened circle or ellipse. For this reason the earth is about three million miles nearer the sun in January than it is in July. At first, we might suspect this change of distance to be responsible for the change of the season, but for the people in the northern hemisphere of the earth, it works out the wrong way. The actual cause of the great difference of temperature from summer to winter is the fact that the axis of the earth, about which it spins, is tipped with respect to the line to the sun, so that in our summer, when the northern hemisphere of the earth is tilted *toward* the sun, we receive its light and heat in a more concentrated form and for a much longer time during the day than in the winter, when the northern hemisphere is tilted *away* from the sun.

So we see that our picture of the earth and its motions has been very radically changed during the short history of mankind as a race. And, frankly speaking, these problems have not been too difficult. From this we gain a better idea of how long it will take the race to solve many of the very practical problems with which it has recently been confronted.

THE MOON

As we all know, the earth is not alone in its annual journey around the sun. Year in and year out, our planet is accompanied by its faithful companion, the moon. It attends the earth much as a dog attends his master, and is now on one side and then on another. The scientist describes this motion just as he describes the motion of the earth around the sun: that is, the moon is said to move in an orbit around the earth.

It is the moon's motion that accounts not only for its changing position among the stars, but it also gives rise to that beautiful phenomenon of the phases of the moon, since its light is only the reflection of the greater light of the sun. There is not one of us who has not watched the beauty of the moon's phases

THE FULL MOON
From a photograph taken by an amateur astronomer with a home-made 16-inch reflecting telescope.

Photo by Frank M. Preucil

changing from night to night. Let us suppose that we first begin to observe the moon on an evening when it appears as a delicately slender crescent just above the western horizon at sunset. We call this phase the "new moon"; here the moon is almost between the earth and the sun, so that we can see only a thin strip of the illuminated portion of our satellite. In a little while the moon sets. On the next evening we shall see it again at sunset, but this time a little higher above the western horizon, and with a somewhat wider crescent. From sunset to sunset it will become visible higher and higher in the sky, successively farther to the east, and we will see more and more of the side that is illuminated. The moon is now said to be "waxing." Also, it will take an increasingly longer and longer time for it to move over to the western horizon where it sets.

Now, when the moon gets to a position where it is about ninety degrees from the sun, its disk will appear as a half circle. If this phase is the first one after new moon (or about seven days from new moon), we call it the "first quarter," since we see only

Courtesy Yerkes Observatory

DIAGRAMMATIC EXPLANATION OF THE PHASES OF THE MOON

THE EARTH-LIT MOON
This phenomenon is also known as "the old moon in the new moon's arms."

Courtesy Yerkes Observatory

one quarter of the surface of the whole moon. About seven days later we see the "full moon," since at that time it is opposite the sun and we see all of the illuminated portion. We remember that the full moon always appears, rising over the eastern horizon, at about the same time that the sun sets in the west.

The moon now rises later and later after sunset, and since we see less and less of the illuminated portion, the moon is said to be "waning." The phases appear in the reverse order of that which we saw from new to full, and the bright portion will face east instead of west. And now, since the moon moves eastward constantly, it will soon "catch up" with the sun, and repeat the cycle of the phases. The interval of time taken by the moon to go from, say, full to full is called the lunar month and is twenty-nine days twelve hours forty-four minutes and three seconds. This is the origin of the interval we call the month.

When the new moon is hanging low in the western sky just after sunset, there may be seen within the thin brilliant crescent, the rest of the disk glowing with a delicately soft light. This interesting effect called the "old moon in the young moon's arms" is due to reflected light from the earth shining on the moon for at this time the earth is "full" as seen from the moon.

THE MOON—JUST A LITTLE FELLOW

Can we measure the distance and size of the earth's companion as we did the earth itself? Everyone knows that a surveyor can determine the distance of a remote object without having to tape off that distance, provided he has a base line and two angles of view. By a similar process on a large scale, the astronomer is able to compute the distance to the moon. In this case the base line used is the distance between two widely separated cities on the earth, and by prearrangement the observation angles of the moon are taken simultaneously by observes at the two stations. The actual result is 238,857 miles on the average. Just as the earth moves in an ellipse around the sun, so the moon moves in an ellipse about the earth. Over the lunar month, the distance from the earth ranges from 221,463 miles to 252,710 miles. It is found, too, that the diameter of the moon is 2,160 miles, or about a quarter of the diameter of the earth.

Perhaps the greatest surprise about the moon comes when we examine its surface with a large telescope. Instead of being smooth, it is extremely rough and jagged. Here and there, all over the surface, we see scattered numerous depressions, looking like great pockmarks. These are called "craters," because they look very much like volcanic craters on the earth's surface. Most of the craters are enormously larger than any on our planet. In fact, there are several so large that if an observer were to stand at the center, he could not see the rim: it would be below the horizon. The largest craters on the moon are over a hundred miles in diameter. Though the small ones—those of five to ten miles in diameter—are by far the more numerous, the total number of these markings runs up into the tens of thousands.

The origin of the craters is not known. Some may be of volcanic origin; others may be the result of a bombardment of

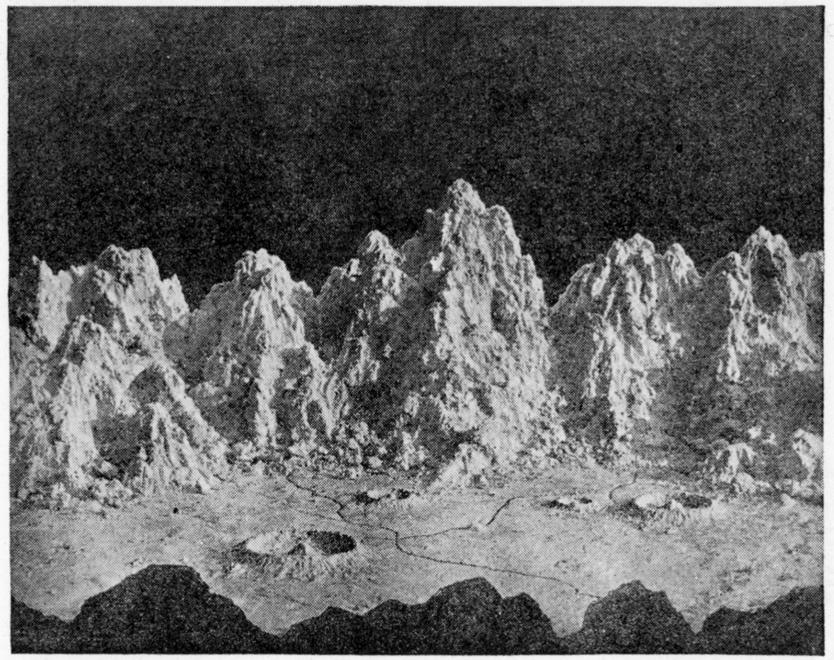

Courtesy Yerkes Observatory

A LUNAR LANDSCAPE

Each peak is higher than the highest mountain on earth. (From a model built to scale from photographs.)

the moon's surface by huge meteors. We know of a few meteoric craters on the earth which from a great distance might look like those on the moon. In addition to these markings, there are many other surprising features on the moon's surface. There are huge plains, hundreds of miles in diameter—curiously enough most of these features are nearly circular—that can be seen with the naked eye, and which make up the features of "the man in the moon." There are mountain ranges as high as any on the earth, and here and there are huge clefts running for hundreds of miles, intersecting both mountain ranges and craters.

What a spectacle the lunar landscape must be, with its enormous craters, great mountain peaks, and broad smooth plains—all without the slightest sign of living things. For the moon has no water or atmosphere. The lack of atmosphere means that all the stars could be seen in the daytime; even the corona of the sun could be seen without eclipse. But the sun beats down mercilessly out of a pitch-black sky. During the lunar day, the temperature gets up to 250 degrees Fahrenheit, well above the boiling-point of water, while it is well below freezing in the shade! At night the thermometer drops to about 120 degrees below zero. Certainly we on the earth, if we were to go to the moon, would find it a bit uncomfortable!

MOON PULLS EARTH—EARTH PULLS MOON

It has already been mentioned that the force of gravity keeps us from flying off the earth; it also keeps the earth in its orbit around the sun, and the moon in its path about the earth. The working of the force of gravity may be seen in another way. The gravitational force exerted on the earth by the moon produces bulges in the seas that cover three-quarters of the surface of our planet. These bulges lie along the line between the earth and moon, with one bulge on the side near the moon, and one on the other side. Now as the earth spins, its surface moves under the bulges of water, so that at any point two tides are produced in the sea each day. An unbelievably large amount of energy is stored up in the tidal waters, and at certain localities the tides are being put to use to give us that all-important source of power—electricity.

It has been known for a long time that the moon always turns the same face towards the earth. This timing is so exact that no one has ever seen the other half of the moon. Scientists now know that this fact is due to the tremendous tidal force that the earth exerts on material of the moon itself.

As previously mentioned, the earth carries the moon with it in the annual journey around the sun. Actually, the motion of the earth-moon system is more complicated. The whole situation may be very easily visualized in the following way: If we put two spheres, of different weight, on a light rod, we shall find that there is a point on the rod at which the whole affair will balance. The principle of the lever will dictate that the heavier sphere will be nearer the balance point (or center of gravity). If the rod were rotated and, at the same time, moved along an elliptic path, the two spheres would rotate about the balance point, and they would seem to wobble about each other while the center of gravity moved along smoothly. We can see that the earth-moon system must behave in the same way (even though there is no material rod joining them). Astronomers have made very accurate observations which show this to be the case. As a matter of fact, it turns out that the balance point of the system lies inside the earth itself at 2,880 miles from its center. A result of this is that, without getting anywhere near the moon, we are able to weigh it. Its weight has been found to be about 1/81 the weight of the earth, or a little more than seventy quintillion tons! Naturally, this huge mass of matter changes the simple picture we described before; and we see that it is the center of gravity of the earth-moon system that follows the earth's orbit around the sun, rather than the center of the earth itself.

Photo by Frank M. Preucil

POLISHED SECTION OF A METEORITE, SHOWING WIDMANSTÄTTER FIGURES

Courtesy Northern Pacific Railway

"THE EARTH OUR HOME"

THIS EARTHLY SPHERE

THE EARTH OUR HOME

AFTER OUR CONSIDERATION of galaxies and nebulae so far distant that we must use terms of light-years to be able to comprehend their positions, the earth on which we live seems petty by comparison. For the sun itself, however important to our existence, is only a star of inferior dimensions; yet it is enormous compared to the earth, which bears about the same size-relation to the sun that a mustard seed bears to a baseball.

The earth, however, has an inalienable hold upon us. It is our home. It is the home of a vast host of plants and animals, as well. They and we are dependent on the happy combination of circumstances which the earth affords. Every fish of the sea, every fowl of the air, every beast of the field, and every flower and tree must find food to nourish its body, energy to carry on its vital activities, and a temperature that is neither too cold nor too hot. The earth, our home, provides suitable food, energy, and temperature. There may be other planets or other places in the universe that also provide them, but we cannot be sure. The fact remains that plants, and animals, and men are true children of the earth. Few, if any, could stand the rigors of outer space; none could survive the tremendous heat of the surface or interior of the sun. They are all bound by incredibly ancient ties to the planet that is their parent.

The sea is one of the most specialized and limited of all the environments that the earth provides. It is laden with a large variety of important chemical substances which serve to nourish its great population, from bacteria to whales. Oxygen dissolved in the water permits the oxidation processes indispensable in the chemistry of life. Various salts dissolved in the water make possible the physiological processes of marine life and have indeed determined the pattern of those processes. Finally, the ocean is remarkably constant in temperature, at least as compared with the atmosphere. The creatures who live in the sea are fitted to live only under conditions which there hold sway. Their remarkable perfection of form and mode of existence would in most cases be quickly destroyed by a slight variation in the happy medium which has meant life to them for countless generations. The jellyfish with its delicate umbrella and waving tentacles swims in glorious splendor through the sea, yet is quickly reduced to a helpless mass when taken out of its home into the air and hot sunlight of the upper world. But even a much less drastic change in environmental conditions would have far-reaching results. A shift in the oxygen or salt content of the water, a variation in the nature or amount of its nutritive material, or a sudden change in temperature corresponding to the blizzards or heat waves of the upper world, would have a disabling and often deadly effect upon the denizens of the deep. Such is the extent of their dependence on their specialized environment.

In the upper world, the environment of the animals, plants, and men is a little less specialized and limited. The polar bear is quite at home where the temperature is most of the time below freezing and sometimes fifty degrees or more below zero. The lizards of the tropics can move about comfortably on sand that is too hot for the hand of man to hold. Certain bacteria can survive remarkable extremes of temperature. The condor of South America soars high in the air, while certain insects and worms spend most of their lives buried deep in the ground.

Man and the rat are both unique among land mammals in their great adaptability, and may be found everywhere except in the regions of extreme cold. Such degrees of adaptation to environment are remarkable. Nevertheless, they are very limited

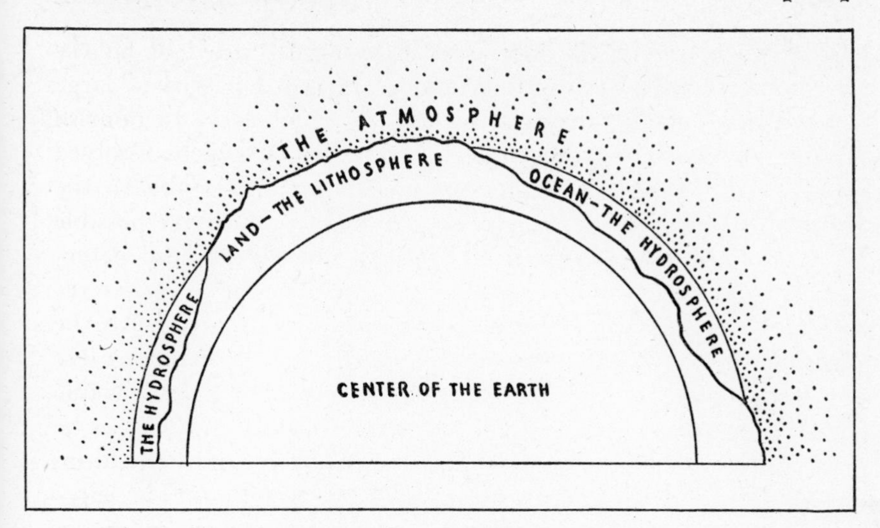

DIAGRAM OF THE SPHERES OF EARTH

in view of the great range of conditions that the universe affords. No animals can exist without the oxygen that the air supplies; plants need both oxygen and carbon dioxide gas. There are places other than the earth that would mean sudden death to any creature of this world. The heat of a desert at noonday is as nothing compared with the heat of the earth's core or the sun. The air into which the condor beats his upward way is merely thin; there is none at all in outer space. The cold of freezing water is warm compared with the cold of frozen air, or of the frozen carbon dioxide gas we use under the name of "dry ice." Even when taken all together, the environments that the earth provides are strictly limited, and in turn limit the activities and natures of plants, animals, and men. The earth happens not only to be our home; it is also the only suitable home in sight!

To make its study more convenient, the earth is usually considered in terms of a number of layer-like portions or "spheres," lying one beneath the other, somewhat like the successive skins on a narcissus bulb. The outermost of these layers is known as the *atmosphere* or gaseous layer, and consists of the familiar air, the material of which winds are made and the support of clouds and airships. Next beneath the atmosphere is the *hydrosphere* or

A SPIRAL NEBULA IN THE BIG DIPPER

Man, a tiny "speck" on a "grain of sand" in the universe, has been able to partially identify the materials of which this mass is composed, though it requires 1,600,000 years for its light to reach the earth.

Courtesy Yerkes Observatory

liquid layer, which is not continuous, like the atmosphere, but is laid down in irregular patches over the earth's surface as oceans, lakes, and streams. Lying in part beneath the hydrosphere, as do ocean and lake bottoms, and in part projecting above it as islands and continents, is the *lithosphere,* or solid portion of the earth. About three-fourths of the lithosphere is kept from contact with the atmosphere by the oceans.

The part of the earth which is capable of supporting life of any kind is only a very small portion of its total volume, certainly not more than twelve and a half miles thick. This distance is the sum of the greatest known depth of the ocean and the greatest height of the land, and within its limits dwell all forms of life of which men have certain knowledge. This region, which includes the hydrosphere, the upper crust of the lithosphere, and the lower portions of the atmosphere, is a mere film compared with the earth's total volume. It is often referred to as the biosphere, or layer of life. Man's permanent home, on which he depends for food, and to which he must always return after brief excursions into the atmosphere, and into or upon the hydrosphere, is the habitable portion of the dry land.

If the surface of the islands and continents seems a bit cramped and insignificant after our telescopic voyages among the realms of space, remember that this small tract on which we live is apparently the only portion of all space sheltering an intelligence capable of seeing and interpreting the great facts of the universe. From our little vantage point of earth we have been able to traverse with eye and brain the stupendous magnitudes of celestial space, and to comprehend, at least in part, the slowly unfurling celestial destinies.

THE OCEAN OF AIR

The atmosphere is a great, all-pervading ocean of gas, far deeper than the ocean of water and completely covering the earth from pole to pole. It penetrates every cave and crevice of the earth and envelops every mountain top. The grass, the trees, and men get from it the most important element of their existence—oxygen. Without an atmosphere we would never hear the rustling of trees or the singing of birds; we would have no music; we would not even hear the human voice; there could be no spoken language. Air is the principal medium which transmits sound waves, and without it the entire globe would be hushed in a silence like the silence of death.

It is the atmosphere which supports the clouds that pour refreshing rain on the dry ground. Without water from the heavens, vast fertile areas of the earth would become barren as any desert sands. Without the atmosphere the sky would lose its blue and become black, for tiny particles of dust buoyed high in the air diffuse the light of the sun and give the sky its beautiful color. The friendly sun, which now brings energy to growing plants and gives health and life to our own bodies, would become a source of terror if it were not for the absorbing and distributing effects of the atmosphere. During the daytime the rocks and sands would

Paul's Photos, Chicago

THE BENEVOLENT ATMOSPHERE

Were it not for the atmosphere and clouds we would be scorched to death by the sun's rays.

become so hot that any form of life would be unthinkable, while every night, without the surrounding blanket of atmosphere, the icy temperature would be as disastrous as the heat of the day.

As the earth spins on its axis and as it revolves around the sun it takes with it the ever-present envelope of air, since there is no outer friction to tear it off. This envelope has no definite upper boundary, but gradually becomes more and more rarefied at higher altitudes. When an automobile tire is inflated to thirty-five pounds pressure (meaning thirty-five pounds in excess of atmospheric pressure, which is fifteen pounds) it will contain approximately three times as much air as it did before inflation. Since three times the normal amount of air has now been forced into the tire, the density will be three times as great as before. This illustrates the general rule that density increases with pressure. The lowest layer of atmosphere, say, one foot in thickness and in immediate contact with the surface of the earth, is continually being compressed by the weight of all the atmosphere for miles above it; therefore it is more dense than any of the layers above. The second layer, one foot in thickness, is being compressed by the weight of all the air above *it*, but not by that below, hence it is slightly less dense than the first layer. The atmosphere, then, becomes less dense at higher altitudes for the simple reason that there is not as much weight bearing down upon it.

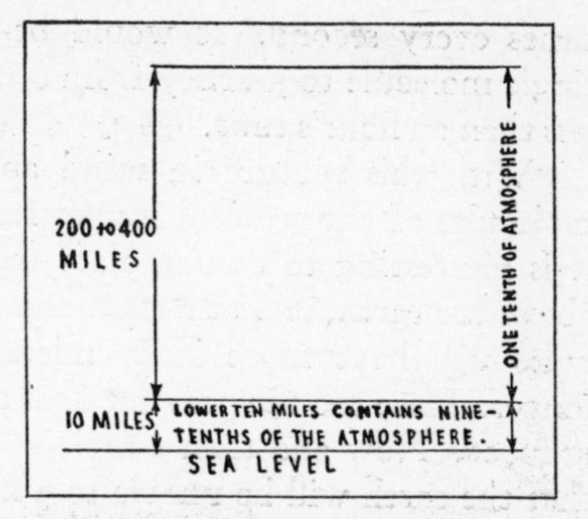

DIAGRAM SHOWING DISTRIBUTION OF THE ATMOSPHERE

A mathematical treatment of the subject would reveal that the falling-off in density takes place more rapidly near the surface of the earth than at higher altitudes so that if one ascends to an altitude of eighteen thousand feet—less than that of many mountain peaks—already half of the mass of the atmosphere has been left below. At an altitude of sixty thousand feet, over nine-tenths of the mass is below, and yet there is evidence that there must be *some* atmosphere as high as five hundred miles. It, however, must be very much rarefied.

A more accurate picture is formed by considering that the air consists of a great collection of infinitesimal particles, or molecules. These may be regarded as being individually incompressible; when the air is compressed, the molecules are merely crowded closer together without being changed either in size or shape. In the lower layers of the atmosphere where the pressure is normally fifteen pounds per square inch, the molecules are so close together that a space no larger than the head of a pin would contain something like thirty thousand million million of them. Not only are the molecules extremely small and very close together but they are continually in motion. A lively swarm of bees would be but a mild picture of their rapid, invisible agitation. The molecules of air under ordinary conditions near the surface of the earth move with the considerable speed of one-third of a mile per second and yet, being so close together, they do not go far without colliding with their neighbors. Any single molecule goes speeding, bumping, glancing, rebounding; it changes its direction many times every second. It would be a very unusual feat for any single molecule to journey from one side of a room to the other in less than an hour's time.

With this picture in mind and remembering also that the molecules of the atmosphere get farther apart at higher altitudes, it is interesting to contemplate their behavior at great altitudes above the earth, say, at a thousand miles or more. Here the molecules will have more independence and their journeys will be longer. Here too the gravitational pull of the earth will be greatly reduced. Now and then a molecule will sail so far out into space that the earth will be unable to pull it back. It then may become a child of the sun instead of the earth. It may be drawn directly into the sun or possibly be captured by Jupiter or some other planet. If headed in the right direction there is also the possibility that it may take up an orbit around the sun and, like a miniature of miniature planets, spend a few eons enjoying a new dignity of time and place!

OF WHAT GASES DOES THE AIR CONSIST?

Science owes much to the famous English chemist, Joseph Priestley, for having demonstrated that the atmosphere consists of several chemical components. He performed the novel experiment of introducing mice into a closed glass vessel and studying the effect of their breathing the imprisoned air. He found that for quite a time they were perfectly at ease but that they eventually died—long before the supply of food ran out or any other necessities were lacking except a change in air. He found that if a second mouse was now introduced into the enclosure it did not live as long as the first animals but died very quickly. The obvious conclusion was that the first mice had, in the process of breathing, removed from the air some constituent that was vital to the support of life. He later found that if a candle were burned in a volume of imprisoned air, it too would render the air unfit to support animal life. Taking some of the same air which had been "spoilt" by mice, he introduced a growing plant and found that this had the effect of restoring the ability to support animal life, thus hinting at the great balance in nature by which plants and animals give and take opposite elements from the atmosphere.

THE AIR HAS BUOYANCY
It is composed of particles which help to support the weight of a man by means of a parachute.

Official photograph, U. S. Army Air Corps

The genius of Priestley did not stop here. In 1774 he heated red oxide of mercury with a burning glass and found that the gas given off caused a candle flame to burn with greatly enhanced brilliancy; mice would become even more active in it than in ordinary air. This gas was oxygen, and Priestley well deserves the credit for its discovery. Priestley had a remarkable career as a chemist, philosopher, preacher, and writer. Moving to America in 1794, he spent the last ten years of his life in Northumberland, Pennsylvania.

During the time of Priestley's experimenting in England, there lived in France the great chemist Lavoisier, whose interest led him to repeat the experiment of heating mercuric oxide. He went a step farther and carefully weighed the materials used and the gas produced. He concluded that air was composed of two major constituents, oxygen and nitrogen, both gases, quite different in behavior but homogeneously mixed. His keen insight admitted also that there might be yet other elements and he even suspected that in the strata at high altitudes, the composition of air might be quite different from that at the surface, a conclusion abundantly supported by the discoveries of modern times.

Although the nature of air was clearly established by these early experiments, it was not until the beginning of the nineteenth century that an exact analysis was made. Then Dumas and Boussingault carefully determined that one hundred parts of air contain twenty-one parts of oxygen (by volume) and seventy-nine parts of nitrogen. They had discovered the truth—but not the whole truth.

It happened that during an eclipse in 1868 two Englishmen, Sir Edward Frankland and Sir Norman Lockyer, found that the sun's spectrum displayed certain lines which could not be identified with any known element on the earth. The investigators rightly concluded that a new element had been discovered and

Paul's Photos, Chicago

DIRIGIBLES, USING THE LIGHTER-THAN-AIR GAS HELIUM, FLOAT IN THE AIR gave it the appropriate name *helium*. Somewhat later Sir William Ramsay was analyzing the gases obtained by heating certain minerals. He found a minute residual portion which he could not identify until he observed its spectrum and found the same lines as were produced by the helium of the sun. The history of science thus contains the unique instance of an element being discovered in the sun before its discovery on the earth. Later helium was found to exist in minute quantities in the atmosphere also. Other work by Ramsay led to the discovery of still other rare elements in the atmosphere, chief of which are argon and neon.

The principal gases of the atmosphere and their respective volume percentages at lower levels are given by the American authority, W. J. Humphreys, as follows:

Nitrogen	78.08
Oxygen	20.94
Argon	0.94
Hydrogen	0.01
Neon	0.0012
Helium	0.0004
Carbon Dioxide	0.03

Samples of air obtained by Captain Albert W. Stevens in the stratosphere at seventy thousand feet showed a slightly smaller proportion of oxygen to nitrogen, although the difference was not as great as was expected. It is believed that at still greater altitudes the proportion of oxygen will continue to decrease. It is probable that the proportion of hydrogen compared with other components is greatly increased at altitudes of forty miles and more.

There has been much speculation as to the amount of carbon dioxide which has been in the atmosphere during the long ages of geological time. The question is an intriguing one because carbon dioxide acts like a great blanket, helping the earth retain its heat instead of radiating it out into space. A greater or less amount of surface heat on a large scale determines the climate and also the types of plant and animal life which will flourish most efficiently. Certain it is, that in some parts of the earth, at least, the climate during the geologic past has changed several times from hot to cold or from cold to hot. One theory teaches that these cycles may have been the result of the relative abundance of carbon dioxide, the cold periods occurring when the atmosphere was thin in the blanketing gas. It has been suggested that during the Carboniferous periods the carbon dioxide may have been abundant and favorable to the types of vegetation which eventually stored up enormous quantities of carbon in the form of coal. But attractive as these arguments are, it must be stated that some of the foremost authorities are inclined to think that the balance of nature has for many ages kept the carbon dioxide content of the atmosphere at just about what it is at the present time. It must be admitted that the problem is complicated by so many factors than any conclusions are largely speculative.

THE AIR IN MOTION

Fortunately for our comfort and indeed for our lives, the air is continually in motion; sweeping away injurious gases which are poured into it, substituting those which have been freshened by ocean spray and falling rain, freely distributing the oxygen supplied by the plants of forest and field. Many localities of the earth owe the mildness of their climate to the heat brought to them by prevailing winds from warmer regions, while other localities, in turn, may be continually chilled by prevailing winds from regions of cold. There is an immense circulation over the entire earth, keeping the components of the air mixed and preventing such extremes of climate as would otherwise exist. Observations restricted to any one locality might suggest that there is but little regularity in the blowing of the wind. Sometimes it blows in gusts, now strong, and again very light; sometimes in one direction and then in another. Observational data gathered from over wide areas reveal that along the surface the air tends to flow from both north and south poles toward the equator, while at high altitudes it is carried back toward the poles.

Common use is made of the facts that warm air in a chimney rises to the top, that a tall chimney draws better than a low one, and that any chimney produces a stronger draft in cold weather than in mild. All this happens because warm air is lighter than cold air; the greater the difference in weight between the column of air inside the chimney and a corresponding column outside,

Paul's Photos, Chicago

FREE BALLOONS ARE USED TO MEASURE AIR DRIFT
The balloon is set free and its movements recorded.

the stronger is the tendency to rise. Similarly, the heat at the earth's equator causes the atmosphere to become lighter while the cold at the poles causes the atmosphere to become dense. The equilibrium being thus disturbed and the air being elastic and free to move, a circulation is set up in a continual attempt at readjustment. This grand-scale circulation from pole to equator constitutes the trade wind, the reliable friend of navigators. Winds which involve the whole surface of the earth and which are due to ever-present causes, are classified as planetary or permanent winds. Local circumstances at times greatly modify the general circulation, especially over the land areas where temperature differences are more extreme.

By a principle of physics, any object moving on the rotating earth has a tendency to deviate slightly to the right, and in the trade winds we find a large-scale illustration of this. In the northern hemisphere, the trades in general blow not directly toward the south but slightly to the west of south, that is, from the northeast. Likewise the southern trades blow from the southwest. Directly over the hot equatorial belt, the air is continually rising and at the surface there is produced a condition of almost permanent calm —the region being known as the doldrum belt. The anti-trades, or higher currents by which the air is carried back to the poles, are less hindered by local variations than are the trades, a fact frequently evidenced by the upper clouds which move with less variation of direction than do the lower clouds. After traveling at high altitudes for a short distance from the equator, the air begins to settle. Some of it gets detached from the main stream of the anti-trades and falls all of the way to the surface, producing a condition of calm or light variable winds known as horse latitude winds. This region is of much consequence to sailing vessels although the effects are less pronounced than at the belt of doldrums.

Most of the anti-trades move on toward the poles but, due to the earth's rotation, they too are subject to a deviation toward the right so that around each pole there is a high altitude circulation known as the circumpolar whirl. The motion of the upper layers being more persistent than that of the lower layers, prevailing westerly winds are produced both at the surface and at high altitudes. The prevailing westerlies have much to do with the path of movement of most of the storms in the United States.

Study of the upper air currents has gained much in recent years from the use of small captive balloons, and also from the high altitude flights of airplanes and man-carrying balloons. Valuable observations along this line were made by travelers and mountain climbers many years ago. When Humboldt ascended the summit of Tenerife in 1799, he found a strong westerly wind blowing, although at the surface there was a wind of quite different direction. Thirty years later, the traveler Captain Basil Hall ascended the same peak and observed that the wind was blowing in a direction directly opposite to that at the base of the mountain. Of just as much value, when altitudes can be ascertained, is the study of movements of the higher clouds.

Aside from the planetary or permanent winds, many of the local disturbances are of much interest and concern in a practical

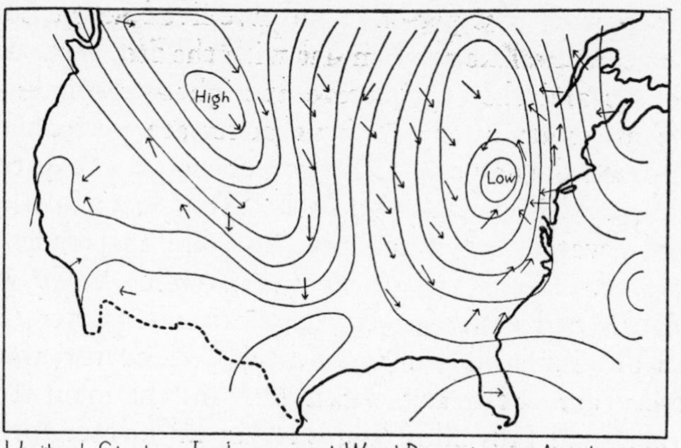

United States-Isobars and Wind Directions, April 11, 1934

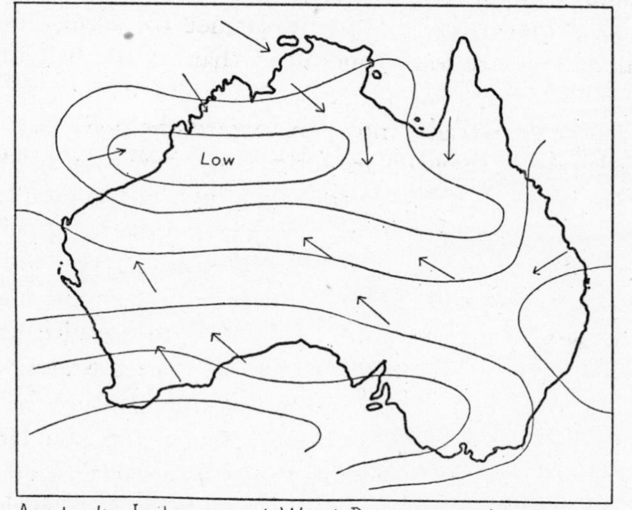

Australia-Isobars and Wind Directions, Aug. 28, 1917
Courtesy Yerkes Observatory

WEATHER MAPS SHOWING WIND DIRECTIONS

Weather maps are drawn to follow the movements of air masses and thus enable weather forecasters to determine the probable direction of winds and the general aspects of the weather. Lows, as shown on the maps, indicate low-pressure areas which are called cyclones—because the winds in a low-pressure area revolve in a circular direction—or storm centers. The direction of the winds in these centers is generally counterclockwise around the storm center. Thunderstorms, low-lying clouds, strong winds, and rain are most probable under low-pressure conditions. These maps are drawn at central meteorological stations from information received from numerous stations at specified times of day and night.

way. For example, those persons who have lived near the seashore or near a large inland lake are familiar with the frequent sea breeze of the daytime and the land breeze at night. It occurs only at times when other atmospheric disturbances are not strongly developed. During the day the land becomes heated so that the overlying air rises and its place is taken by a cooler mass flowing in from over the water. At night, since the land cools more swiftly than the water, the circumstances are reversed. Similar causes, on a larger scale and with seasonal variations, give rise to the monsoon winds of China, India, and other parts of the world. In summer there are prevailing winds blowing far to the inland, while in winter the prevailing winds are in the opposite direction.

THE MAGIC OF DEW AND FROST

The amount of moisture which air can hold depends on the temperature. The colder the air, the less moisture it can hold. It follows that if air is already nearly saturated with water vapor and the temperature is then lowered, condensation must take place. A common illustration is the "sweat" which forms on the outside of a pitcher of ice water on a warm humid day. A similar effect often occurs at night in warm weather when the air is heavily laden with moisture. The stones, blades of grass and other solid objects radiate their heat rapidly and become cooler than the surrounding air; thus condensation first takes place on these objects, producing the dew which we find in the morning. Near bodies of water and in low moist areas, dew will form more abundantly. Dew will form more readily on clear nights than when it is cloudy, because without the blanketing effect of the clouds, radiation can take place more rapidly and thus the temperature is likely to fall more swiftly.

During the autumn and spring when the temperature of the atmosphere at night falls low but yet not to freezing, moisture may nevertheless be found frozen on the same objects which at other times would merely collect drops of dew. Here again radiation is the explanation; at the immediate surface of objects which collect frost, the temperature must be at least as low as the freezing point. Frost is not dew that has frozen but moisture which

Paul's Photos, Chicago

CLOUDS ARE FORMED OF WATER VAPOR CONDENSING AROUND TINY PARTICLES OF DUST

has collected atom by atom, directly into the crystalline state. When the crystals form in the tiny cells of the plant tissues, as in leaves or tiny shoots, they may kill the protoplasm and possibly rupture the cell walls; hence the damaging effects of early frosts in the fall of the year. There is commonly much confidence in the rule that frost is liable to be more severe on a moonlight night. The rule is a good one although the moon itself is free from blame. It is the absence of clouds which is responsible; heat radiates away from the earth more readily than if the sky were covered.

In the winter time, if window panes are cooled to freezing or below, while at the same time there is sufficient moisture in the air inside the house, frost will form in various crystal formations on the glass. The more beautiful patterns of large crystals are formed when the action is slow; the laws of crystallization arrange the particles to perfection. When the freezing is rapid, the crystals are so small that their structure is not noticeable. If frost does not form on the windows when the temperature is low it probably indicates a lack of moisture in the air of the room and should be a reminder that more is needed for health and comfort.

DUST AND WATER DROPLETS

While the formation of the dew and frost indicates a saturated condition at the cold surfaces of solid objects, it may also happen that saturation is reached in mid air. How then is condensation to take place? Upon what objects can the droplets form? The answer is—dust! The ever-present dust particles of the atmosphere serve as nuclei, or cores, on which condensation starts as soon as the condition of saturation is reached. Each tiny dust particle thus accumulates a few molecules of water vapor, then more and more until at last there is produced a droplet scarcely big enough to see, but which with a multitude of others constitutes the condition we know as fog. Each tiny drop is spherical in shape because the surface tension pulling in from all sides has a large effect compared with the weight, and a sphere is the geometrical shape which has least surface for a given weight. There are many interesting circumstances regarding these minute spheres of water suspended in the air, rising almost as easily as falling while wafted about by the slightest breeze.

How can it be that a droplet of water defies the force of gravity and stays up without wind or wings? In perfectly quiet air it *would* fall, but very slowly, because its surface in contact with the air is large compared to its weight. For illustration consider the relation between the surface area and weight of a brick. Break the brick into two pieces and the total surface area will have been increased by the amount of the two new faces, while the total weight remains the same. Now break it again and again until it is reduced to a fine dust. The total weight is unchanged but the total surface area has been increased to many square feet. At first the brick would fall with a thud; now the particles can be lifted by the breath, and may settle on picture frames and lamp fixtures, or possibly be carried for many miles by the wind.

Another illustration is furnished by the slow falling of the plumed seeds of such plants as milkweed and dandelion. A scientist once measured with a powerful microscope the diameter of the filaments of a milkweed plume, then counted the filaments and multiplied them by the average length, thus calculating the total area subject to the friction of the air. It amounted to nearly four square inches; in proportion to the weight of the seed it would be equivalent to eighty square feet per ounce!

The particles in a fog may grow through more condensation; by numerous collisions many will combine to produce larger particles. The result is then better described as mist. Some writers have supposed that many particles of mist enclose minute bubbles of air. This would further increase their floating ability but it is doubtful whether the condition holds true in general.

THE WHITE FLEECE OF THE SKY

A cloud is nothing more or less than a fog, though the term is applied only to the large masses which float over our heads. At higher altitudes the temperature becomes lower; there is also a falling off in the amount of moisture. Therefore at a certain height there is a balance between temperature and moisture, and conden-

Courtesy Northern Pacific Ry.

WHITE FLEECE OF THE SKY

sation takes place to form a cloud. If the cloud should fall lower it would evaporate because of the increase in heat, while if it should rise it would evaporate because of the drier condition of the upper air. The altitude of equilibrium varies greatly with circumstances and indeed may exist for more than one layer at the same time, as is often witnessed by two or more layers of clouds at different heights.

The large "woolpack" clouds which seem to pile one upon the other in great masses and which have well defined outlines against the blue sky are known as *cumulus* clouds. The lower side is likely to be slightly less than a mile in altitude and the thickness may be half a mile. These are the clouds which perhaps give most play to the imagination, with their whiteness or variable tints and their incessantly changing shapes. It is not difficult to see in them the forms of men, birds, monsters, or mountains.

The *cirrus* clouds are the white delicate filaments seen at great altitudes. They may resemble threads of silk swept by a broom, or tangled skeins, or an irregular network, or again they may

Paul's Photos, Chicago

CIRRUS CLOUDS

Paul's Photos, Chicago

NIMBUS CLOUDS

resemble goose feathers thrown into the sky. They are the highest of all clouds, sometimes floating seven miles or more above the earth. The temperature at these altitudes being well below the freezing point, it is practically certain that the cirrus clouds consist of snow flakes or small ice crystals.

To low drifting clouds wide in extent, the term *stratus* is applied. They may be fairly dense but are seldom of great thickness. Low, thick clouds of wide extent from which rain or snow is falling, are called *nimbus* clouds. In addition to the four general types of clouds just mentioned there are many forms which may be better described by combination terms: cirro-stratus, cirro-cumulus, strato-cumulus, cumulo-nimbus, etc.

RAIN, HAIL AND SNOW

In the formation of rain there is usually a rising current of moisture-laden air which, on reaching higher altitudes, cools and condenses at a rapid rate, especially if meeting already existing clouds. As the droplets grow large enough to fall at an appreciable rate they have a sort of filtering action on the rising air through which they pass, robbing it of moisture to add to their own size. The drops thus become larger and fall still faster, but due to the resistance of the air there is a limit to their swiftness. When a drop of water reaches a speed of about twenty-six feet per second the disturbing influence of the friction of the air becomes greater than the internal cohesive forces of the drop and so it promptly breaks into smaller drops and the speed is again reduced.

Sometimes the condensing region of the atmosphere is subject to very great turbulence, as during a thunderstorm, and the draught may be strong enough to carry upward drops as large as any that ever reach the earth. If at the same time regions of snow are encountered, as is likely to be the case at high altitudes, a nucleus of ice is formed which in the course of the onrush may pass alternately through regions of rain and snow and grow to a surprising diameter. Such built-up ice drops are called hailstones. Hailstones have been found which were over three inches in diameter after reaching the ground. An exceedingly high wind

Paul's Photos, Chicago

HAILSTONES MUCH LARGER THAN EGGS!

ENLARGED VIEWS OF SNOW-FLAKES SHOWING SIMILAR GEOMETRICAL ARRANGEMENT BUT VARYING PATTERNS

Courtesy American Museum of Natural History, N. Y.

velocity is required to keep hailstones suspended after growing to such a size. Humphreys has estimated that to sustain a stone one inch in diameter, the upward velocity of the air needs to be almost sixty miles per hour and over one hundred miles per hour for a stone three inches in diameter.

Snow is formed when the temperature is not very far below freezing and the moisture not greatly beyond the saturation point —conditions which give sufficient time for large, perfect crystals to form. These crystals tend to take the shape of filaments which form six-sided figures of infinite variety and beauty. No two snow crystals are ever just alike and yet all conform to the same geometrical plan.

RIDDLES OF THE STRATOSPHERE

We have noted that, above the surface of the earth, the air becomes less and less dense, until finally there is no air at all, but only the scattered infrequent molecules that characterize outer space. Above the region of clouds and snow, of rain and wind, beginning at a height of about five or six miles, there is a realm of thin air that is called the stratosphere. Into the under-regions of this realm man has penetrated by means of titanic balloons, Piccard ascending in 1931 and Stevens and Anderson entering their air-tight gondola and going up from the Black Hills in 1935. The stratosphere is a quiet, windless region, as is shown by the fact that its temperature does not, like the lower air, vary by levels but is vertically constant over each point on the surface of the earth.

Man has long sought to know how high a stratosphere of appreciable density extends. The ancient Arabs had an answer. They reasoned, rightly, that the atmosphere is the cause of twilight, bending the sun's rays down to earth after the sun itself has disappeared behind the horizon. Therefore, they reasoned, the height of the atmosphere could be deduced from the duration of twilight. Forty miles was the value they obtained. Moderns, using the same method, have found the figure to be nearer a hundred or a hundred and fifty miles.

A study of the duration of twilight, however, is only one way of getting an answer. Other men have tried to discover the height at which meteors become incandescent because of the friction of the stratosphere. Still others have turned their attention to the *aurora borealis*, the "northern lights" that have for centuries fascinated dwellers of the temperate zones. For centuries men have been drawn from their warm cottages to watch in awe the panoply of luminescent streamers and columns that stand out mysteriously against the far northern or far southern night sky, constituting the *aurora polaris* and the *aurora australis*. What are they? Where do they arise? How high do they go? Eventually scientists began to consider these profound and intriguing questions.

What are they? Here the answer made by modern science is truly amazing. Imaginatively directed study showed that there was a relation between the northern lights and the spots on the sun, that a little while after prominent sunspots were directed toward the earth a strong auroral display would often be seen. This observed correlation led to the belief that sunspots indirectly cause

Black Star Photo

RELEASING A WEATHER BUREAU BALLOON WITH PARACHUTE ATTACHED
Meteorological balloons ascend as high as 20 miles.

Black Star photo by Ernst Mayer

A POLAR EXPEDITION STUDYING THE AURORA BOREALIS
Notice how the aurora illuminates the landscape.

the aurora borealis. Sunspots are vortexes in the surface of the sun. From these vortexes, as from the mouths of titanic cannon, a mass of electrified particles or some form of electrical energy is blasted in the direction of the earth! When the blast reaches the earth it comes under the influence of the earth's magnetic field and is drawn to the poles, where it bombards the rarefied air of the stratosphere, making it glow like a Crookes tube or neon sign! A study of the spectrum of the aurora has tended to confirm this audacious theory; it has been proved that the characteristic green of the northern lights can be reproduced artificially by subjecting rarefied oxygen to an electrical discharge.

Where do they arise? This is a question that has led to startling theories. Some men have even claimed that there is a vast hole in the earth at the north pole, and that the northern lights gleam up through that hole from the center of the earth. This theory was disproved by polar exploration, and especially by the recent Russian flight across the pole itself. According to the sunspot theory, the northern lights begin high in the stratosphere. For a long time it was believed that they also ended there. Reputable observers far to the north, however, have claimed to see the tails of the glowing streamers close to earth, as between themselves and a nearby cliff or berg. Truly, there is today more mystery than ever connected with the aurora borealis. The lights of the icy North and the frigid South remain a curious enigma and a fruitful subject for speculation.

How high do they go? This is an especially important question, since it is linked with the question of the height of the atmosphere. To determine the extreme altitude of a particular streamer the same method must be used as to determine the height of a tree or a mountain; one observation is not enough; two observations must be taken, and those from different locations. It proved, however, difficult for the human eye to observe accurately the upper limits of streamers, and still more difficult for two separated observers to agree that they were talking about the same streamer. Photography solved this problem. Photographs of the aurora against the background of stars were not doubtful and could not lie. By means of photographs the general upper limit of the aurora

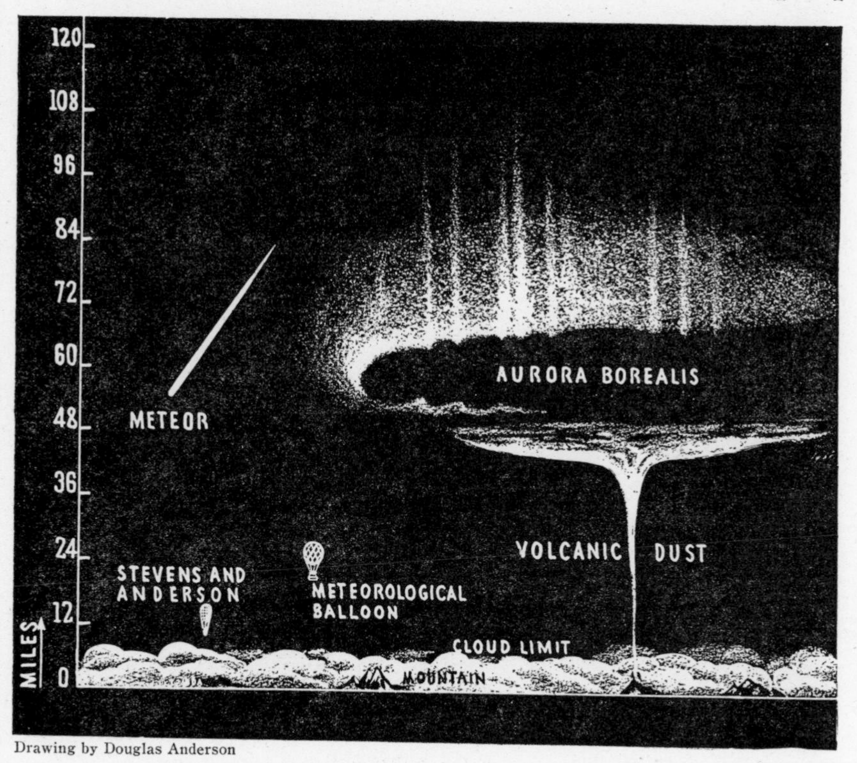

Drawing by Douglas Anderson

DIAGRAM SHOWING THE RELATIVE HEIGHT OF AURORAL PHENOMENA

was determined to be from fifty to two hundred and fifty miles. During a peculiar auroral display in 1926 the sensitive photographic plate caught faint streamers invisible to the human eye; these seemed to extend to a height of six hundred miles!

At even lesser heights in the stratosphere science believes that other strange conditions hold sway. Stevens and Anderson recorded temperatures as low as seventy-eight degrees below zero. However, their flight took them only about fourteen miles up. Some scientists have claimed that, at an altitude of thirty or forty miles, the stratosphere becomes definitely warm.

A study of the behavior of radio waves has indicated that, when they start off toward outer space, something reflects them back toward the earth. This is supposed to be a layer of ionized gas which conducts electricity easily, as well as reflecting radio

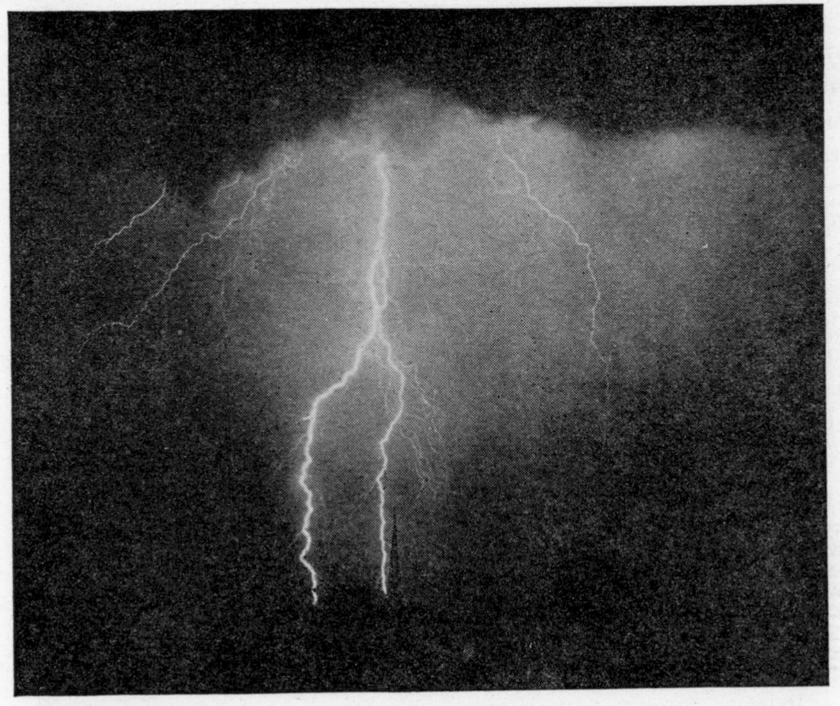

Paul's Photos, Chicago

LIGHTNING—A DISCHARGE OF ATMOSPHERIC ELECTRICITY

waves. It is named the Heaviside layer, after its chief investigator. In the daytime it exists at a height of about twenty-five miles in the stratosphere, but at night it rises twenty-five miles higher. During the day it may be due to the action of ultraviolet rays upon molecules of rarefied gas; during the night it may be due to the dissociation of ozone. Ozone is a form of oxygen, a bluish gas caused by electrical discharges through atmosphere. This brings us back once more to electricity and the possible influence of sunspots. It constitutes one more indication that the stratosphere is a realm of mysteries, whose further elucidation may do much to advance scientific knowledge.

Without the Heaviside layer, long-distance radio broadcasting would be impossible. The only other heavenly body known to have a Heaviside layer is the recently-discovered invisible giant star, Epsilon Aurigae.

Thus we see that the atmosphere is not only the means of man's continued existence, the support of moisture and clouds, and the cause of the blueness of the sky. It is also a link between man and the strange wonders of the sun, earth's magnetism, the stars, and empty space.

THE REALM OF WATER AND WAVES

Hydrosphere, as a name, is used to describe all of the aqueous envelope of the earth, including the oceans, lakes, rivers, the moisture which is held in the atmosphere, and the water which has penetrated to the depths of the lithosphere, the solid portion of earth.

In view of the fact that the oceans and seas form, by far, the greater part of the hydrosphere, any description of the hydrosphere necessarily contains a great deal of description of them. This description is called oceanography, the science that tells us of the mystery and magnitude, of the dangers, depths and denizens, of the extent and explorations, and of the genesis, grandeur and growth of the oceans.

Primitive man was absolutely terrified by the vast expanses of water and would have nothing to do with them, even as many people today are frightened by the boundless deep. With this in mind, it is easy to imagine the great debt that the modern world owes to that first man, or men, who fearlessly set out in a hollowed tree trunk to explore the uncharted seas. The world knew no oceanography until the days of Ancient Greece. That wonderful civilization learned much about the habits and characteristics of the Mediterranean Sea but even in their eyes the world to the west of the Pillars of Hercules, or Gibraltar as it is now called, was filled with colossal dangers, unknown depths, terrific storms, and monsters so large as to be able to swallow a ship at one gulp. The Phoenicians, who preceded the Greeks, knew better than this for we can be reasonably sure that they not only discovered Britain but also circumnavigated Africa. However, they were clever businessmen as well as adventurous sailors; they wanted to keep their trade to themselves, so they concocted wild tales which the Greeks took as the truth.

Not for long though, because in the fourth century B.C., the Greek Pytheas plowed into the Atlantic and sailed to the shores of Britain. Three centuries later Hippalus discovered the monsoon winds of the Indian Ocean and used them to sail the open sea, a much speedier means than hugging the coasts, which had been the procedure up that time.

THE BEGINNINGS OF OCEANOGRAPHY

Through the dark ages oceanography lay dormant, with many other sciences, until those memorable thirty years between 1492 and 1522 when such history-making voyages as Columbus' crossing the Atlantic, da Gama's sailing around the continent of Africa, and Magellan's circumnavigating the globe took place. These voyages increased the knowledge of the extent of the oceans, their currents and winds, but it was not until the early days of the

Courtesy U. S. Coast and Geodetic Survey

THIS SHIP, THE "HYDOGRAPHER," IS USED IN STUDYING THE SEA

nineteenth century that oceanography had its start as an organized science. It was then that comparatively accurate maps were made and a knowledge was developed as to what the ocean floor looked like. But even today there is much to be learned about the hydrosphere. Also, that which is known about it is interpreted differently by different scientists. Nearly everyone, however, is agreed upon the following facts.

As a continuous watery unit, the hydrosphere covers 140 million square miles or seventy-one per cent of the earth's surface, the remaining twenty-nine per cent being land. It has an average depth of 275 fathoms (one fathom equaling six feet). In other words, if all seas and oceans were everywhere equally deep, they would have a depth of over two miles. Not only is there much greater water surface on this planet but also the depths of the oceans are greater than the heights of the land. Thus, the highest known mountain in the world, Mt. Everest, 29,002 feet high, could be placed in the deepest known "deep," the Swires Deep off the island of Mindanao in the Philippines, and the mountain's peak would be covered by more than three thousand feet of water.

It is extremely difficult to determine how the oceans came into being. To know their origin is to know the origin of the earth itself. Although there are a number of theories none of them has been proved to the satisfaction of all scientists. It has been suggested that the bed of the Pacific Ocean was formed when a huge piece of material was thrown off from the earth. The material went to form the moon, while the cavity it left filled with water and became a great ocean. Others believe in the theory of "Continental Drift" and argue that at one time there was but one continent. In the course of time the two Americas drifted away to the west. This is suggested by the fact that eastern South America seems to fit into the coastline of Africa while North America and Greenland seem to fit into the coastline of Western Europe. In any case, when the crust of the Earth began to cool, and shrink, and crinkle, some places were left high and some low. Then the great steamy clouds of a younger earth cooled and condensed, filling the depressions and making the oceans.

Courtesy Yerkes Observatory

THE MOON AND ITS "SEAS"

The darker, depressed areas of the moon have been named seas although they are waterless. They are great plains that are relatively level and little marked with craters or mountains. They were first named seas by Galileo and his contemporaries, who chose such names as Mare Serenitatis—the Sea of Serenity, Mare Nectaris—the Sea of Nectar, and Mare Tranquilitatis—the Sea of Tranquillity. These names have come down to us unchanged. During those early years of astronomy star gazers expected the moon to exhibit the characteristics of the earth and thus were not surprised to see resemblances to seas. These features of the moon are easily recognizable even without the aid of binoculars or telescopes.

WAS THERE A LOST CONTINENT?

Another great point of argument in the world of science revolves around the enchanting story of the lost continent of Atlantis. Because many scientists have derided the idea of an island or civilized continent being swallowed by the sea, most people hear of Atlantis only through the Sunday sections of the newspapers. Nevertheless, a certain group of learned men argue rather convincingly that Atlantis did exist and that it and its inhabitants were swallowed by the waters of the ocean during a great cataclysm.

STUDYING THE OCEAN'S FLOOR
A diver being lowered to make underwater observations.
Paul's Photos, Chicago

It was the philosopher Plato who first popularized the story of the lost land and he put the date of its disappearance some nine thousand years before his time. He heard the story from his relative Solon who had it from an Egyptian priest. Therefore the scientists argue that, since most legends have some basis of truth, there probably did exist a body of land that would roughly answer to the description of Atlantis.

According to Plato Atlantis was a very beautiful and happy land. It lay in the Atlantic, westward from Gibraltar, in a region of such mild weather that the fields and orchards were always giving bumper crops at a minimum of the inhabitants' effort. There were great cities, splendid buildings, enormous temples, canals, and roads. The people, for their part, were industrious, honest, and honorable; they despised everything but virtue. However, their wonderful civilization became decadent. Their king wanted greater glory and started to conquer the nearby lands in Africa and Europe. On the eve of the departure of a great navy a major cataclysm began. Storms, earthquakes and tidal waves shook the world and in a single day and night Atlantis disappeared under the tumultuous waves.

As a matter of fact, there is a good deal of geological evidence to show that the eastern bottom of the Atlantic Ocean has subsided in recent times to the extent that only the peaks of a few mountains remain above the surface of the sea. These mountain peaks form the Cape Verde, Canary, and Azores Islands. However, science still does not possess enough evidence definitely to prove or disprove the past existence of Atlantis. Until that evidence is forthcoming, we shall have to consider it a very interesting possibility.

THE PORT OF MISSING SHIPS

Whether it was the story of Atlantis or the terrible tale told by the Phoenicians of the dangers of the Atlantic that caused sailors to fear the ocean has yet to be determined. At any rate, up to the days of Columbus the Atlantic was pictured variously as a place where boats became stranded because it was so shallow; as

Black Star photo by W. Bardili

MEASURING THE OCEAN'S DEPTH BY MEANS OF SOUND WAVES

the end or jumping-off place of the world; as the area of high winds, no winds, whirlpools, phantom ships, spirits, devils, and as the sea where seaweed was so thick that ships were stopped, overgrown, and finally sunk by the marine plants.

In reference to the seaweed, the existence of the Sargasso Sea was long known, and sailors carefully avoided it. The sailors of Columbus were terrified when the brave admiral's tiny boats steadily plowed through this area from which there was supposed to be no escape.

If there were no real Sargasso Sea there might still have been a legend about one because the human mind, which is surrounded by motion of all kinds, the blowing winds, the falling leaves, and rising and falling waves, likes to imagine a place where motion or change do not exist. At the same time the mind wanted a place where there was something alive and quiet in addition to the absence of motion and change. This is a perfect description of the Sargasso Sea. Even when people sail through it today, they feel a sense of mystery, of things slowly dying, and of intense silence and quiet. No wonder that the early mariners were terrified by this spot. In it they saw great patches of seaweed that scarcely moved but stretched out on the surface of the water in long lines like so many sea serpents. There were the rotting hulls of old ships that had been wrecked elsewhere but were still afloat. There were pieces of wood and other floating objects that lazily rose and fell on the slight swell of the sea in a region where the wind seldom blew with any vigor. It was certainly the Port of Missing Ships in accordance with all the old medieval and classical legends.

SEA LIFE AS IT GREW ON WHARF PILING ON THE MAINE COAST

Courtesy Buffalo Museum of Science

Oceanography has given a very simple explanation of the Sargasso Sea. The north equatorial current which flows westward from the west coast of the Sahara and the Gulf Stream which flows north and east from North America to Europe describe a large circle and produce a circular motion in the waters around which they flow. This circular current causes objects caught within the circle to drift to the middle. The middle area is the Sargasso Sea. There is nothing terrifying about such an explanation, but the mariners in the days before Columbus knew little of oceanography.

It is no wonder, then, that the early sailors were so afraid of the Atlantic that they called it the Terrible Ocean. In the Middle Ages the oceans acted as a barrier to transportation and the exchange of thoughts and ideas, the fundamental necessities for an advance in civilization. There was one exception to this. Fearless mariners with long blond hair and bright blue eyes, bearing such names as Ottar the Swart, Eric Blood-ax, Sweyn Splitbeard, Sigurd Snake-eye and Thornfinn Skull-cleaver, sailed the open and stormy seas in their tiny craft and knew no fear. They discovered America five centuries before Columbus landed on these shores. They sailed and ravaged the coast of France and England and even entered the Pillars of Hercules to storm and pillage the countries of the Mediterranean. These were the Vikings or Norsemen. Unfortunately, their voyages across the Atlantic received little publicity; so the fear of the Terrible Ocean still persisted.

Thus it remained for Columbus to prove to the world that the dangerous Atlantic crossing could be made. When one realizes the perils of those days Columbus must be regarded as a most valiant man. Even now danger is not removed; one has only to think back to the "Titanic" or the "Vestris" for two out of many examples of the sudden perils of the sea. Mention of the "Marie Celeste" and the "Cyclops" instantly call to mind the eerie terrors of ocean.

But since the days of the Genoese admiral the oceans have increasingly become routes and highways rather than barriers or walls. Their economic importance is difficult to realize. Without them it would be almost impossible to enjoy foreign and exotic

Courtesy Chicago Historical Society

THE FLAGSHIP OF COLUMBUS

products from other lands. For example, the shipping of coffee from Brazil to the United States would be inconceivable by train because no one, except the very rich, could afford to pay the final price of that delicious beverage. Along the same line it is interesting to note that the steel mills in Baltimore, Maryland, use iron ore that is shipped from Cuba and Chile rather than the ore from Birmingham or Duluth. The reason is that the American ore must, in part at least, be shipped by train; this makes it more expensive than the ore that comes by water from the far-off south. Thus the oceans really make the world into a united whole rather than divide it into isolated continents.

FACTS AND MYSTERIES

Any story of the ocean would be incomplete if it failed to mention some of the interesting phenomena which occur in large bodies of water, such as color, storms, tides, currents, icebergs, waves, whirlpools, and waterspouts.

Paul's Photos, Chicago

SURF BREAKING OVER AN ENGLISH SEA WALL DURING A STORM

The color of the oceans and seas is not, as some people have suggested, due simply to a reflection of the sky. After all, although the ocean is a sky blue in its deeper parts, much of it is light or dark green. The color of a body of water depends on its transparency and the transparency is influenced by the amount of plankton and mineral matter that is held in suspension. Plankton consists of marine organisms carried along by the current. The more transparent the water is, the more colors it absorbs. However, it tends to absorb the longer wavelengths of light more readily than the shorter, such as blue. It reflects the blue and thus its color is blue. However, if there is much plankton in the water these organisms reflect red and yellow, making the water greenish in appearance.

Two of the terrors of early mariners are especially famous, Charybdis and the Maelstrom. They are both whirlpools, the first off the coast of Sicily and the second off the coast of Norway. Whirlpools are caused by the strange configuration of channels or conflicting currents, or wind blowing in the direction opposite the tide. In the northern hemisphere whirlpools turn in a counter-clockwise direction while in the southern their direction is that of the hands of a clock. Although some of the whirlpools of the world could easily wreck the small ancient ships, none of the large modern craft have any fear of them.

Another terrifying object of the sea is the waterspout. This is nothing but a sea-going tornado, yet it is very ominous and horrible in appearance, and may work destruction to any ship in its path. It takes the form of the land tornado, an inverted cone descending from a very black storm cloud. The cone averages twenty-five feet in diameter and is from two to three hundred feet high. Strangely enough, most of the water in waterspouts is fresh as it comes from the storm cloud above; very little is sucked up

Courtesy Northern Pacific Railway

A TERROR OF THE SEA

Ships do not sail close to ice barriers because great sections frequently break off and fall

from the sea. The ancient method of dispelling them was to shoot at them with cannon, make the sign of the cross, or pray. Today, with faster vessels, waterspouts can usually be avoided as they seldom last more than half an hour.

One phenomenon which was sometimes welcomed and sometimes feared by sailors is St. Elmo's Fire. This is a discharge of atmospheric electricity that takes place along the upper parts of a vessel's masts or rigging on stormy nights. It gives a soft and weird glow which some sailors thought to be the spirit of St. Elmo (St. Erasmus) the patron saint of Mediterranean sailors. Others thought it to be an omen of shipwreck.

One feature of the sea that is as much a danger to modern shipping as it was to the commerce of the olden times is the presence of icebergs. These huge mountains of ice are the broken ends of seaside glaciers which float along on the currents and imperil all that they approach. Their season of greatest danger is the spring and early summer when it becomes warm enough for them to break away from the polar rivers of ice. The United States Coast Guard now maintains a vigilant watch for these frozen monsters, warning all shipping of their approach, and blowing them up with dynamite or gunfire when possible. Some are so large that many cases of dynamite make only a small dent in their sides. The service of the Coast Guard, however, helps to prevent the occurence of another such disaster as that which sent the "Titanic" to the bottom.

PECULIARITIES OF THE TIDES

The name tide is given to the rise and fall of water on the shores of the oceans and seas. In some places, the Bay of Fundy near Nova Scotia for one, the tide rises almost fifty feet. In others, such as the Mediterranean Sea, its rise and fall are scarcely noticeable. It is a well-known fact that all bodies exert a gravitational attraction upon one another. The attraction or "pull" of the sun and noon on dry land has little effect because the land is rigid enough to withstand it, but the waters of the hydrosphere are attracted and piled up. The tides travel with the passage of the sun and moon; every twelve hours and twenty-five minutes they

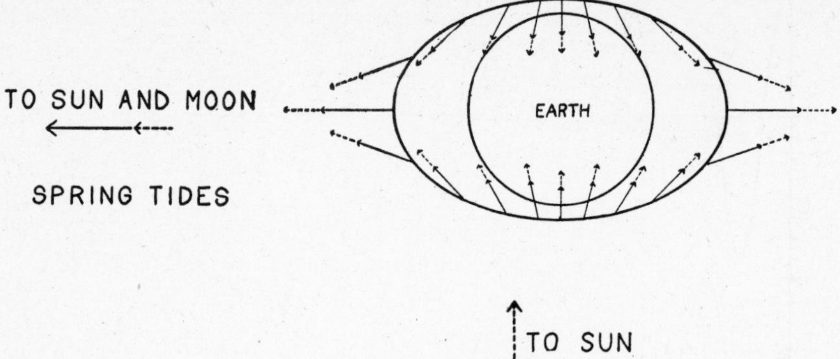

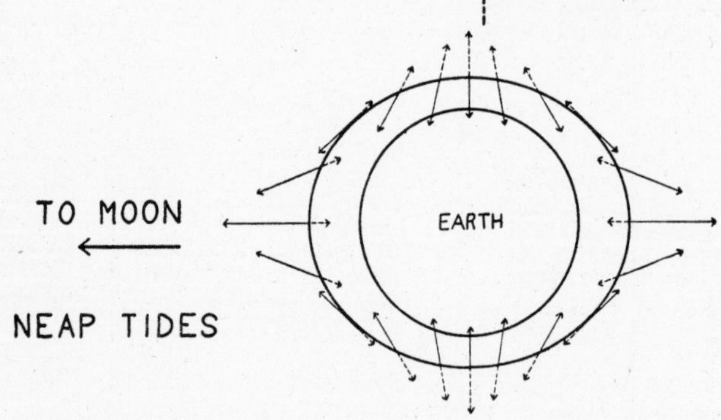

Courtesy Yerkes Observatory

DIAGRAMMATIC EXPLANATION OF THE TIDES

wash the shores of the land. The differences in the configuration of the land cause the differences in the feet of rise. A narrow river-mouth will cause the tidal water to pile up higher than in a wide-mouthed river.

Tides are somewhat like waves except that tides actually move while there is no horizontal motion to a wave. It is only the *form* of the wave that moves forward. The particles of water which form a wave only describe a curve and come to rest about where they started. The same principle is found in whipping up and down one end of a rope, the other end of which has been tied to an immovable object. The *forms* of waves move forward on the rope but the rope itself moves forward not one inch. The largest waves in the world are found in the North Atlantic and in the southern oceans. In these regions waves are sometimes over five

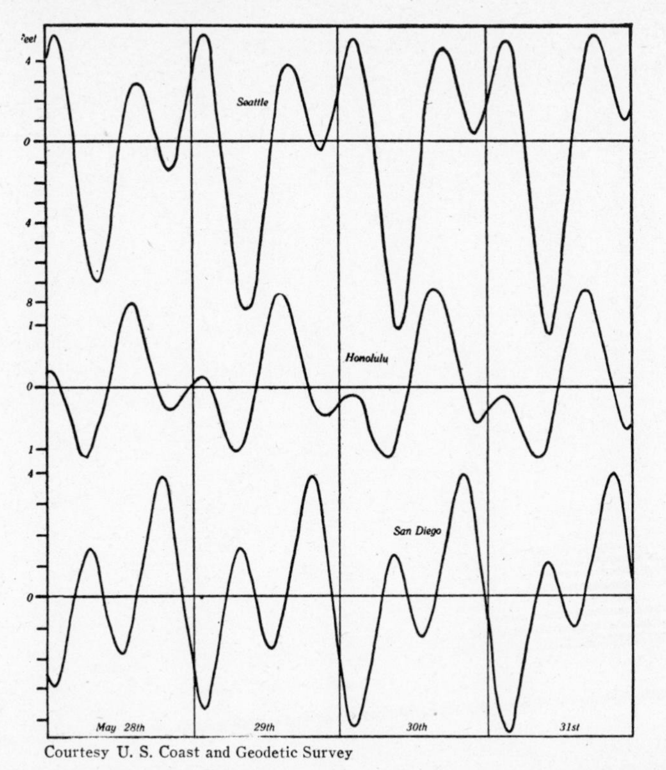

Courtesy U. S. Coast and Geodetic Survey

TIDES ARE DIFFERENT AT DIFFERENT PLACES, AS THIS CHART SHOWS

hundred feet long, from crest to crest, and from fifty to sixty feet high, from crest to trough.

The currents of the oceans are caused by the prevailing winds which blow above them. Many of them are also affected by the rotation of the earth, in that their original course or direction is deflected.

Many men have spent a lifetime in studying the mysteries of the oceans, in charting their intricate coastlines, in plumbing their deeps with weights and with sound waves, and in searching for reefs and rocks and islands. The fruits of their labor are the great charts by which the courses of ships are set and directed. Even those charts are full of little islands marked "P. D." and "E. D."—"position doubtful" and "existence doubtful." This shows that man's knowledge of the sea is still incomplete and uncertain.

Moreover, new lands are slowly rising, old lands sinking; the sea is always changing. There are always new mysteries for our modern Phoenicians and Norsemen. The tides link the sea with the sun and moon. Rain and clouds link the sea with the atmosphere. More than the rest of man's environment, it remains part and symbol of the unbounded and mysterious universe, restless and everchanging.

HOW MEN TRIED TO READ EARTH'S BOOK

If we had been in existence at some time previous to the eighteenth century, we could not have had a scientific understanding of the origin and structure of our world. Instead we would have had to adopt partial or mysterious explanations, according to the period and country in which we lived. As early Greeks we might have held the religious view then current that the earth

Courtesy of and copyright by J. E. Haynes, St. Paul

THE BROAD BOOK OF EARTH

was created by Uranus, the first of the gods, with the help of his Titan children. Later in the Greek era we could have agreed with Plato that the earth was produced by interaction of the four primary "elements," earth, air, fire, and water. In Aristotle's time earthquakes were thought to be the result of great winds storming through the earth's hollow interior, shaking its crust and ultimately escaping through the throats of erupting volcanoes.

Fossils in particular, the vestiges of earlier forms of life preserved in various ways, were a source of mystification in all ages. They were variously considered freaks of nature, "star-seeds," and cryptic messages from God.

The history of earth's origin and the development of its present forms is to be found in the earth itself. The chapters of this planetary history are the principal geological ages, and its pages are the layers or strata of rock, laid down in orderly time-succession on the continents. If these pages had remained in their original chronological order and were all exposed to inspection, our knowledge of the history might become complete; but many of the strata have been deeply buried or worn away. Others have been so altered by compression and chemical change that as pages they are nearly illegible.

It was not until the latter part of the eighteenth century that men began making co-operative and persistent efforts to assemble, decipher, and translate for us the parts of earth's aged manuscript. Thus they laid the foundations on which present methods of geology are based. Serious geological studies had of course been attempted as long before this time as the ancient Greek era, but these studies were based on insufficient scientific observation, and did not in most cases open up avenues which could profitably be explored further.

James Hutton, a Scotchman, may be considered the founder of the modern science of geology. His great work, *Theory of the Earth,* published in 1788, dealt with the natural processes of rock formation and movement. He rightly maintained that the forces which had produced the structures of the earth were still active, and might be observed in operation. Before his time it had been

Courtesy Northern Pacific Ry. Photo by Haynes

HERE A MIGHTY RIVER CUT A GORGE BETWEEN THE PAGES OF EARTH'S BOOK

customary to assume that most geological forces had done all their work in the remote past. Of course with such an assumption as this men were disposed to regard many of the more obscure portions of earth's history as beyond their comprehension. It was an unprogressive viewpoint, which Hutton's philosophy did much to render obsolete.

William Smith, an Englishman living at Hutton's time, was surveying the rock formations near the city of Bath when he noticed that one of the outcropping strata contained a group of fossils which he could not find in the other strata above and below it. He reflected that these fossils might be used to identify the same stratum wherever it was visible above the earth's surface, no matter how far away from the original outcrop or how distorted. Identifying it by this means, he succeeded in tracing the stratum through the English Midlands to the spot where it emerged again on the Yorkshire coast. Prior to Smith's discovery it would have been impossible for anyone to assert that the rock layers of Bath and of Yorkshire were parts of a single whole; but the fossils contained in them told "Strata" Smith that the rocks were parts of a stratum originally continuous, laid down at a single period in earth's history. This means of stratum identification enabled him to map both the exposed and the hidden rock layers of a large part of England.

Our ability to explain earth movements, to determine the time order of geological events, and to locate hidden mineral treasures depends in large part on the location and identification of strata. Although they were originally laid down horizontally, or nearly so, the strata have undergone extensive shifts, having been upheaved and repeatedly depressed; broken by earthquakes, overturned, and pulled apart by lateral movements of the earth's crust; worn down by water and ice, and then redeposited far from their

Courtesy Atchison, Topeka and Santa Fe Railway Co.

METEORITE CRATER NEAR WINSLOW, ARIZONA

original location. Without noting the fossil contents of the rock layers, as Smith taught us to do, and analyzing their mineral content, we could never make an orderly arrangement of this jumble of data.

Smith's work was also important in the field of historical biology, since it stimulated the evolutionary studies of the naturalist, Lamarck. This Frenchman was the first person to demonstrate convincingly the gradual changes in the forms of life, exhibited by the successive layers of fossil-bearing rock.

THEORIES OF EARTH'S ORIGIN

Since the beginning of the present century important investigations have been made as to the origin of the earth, and the condition of its interior. As a result of these studies, the once widely-credited *nebular hypothesis*, published by La Place in 1796, lost general acceptance. According to the Laplacian doctrine the cooling sun threw off a succession of gaseous rings, which took on spherical forms as the planets. In cooling they

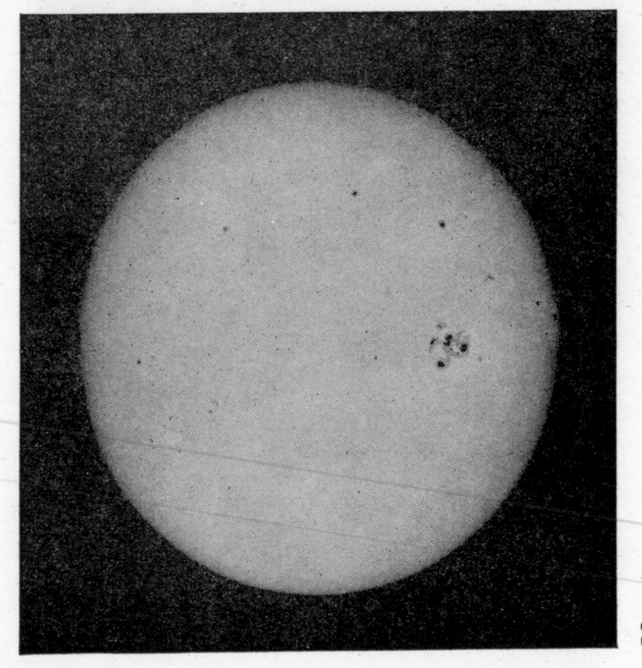

EARTH'S "PARENT," THE SUN

As viewed through a refracting telescope.

Courtesy Yerkes Observatory

were reduced from a gaseous to a liquid state, and finally developed solid crusts, as ice forms on the surface of water. The earth was believed to have a liquid, molten interior—the source of the lava ejected by volcanoes.

A number of discrepancies in this hypothesis were noted, especially the fact that earthquake waves passing through the center of the earth move much more rapidly than would be possible through a liquid medium. Furthermore, it has been pointed out that the friction generated by the supposedly liquid center of the earth against its outer crust would have been great enough to stop its rotation entirely. Nor do gases under known conditions behave in such a way that they could possibly have left the sun in the form of rings. Even had they done so, they and their satellites should all be rotating in the same direction, to bear out La Place's theories. A number of them have been discovered, however, which revolve in the contrary direction.

THEORY FROM CHICAGO

Two men of the University of Chicago were the originators of the now famous *planetesimal hypothesis,* which has largely superseded the nebular hypothesis mentioned above. According to the more recently proposed system, the planetary materials were not emitted from the sun as rings, but were torn from it by a star, approaching near enough to overcome the sun's gravity. Portions of the material at the sun's surface were drawn out in great tidal movements and detached from the sun entirely. The gravities of the sun and the moving star, changing relatively to each other, caused the planetary masses to assume elliptical orbits about the sun. In addition to the planets, many smaller bodies of solar material known as *planetesimals* were drawn out into space, and assumed orbits of their own. The planets were originally much smaller than they now are, but gradually added the planetesimals to their mass by drawing them in when the planets and the planetesimals came close together. So the planets built themselves up to their present size.

DID ONE OF THESE STARS PASS CLOSE TO THE SUN AND THUS FORM THE PLANETS?

Courtesy Yerkes Observatory

THE AGE OF THE EARTH

The present century has also witnessed the development of a method more accurate than any previously known for estimating the age of the earth. This method employs the so-called "radio-active time clock," and is based on the discovery that certain radio-active elements such as thorium and uranium disintegrate into other elements at definite rates of speed. A given quantity of uranium, for instance, requires about five billion years to lose half its volume, which is turned into lead and helium. Therefore, if the quantities of lead and helium in a piece of rock are measured, and compared with the quantity of uranium remaining in it, it is possible to know approximately how many years have elapsed since the rock was formed from the liquid state. Geologists estimate that, according to the data of radioactive elements, the earth must be not less than two billion years old.

THE SHAPE OF THE LITHOSPHERE

The *lithosphere,* or solid portion of the earth, is naturally of the first importance to man, since it is the home to which he must always return after his brief excursions upon the oceans or into the atmosphere. It is also the portion of earth most interesting to geologists, since it is readily accessible for observation and has structures permanent enough to be carefully studied.

The surface of the lithosphere is so irregular that the waters of the *hydrosphere,* or liquid layer, are held by gravity in its deepest hollows. These are the ocean basins, above which the continents project to an average height of half a mile above sea level.

In order to draw off the waters of these oceans, so as to expose to the atmosphere and to our inspection the entire outer surface of the lithosphere, we should first have to find a place to store about 320 million cubic miles of water. Having done so, we should be able to view the 140 million square miles of the lithosphere which the water now hides from us, that is, 72 per cent of its total area. If we should walk over the ocean bottoms thus exposed, the landscape meeting our eyes would probably prove disappointing. It consists for the most part of vast lifeless plains, covered with a fine deposit of red clay derived from volcanic dust, and is so uniformly flat that we could not see the slightest irregularities.

Moving over this dreary plain, we might chance to wander at last down a slight slope into one of the lower portions of the ocean bed, some thirty thousand feet below the level of the sea and lying parallel to the continental platforms, to which they rise on their landward sides with extreme steepness. Climbing without difficulty back up the gentle gradient again toward the ocean's center, we might chance upon one of the smooth volcanic cones which have built themselves up little by little from the ocean floor. Certain of the Hawaiian peaks of this kind rise nearly thirty thousand feet above the base level of sea bottom.

Courtesy Northern Pacific Railway

PART OF EARTH'S LITHOSPHERE
The Crazy Mountains, a section of the Montana Rockies.

Courtesy Field Museum of Natural History, Chicago

A LAVA BED DESCENDING INTO THE SEA

Viewed thus with the ocean beds emptied, the seven continents would appear about ten million square miles or one-twelfth larger than they now do. This additional twelfth consists of the continental shelves, and is the area which the continents have lost due to the encroachments of the sea. These shelves slope gently downward from the continents which they fringe, and have an average depth of 600 feet below sea level. At the edges of these shelves the descent to the true ocean basins is extremely abrupt, making it very clear that the shelves are really part of the continents.

Compared with the smooth ocean basins, those parts of the lithosphere above sea level are extremely irregular, projecting to lofty mountain peaks, and traversed with gorges and valleys which merge into plains. The irregularity of the dry land as compared with sea bottom is due to certain erosive agents which cannot operate under water. These include sudden temperature changes, winds which pick up dust and redeposit it in piles, and most important, the rivers which are constantly gnawing at the soil, dissecting away the softer portions of hillsides and mountain slopes,

Courtesy Northern Pacific Railway

THIS MOUNTAIN, HIGH AS IT IS, COULD BE SUNK DEEP IN THE SEA AND BE LOST TO SIGHT

and leaving their skeletons exposed. But the bottom layers of sea water are nearly constant in temperature, and are scarcely stirred by the currents which sweep at the surface. The solid materials which are carried from the continents into the ocean basins by rivers or dust-bearing winds sift evenly down over the sea bottom.

The average depth of the oceans is about two and one-half miles. Their cubic content is so great that if all the projections of the lithosphere were planed down to fill its lowest basins, the ocean would cover the entire solid portion of the earth to a depth of two miles. Such a planing action is in fact the total effect of earth's various erosive forces, and if this effect were not being constantly offset by another process, the uplifting of continental shelves, we might predict the eventual disappearance of all our land into the domain of the sea.

THE MATERIALS OF THE LITHOSPHERE

There are more than ninety known elements which enter into the composition of our planet, some of them, like praseodymium and dysprosium so rare that few of us have heard their names. Of these ninety-odd only eight are present in the earth-crust to the extent of one per cent or more of its mass. Here is a list of these eight predominant elements in the lithosphere, with the percentage of the total for each:

Elements	Percentage by weight
Oxygen	46.46
Silicon	27.61
Aluminum	8.07
Iron	5.06
Calcium	3.64
Sodium	2.75
Potassium	2.58
Magnesium	2.07

It is evident from this list that almost one-half the weight of the earth's shell consists of oxygen, while silicon constitutes more than one quarter. Oxygen in its pure state is normally a gas, while pure silicon is a non-metallic solid. The other six principal

Courtesy G. W. Stose, U. S. Geological Survey

FOLDS OF QUARTZITE, A TYPICAL MINERAL

constituents are true metals. But none of these eight elements are found in a free or pure state in the crust of the earth, being combined in definite proportions to form minerals.

Minerals are solid chemical masses of natural occurrence, and are composed either of single elements, or of two or more in combination. They usually tend to assume crystalline formation, that is, their particles are geometrical with facets bounded by angles characteristic of the minerals in which the crystals occur. Rocks, the usual form in which the minerals occur, are generally in crystalline form, and may contain one or many minerals in physical mixture.

If we clear away the plant life with which the upper surface of the lithosphere is carpeted, we come usually to the *mantle-rock.* This is not rock as we think of it, but a comparatively loose mass of clay, sand, rock fragments, and gravel, with small additions of organic material from animals and plants, which greatly increase the soil's fertility. This mantle-rock may vary greatly in thick-

Courtesy Northern Pacific Railway

WINDYGAP GLACIER, MONTANA—NOTE THE LOOSE ROCK

ness, being hundreds of feet deep in some places, where it was deposited by winds or muddy rivers. Glaciers too, the ice-rivers found in the frigid zones or at high altitudes, pick up rocks or gravel from their beds, and bear them downward frozen in the ice to the levels where melting occurs. Here the mantle-rock is deposited in large heaps known as *moraines*. In certain places, where the slopes are so steep that the loose rock or soil is readily blown or washed away, the mantle-rock may be wanting. In such cases the bedrock is exposed to the atmosphere, the mantle-rock being removed about as fast as it is produced.

Below the finer layers of the mantle-rock (which we usually call soil) are less completely disintegrated rock layers, which have been only slightly decayed by chemical combination with the elements of the water and the atmosphere. Digging beneath these loose portions of the rock which have not yet been reduced to the consistency of soil, we come at last to the solid rock, which is found at varying depths under all portions of the crust of the lithosphere.

Rocks are classified according to their mode of origin and the processes which they have undergone, into three general sorts, *igneous, sedimentary,* and *metamorphic.*

IGNEOUS ROCKS

Igneous rock is so named from *ignis,* the Latin word for fire. It originates as hot liquid matter under the earth's crust, and is forced toward the surface of the lithosphere by the downward pressure of the overlying rock masses, or by the tendency to expansion of the gases and water vapor compressed within it. As it rises and seeks an outlet this hot material or *magma* may encounter the outlet of a volcanic cone, from the top of which it is forcibly hurled into the air as cinders or dust, and strewn on the surrounding country. Or it may maintain a semi-liquid state, comparable to thick corn-meal mush, and flow down the sides of the cone as lava. If the magma can find no opening to the surface, it rises between the joints of the rock masses above it until it finds a space between the strata where it can solidify in horizontal layers. If it cannot find such an opening, it hardens in the

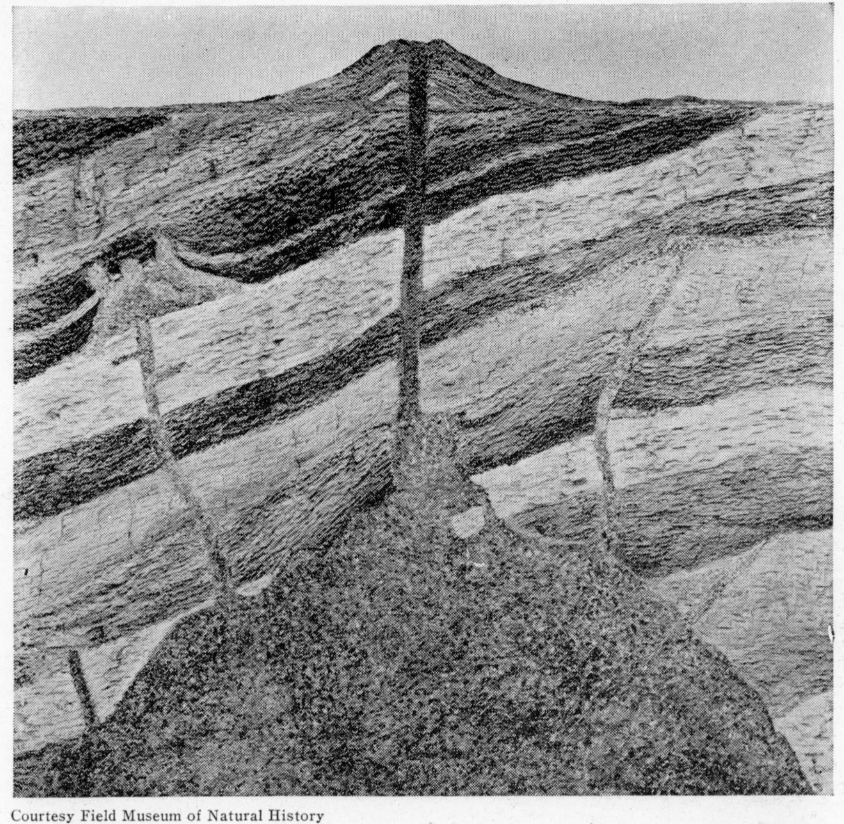

Courtesy Field Museum of Natural History

A CROSS-SECTION MODEL SHOWING IGNEOUS INTRUSIONS, OR DIKES

rock fissures themselves to form thick vertical walls known as dikes. Granite, basalt, and obsidian are the best known sorts of igneous rock, beside the various forms of lava.

SEDIMENTARY ROCKS

Rocks of the second great class, the sedimentary rocks, are usually distinguishable from the igneous rocks by their banded or stratified formation. Cross sections of some sandstones and shales reveal ribbon-like bands of varying colors and textures, and sometimes within a single stratum a definite size gradation of materials can be observed, with the coarsest gravels at the bottom, and the finest silts at the top.

Sedimentary rocks with clearly defined bandings and strata occur far from the present borders of the oceans, even on the tops of the highest mountains. Nevertheless we can assert confidently that most sedimentary rocks were formed under water, usually in the sea, as no other mode of origin would account for the existence of the strata and the bands. The elevation to their present lofty position has been accomplished through tremendous up-thrusting movements of the earth's crust. Additional proofs of the under-water origin of sedimentary rocks are furnished by the fossil shells of marine animals, which are often found in great quantities embedded in the stratified rock thousands of feet above sea level.

If you have ever observed how dirty water in an aquarium which has been disturbed clears itself again, you understand al-

PALISADES ALONG THE YELLOWSTONE RIVER
The rock bands are almost as even as man-made walls.

ready how the layers and bands of the sedimentary rock are formed. First of all, the shells and coarser sand-grains stirred up from the bottom sink again rapidly because of their weight. Next the finer sand redistributes itself fairly evenly over the bottom of the tank. It may be hours or days before the finest mud in the water is precipitated to the bottom, leaving the water clear. After this takes place, if you look through the side wall of the aquarium you will see the same bands of material that may be observed in a section of stratified rock. Gravity causes the mixed materials to be sorted out, with the largest and heaviest ones at the bottom, while the water has just enough sustaining power to retard the sinking of the lighter materials, and to cause their even horizontal distribution.

That is the way in which sedimentation occurs along the shores of large bodies of water. The rivers bring down great quantities of mud and sand from the mountains and plains, and empty them into the comparatively quiet waters of the oceans

Courtesy Northern Pacific Railway

POMPEY'S PILLAR IN MONTANA
Picture shows clearly varying thicknesses of strata.

and the lakes. Since the carrying power of water depends on its velocity, as soon as the forward motion of the stream is checked, the materials it bears begin to sink in the order of their weight. Thus bands within a single stratum are formed.

If the rivers dry up or change their outlets, the supply of eroded materials furnished the forming stratum ceases. Other materials then become predominant, such as calcium carbonate, precipitated directly from the sea water or laid down by the limy shells of marine mollusks. By this sudden change in sedimentary materials the mud-stratum may be distinguished from the later stratum of limestone formed above it.

SEACOAST EROSION

In addition to the rivers, depositing their burden of soil and sand constantly in the ocean, the ocean itself secures much sedimentary material by cutting back its shores. This action, duplicated on a smaller scale by lakes, takes place wherever large bodies of water are in motion at the borders of the land.

If you have ever been on the seacoast during a storm you have some conception of the tremendous power of the sea to wear the land away. Far out you may see the successive lines of waves rolling smoothly and with slow majesty landward. As they come nearer the shore their speed is increased and their crests become steeper. Finally they start to "drag bottom," collapsing as breakers which hurl themselves with fury on the land. The shock of their impact may be distinctly felt; and under the heavy booming you may hear the sharp rattling grind of pebbles and sand grating together. These are the abrading surfaces by which each wave is able to rasp the land margin, as if it were a gigantic file.

Upon broad and level beaches the waves have already done most of their land-reducing work, and confine themselves to grinding the sand and rock fragments ever smaller, or to depositing these materials. But in steep and rocky sections of the coast, the sea's work may be progressing rapidly. The precipitous sea cliffs of New England and of the Aran Islands west of Ireland are undergoing steady wave disintegration. Though rising steeply from the water, these cliffs will be found to have fairly level terraces extending outward a little below the surface of the water. These terraces exist because the waves are active only at the surface, cutting a horizontal groove into the cliff-side as a logger's saw grooves a tree trunk. As this groove works its way into the cliff, undercutting it and forming caves, the weight of the rock above causes a collapse, so that the cliff presents a vertical front once more. The removed materials may help to build up the submarine cliff terrace, or they may be ground down to fine sand by mutual friction, and transported by shore currents to beds of sedimentation. Here they are deposited more or less evenly, and are slowly cemented together to form stratified rock, through the binding agency of lime, silica, or magnesium.

A dramatic example of the sea's encroachment on the land within recent time is furnished us by Heligoland. This is a sandstone island of the North Sea, best known today as the scene of

Courtesy W. Cross, U. S. Geological Survey

THE WHITER ROCK IS AN OVERTHRUST OF MILLSAP LIMESTONE

RIPPLE-MARKED SANDSTONE

Some sandstone deposits retain the rippled surface imparted to them by the action of wind or water eons ago.

Courtesy Field Museum of Natural History

the first naval battle of the World War. In the ninth century of the Christian Era, this island had a coastline of 120 miles. By the fourteenth century this had been reduced to forty-five miles. At present all that is left of this once important feudal fief is a battered remnant scarcely a mile long. All the rest has disappeared into the insatiable maw of the ocean. The German government hopes to save the island from complete extinction by the heavy concrete walls with which it has surrounded it.

There are many kinds of sedimentary rocks. Among them is limestone, composed of calcium carbonate more or less mixed with impurities, and grayish or white in color. Another is sandstone, composed of sand grains more or less firmly united by cementing agents like lime or iron oxide. The latter often gives to sandstone the rust-colored bands found in it. Shale, one of the most abundant of all rocks, is known as a "mud stone," due to its constituency of compressed clay and sand grains. It is soft, and flakes so readily that its use to man is limited.

METAMORPHIC, OR "ALTERED" ROCKS

Rocks of the third broad class, the metamorphic rocks, derive their name from the Greek *metamorphosis,* meaning "a change of form." These rocks are produced from rocks of the igneous and sedimentary classes which have been acted upon by heat or pressure. They may be so altered in structure that it is nearly impossible to determine whether they were originally sedimentary or igneous. The crystals characteristic of the igneous rocks may be much changed by pressure, and new minerals may be formed, while the strata or bandings of the sedimentary rocks may be entirely destroyed. When particles of shale, a "mud rock," are squeezed, they tend to expand in the direction of least pressure, and may thus form broad crystals of mica, so thin as to be usable in the windows of stoves, where a transparent substance resistant to fire is required.

The familiar slate with which we roof our houses is another form into which shale may be converted, but it had to undergo a chequered history before becoming suitable to our use. It origi-

FLUORITE, A CRYSTALLINE MINERAL

Courtesy Field Museum of Natural History

nated as igneous rock, was eroded by water or atmosphere, and its particles were deposited in sedimentation beds as mud. Here it was cemented into shale, and was then buried deep in the earth and subjected to great pressures. This pressure has altered its structure, squeezing it into thin "cleavage plates," at which it can be split into thicknesses suitable for shingles.

Other common metamorphic rocks are gneiss (pronounced "nice"), derived from granite; marble, crystallized from limestone under pressure; and quartzite, a compressed form of sandstone.

THE EARTH IS CHANGING

Most people have observed and are somewhat conscious of the gradual changes in the formations of the earth, wrought by erosion. But the average person, unless he has witnessed some great convulsion of nature such as an earthquake or an eruption, thinks of the earth as the ultimately solid thing of his experience. He does not realize that it is subject to sudden changes of great extent any more than he senses its daily rotation, or the considerable rise and fall of the earth-tides under his feet.

One of the most interesting documents in earth's history-book may be seen at Pozzuoli, a small town beside the Bay of Naples. This document demonstrates the extent of geographical change within historic time.

If you are in Italy and chance to visit little Pozzuoli, your guide will probably call your attention to three marble columns. These form a part of the ancient ruined temple of Jupiter Serapis and rear their forty feet of height not far from the present shore, on the site of the old Roman city of Puteoli. Examining the surface of the columns carefully you will see that they are roughened by the openings of small tunnels into the marble. Within them have been found shells of *Lithodomus*, a mollusk of the Mediterranean which is remarkable for its ability to drill out homes for itself from solid rock.

From these and other indications of the nearby shore, it becomes evident that the entire area subsided not less than forty

Courtesy Field Museum of Natural History

EROSION CHANGING THE EARTH

Courtesy Northern Pacific Railway

THE WEIRD BADLANDS OF WESTERN NORTH DAKOTA

Courtesy Idaho State Chamber of Commerce

THE CRACKED AND FISSURED SURFACE OF LAVA

feet, bringing the temple of Jupiter Serapis well below sea-level. Before the re-emergence of the land Lithodomus faithfully inscribed the message to man which we read today.

Written records of the past also furnish us with abundant evidence of changes of the earth of great extent, both gradual and sudden.

The Mongolian invasions of Europe, notably the invasions of the Huns from the fourth to the sixth centuries, A.D., are ascribed by historians to the increasing scope of desert conditions in Asia, by which the hungry hordes were forced from their ancestral homes. In like manner the extension of Mohammedanism westward as far as Spain is believed to be due in part to the increasing dryness of central Arabia.

Volcanic activity provides some examples of recent earth changes of astonishing dimensions. The mountain known as Jorullo originated in 1759 when a level plain in Mexico, far from any known volcano, opened suddenly during an earthquake, and volcanic matter began to erupt through the fissure. In a single night such quantities were ejected that a cone was formed of considerable height. Since then the mountain has added to itself by further eruptions of cinders and lava, so that its present height is over four thousand feet. In Camiguin, an island of the Philippine archipelago, another mountain rose with startling suddenness in 1871. As in the case of Jorullo, a fissure appeared in a plain, through which an eruption took place. This continued for four years, at the end of which the volcanic cone thus formed had an estimated height of nineteen hundred feet.

The many forces by which land forms are changed, either gradually or by sudden spasms, are classified in three groups. These are *gradation,* the leveling down of land surfaces by wind, ice, or water; *diastrophism,* the deformation of the earth's crust; and *vulcanism,* the rising of hot mineral matter through or into the earth's outer rock layer. The general tendency of gradation is downward, the eroded materials of the land being transported bit by bit from their original locations, and deposited at lower levels in stream beds, on the ocean floor, and on the submerged margins of continents. Diastrophism, the movement of the earth's rocky crust, may be either upward, downward, or sideward, and is responsible for earthquakes, the upheaval of mountains, and the rising and sinking of coasts. Its effects therefore are either to increase or decrease the total land area. Vulcanism is generally an upbuilding force, adding to the land the materials ejected from the earth's interior.

Each of these primary forces accomplishes its object by a variety of means, which require separate consideration to understand the sum of their effects, so vital to humanity's future.

EROSION, THE LEVELER OF EARTH

The gradation of the lithosphere is accomplished by various agents of erosion, which gnaw constantly at the structures of the earth, seeking to reduce mountains, plateaus, and plains to one dead level at sea bottom. If gradation were not being counteracted by other geological forces, our descendants would have to resign themselves to the gloomy prospect of seeing the land swallowed up little by little by the hungry sea. Mankind and the surviving animal and plant species of the land would live huddled in extreme congestion until the surf rolled over the ultimate core of the continents.

Courtesy Northern Pacific Railway

AN EXAMPLE OF HIGH-PRESSURE EROSION
Lower Falls of the Yellowstone River.

The atmosphere serves as an erosive agent in various ways, both mechanical and chemical. When in motion as wind it can pick up dust and the tinier particles of the mantle rock, and circulate these widely over the surface of the globe. Much dust from the continents descends over the oceans, settling in the depths where it is forever lost to men. Other dust is deposited on the land, and is known as loess, sometimes accumulating in layers several hundred feet thick. These deposits are most frequently found near deserts, though some occur in Europe and in the glaciated sections of North America. There are extensive loess beds in northwestern China, brought there by the wind scouring over the dry soil of the Gobi Desert. Loess, though soft, is remarkable for its ability to stand a long time in vertical cliffs, which accounts for certain sunken roadbeds in China, worn deep into the soil by wheels and feet padding through the centuries.

Courtesy Southern Pacific Co.

BALANCED ROCK, A PRODUCT OF EROSION

The loess beds of Europe and the central United States were laid down in the Glacial Epoch, thus providing us with an interesting sidelight on the recent dust storms of the Great Plains area. In the current consternation man is being given all the blame for these storms, and the consequent loss of valuable topsoil. But the loess beds show that much greater dust storms occurred long before man could have caused them by unsound methods of agriculture and lumbering.

Winds which carry sharp sands may abrade and wear away the surface of rocks, as the commercial sand blast is used to refurbish the exterior stone of skyscrapers. Since the softer materials are worn away first, "stone mushrooms" and isolated pillars of rock with more or less rounded sides are sometimes found in the deserts, far from other prominent features of the landscape.

VAGABONDS OF COAST AND DESERT

Wherever dry sand accumulates the land is likely to be encumbered with sand dunes hundreds of feet high advancing relentlessly over a broad front. In the desert this sand may be produced either by wind erosion, or by a sea which covered it in earlier ages. On seas and lake shores sand is formed by the grinding action of waves already described. But however formed, wind-blown sand tends to accumulate on the leeward side of obstructions, and thus a small bush or boulder may become the nucleus of a large dune.

Dunes are often crescent-shaped, and on the moderately inclined inner surface of such a dune, known as the blowout, even a moderate wind is sufficient to carry the sand up to the dune ridge. The shape of the blowout and the heat of the sand cause strong air currents, so that the sand grains strike against obstacles with stinging force sufficient to frost the surface of glass. The whole surface of the sand seems to be alive when the wind blows, the superficial grains appearing to be crawling over one another. At the top of the blowout the dune descends in a steep slope to the lower ground on which it is encroaching. Halfway down this slope the top branches of buried trees are visible, struggling to keep their topmost leaves in the life-giving sunlight. Lower down only the boles of the trees are covered, and beyond the farthest advance

Courtesy Field Museum of Natural History

A SAND DUNE

of the tongues of sand are forest giants awaiting their turn to be overwhelmed.

Long after such a forest has been covered, the dune may pass on, leaving behind a few silvery tree trunks, desiccated and stripped of bark, like ghosts of the rich forest that was.

Farms, woodlands, and even whole villages may be buried under dune-sand. On the shores of the Baltic Sea are villages which have been thus covered up and exhumed again long afterward by the forward movement of the dunes. The rapid advance of hills of sand over useful and populous soil areas is so destructive that methods of checking them have been practiced both by private individuals and by governmental agencies. There are certain grasses and other plants which are well adapted to dry conditions by the dense mats of fine roots with which they anchor themselves in shifting soil. These roots so bind the sand that the dune is immobilized little by little, permitting its gradual colonization by larger plants and trees. Through this process a layer of fertile humus is built up, nourishing a protective ground cover of vegetation.

Even after a dune has been well forested by this slow stabilization process, such small causes as the uprooting of a bush or the death of a tree may tear through the guard layer of humus, giving the wind a new chance to dry out and carry away the exposed sand. So the wooded and harmless dune may revert again to its old life as a menacing wanderer.

Courtesy Southern Pacific Co.

EROSION WILL EVENTUALLY LEVEL THIS CRINKLED CRUST OF EARTH

DOWN TO THE SEA IN RIVERS

It is estimated that over six thousand cubic miles of water are borne to the oceans every year by the rivers of the earth. Within the United States alone running water has an annual working capacity of about 400 million horse-power. Man uses some of this great fund of energy to drive his machines, but the rest does its natural work of wearing down the prominences of the continent, and of transporting some of this loosened material into the sea. The rivers of the United States bear an annual load of about 783 million tons of eroded matter down to the coasts, where it is deposited on the continental shelves or sinks to the ocean bottom. So great a loss, if suffered evenly by the entire country, would wear down one foot of its elevation in about eight thousand years.

Courtesy Atchison, Topeka and Santa Fe Railway Co.

CANYON DIABLO, ARIZONA
Where man has spanned a gorge cut by water.

Courtesy Atchison, Topeka and Santa Fe Railway Co.

THE GRAND CANYON, A PRODUCT OF EROSION

Running water is one of the most powerful agents of erosion, working over the land as a whole, instead of being restricted to a narrow band at the sea coast, as the oceans are. In arid deserts running water has ceased to be a factor of first importance, as here most of its work was done earlier. In regions of intense and perpetual cold, water does its work in the form of ice, which produces quite different effects from those of water in its liquid state.

If you have watched rain running in a gravel pit, or have watered a garden, you have had a chance to see erosion going on in miniature. The forces at work here are those by which rills have become rivers, mountains have been transformed into hills and placid valleys, and plateaus have been reduced to a maze of flat-topped buttes traversed by gorges and ravines. Of course in your back yard there are not such various conditions as prevail over a continent through geological ages, but the same principles operate. If the soil of your garden is very dry, most of the water coming from the nozzle of the hose will penetrate among the fine earth grains, working deeper and deeper. It may eventually reach the general level of flowing water under ground, known as the *water table,* and become *ground water.* But if you continue sprinkling long enough the soil will become saturated, and additional water poured on it will start running over the surface of the ground, seeking a path downward in response to the call of gravity. The ground may look perfectly level to you, but the water knows better. Soon, instead of flowing as a sheet over the whole surface, it is running in many little twisting channels. The water in these rills carries bits of soil with it, thus widening and deepening its bed. Presently the many little run-offs unite to form larger ones part way down their course. These are miniature river systems, complete with their tributaries and individual watersheds. By the time so much material has been washed away that the streamlets are too small for their beds, little river valleys have been formed, whose side walls become less and less steep as side-wash levels down their banks. You will find the washed-out material deposited at the foot of the streams, where it is spread out in flattish fan-shaped piles of fine silt.

Where these deposits occur on a large scale, as at the mouths of rivers emptying into lakes or ocean, *deltas* are formed. These formations bear the name "delta" because of their fancied resemblance to the shape of △, the fourth letter of the Greek alphabet. Since the carrying power of a stream depends on its velocity, when river currents are suddenly checked on entering large bodies of water their loads settle and accumulate, ultimately emerging from the sea as low plains of great fertility. The large and famous deltas of the Nile, the Hwang Ho, and the Mississippi are the rivers' gifts to man. Yet these great streams are but "Indian givers," since they add to the land only by reducing its volume above sea-level.

THE AGING LANDSCAPE

As rills enlarge to rivers, and gullies become valleys by the washing out of delta-forming materials, the landscape passes through distinct stages of development. Each stage exhibits char-

Courtesy J. E. Haynes, St. Paul

THIS LANDSCAPE IS YOUNG, BUT EROSION IS AGING IT

acteristic features, according to which mountains, valleys, and plateaus are known as "youthful," "mature," or "old." Such nomenclature is not fanciful, since the features of the land go through a definite cycle of birth and death. Mountains and plateaus are born beneath the sea at the margins of the continents, from which they are uplifted into the air by the birth pangs of the earth's crust. They are Gargantuan babies and reverse the biological cycle by being largest when young, becoming ever smaller and less conspicuous as they mature. Young mountains, such as the Rockies and the Andes, have jagged outlines, very steep slopes, and comparatively simple drainage systems of a few rivers without many tributaries. The Appalachians of eastern North America are ancient mountains, thoroughly dissected by erosion, and shriveled from their once magnificent height like senile old men. Their greatest elevation is only a trifle over 6,700 feet. Compared with them, the Rocky Mountains are still young fellows in their prime.

Unlike mountains, valleys grow larger as they age, and their slopes become more and more gradual. A young river valley, such as that of the Yellowstone, usually narrows at its bottom like the letter "V," and is not much more than wide enough for the stream running through it. A mature river valley, of which the Mississippi Valley is a good example, has generally a broad flood plain much too large for the river upon it, and side walls far apart consisting of gently rolling hills.

The power of rainfall to alter the gross features of the landscape is well illustrated in Puerto Rico, an island possession of the United States. It is about one hundred miles long and thirty-five miles wide, and stretches from east to west along the north edge of the Caribbean Sea. With the other Antilles, it comprises one of the greatest mountain chains of the earth, known to geologists as the Antillean Range, though by far the greater part of the range is under water.

The mountain system known as the Cordillera Central runs from end to end of the island, much nearer the southern coast which it parallels than the Atlantic on the north. These mountains do not now rise over 4,500 feet, but were once much higher

Courtesy Northern Pacific Railway

ROCK FORMATION IN SHOSHONE CANYON, KNOWN AS THE "HOLY CITY"

than at present, dividing the island lengthwise into equal northern and southern slopes. Since the island's rainfall is all supplied by the prevailing northeast trade winds, the northern side of the mountain crest has always robbed the southern side of its rain. Through the ages the effect has been to erode the northern slopes more and more, forming a broad plain which slopes gradually toward the Atlantic. The median crest has been shifted steadily southward by the uneven distribution of rainfall; and the semiarid southern slopes, being little eroded, descend steeply to a very narrow coastal plain.

WHEN ICE WAS KING

In certain cold regions of the earth which now support only a sparse population of a few of the hardiest plant and animal forms, fossil animals have been dug from the preserving ice or

Courtesy Northern Pacific Railway

GLACIERS LIKE THIS ONCE CAME FAR DOWN INTO THE UNITED STATES

mud which closely resemble species now able to survive only in the tropics. Some of the most frigid parts of North America contain coal beds formed from luxuriant tropical vegetation, in marked contrast to the tundra plants growing there at present. It is therefore clear that almost tropical temperatures must once have prevailed here.

On the other hand, there are numerous evidences to show that Canada and a large part of the northern United States were once covered by a vast ice sheet hundreds or even thousands of feet thick. Corn fields, rich meadows, and forests of broad-leaved trees flourish in our present temperate conditions. But a more detailed inspection shows us heaps of gravel and boulders mixed helter-skelter, many shallow lake-beds not formed by rivers, and rocks which have been scoured and scratched. Such topographical features can be the result of only the great perennial mass of ice which once crept across the land.

In Bronx Park, New York, there is a surprising memento of a glacial visitation. It is an immense boulder perched on a slab of bare rock. This slab is roughly planed flat, with many long parallel grooves gouged out in the direction of movement of the ice which once covered it. The slab and the boulder are different kinds of rock, indicating that the ice sheet brought the boulder down with it from the north, and dropped it here when the ice melted.

The many small lakes of the northern states, especially numerous in Maine, New Hampshire, New York, and Minnesota, were produced by glacial action. The largest and best-known lakes originating in this way are the Great Lakes, the Finger Lakes of New York, and the large Alpine Lakes of Switzerland and northern Italy.

How can we reconcile such contrary evidences as these telling us on the one hand of polar conditions, and of tropical temperatures on the other? The truth is that in the eons since life began our planet has gone through a series of climatic changes of long duration and great extent. In the ages of increasing cold the Ice King extended his dominions from the poles toward the Equator, oppressing the conquered lands with heavy and impenetrable ice as he advanced. As the ice fronts moved down over the continents, plant and animal species were destroyed, except for the few that succeeded in migrating toward the tropics.

Such glacial periods have been followed by periods of warm temperatures, much warmer than we have today. During such epochs the warm zones grew from the Equator toward the poles, and melted the glacial sheets before them. Tropical and subtropical species of life then were able to recolonize the high latitudes of earth.

Four or possibly five such cycles of advancing and retreating ice are known to have occurred in the Northern Hemisphere. For the Southern Hemisphere the data by which such cycles can be enumerated are less complete. At present we live in an age of diminishing glaciation demonstrated by the retreating fronts of glaciers, both on mountains and in arctic regions.

At its greatest extent the North American ice sheet covered the entire continent as far south as Long Island, the Ohio River, the Missouri River, and a line from central North Dakota westward to the Pacific Ocean. However, there was a region of con-

Courtesy Field Museum of Natural History

A MODEL SHOWING HOW AN ANCIENT ICE SHEET CREPT DOWN OVER THE REGION OF THE GREAT LAKES

siderable extent centering in southern Wisconsin which was surrounded but not covered by ice. This is known as the Driftless Area.

The northwestern part of Europe was also covered by an ice sheet, extending over Scandinavia, the Baltic Sea and the lands east of it, most of the British Isles, and large parts of present-day Germany and Poland. The Southern Hemisphere too had its glacial epochs, during which the ice moved northward into Africa, South America, and New Zealand.

The causes of these world-wide climatic changes are a matter of disagreement. They have been attributed to all sorts of causes—to changes in solar radiation, a varying volume of carbon dioxide in the atmosphere, alteration of the elliptical orbit of the earth, and to shifting ocean currents. We need not concern ourselves very much with these controversies. But it is interesting to note the correlation between the total volume of ice on the earth and the elevation of the continents above sea-level. During eras of frigidity so much of the water of the hydrosphere is bound up in the continental ice sheets that the general level of the oceans is lowered. But when the ice melts back in warmer ages, the water which is released floods the ocean basins until they spill over onto the continents. The coldest eons of earth's history are therefore those at which the land area is the greatest, and the warmest periods are those at which the greatest amount of land is submerged. If the human species survives long enough our remote descendants may find the advantages of a widespread genial climate offset by the reduction of land area associated with this warmth.

RIVERS OF ICE

In addition to the continuous masses of moving ice known as continental glaciers, during the glacial era sporadic icecaps covered the higher mountain regions in nearly all parts of the world. From them rivers of ice flowed far down over the surrounding land. With the retreat of the continental glaciers, the mountain icecaps too diminished, melting away entirely in many cases, or at most maintaining themselves only on the heights. Such reduced glaciers

Photo by Beaumont and Hohman, Seattle

A RIVER OF ICE CURVES DOWN TO THE SEA

may be seen in the Alps, the Rockies, and in many other lofty regions.

Such mountain glaciers are called rivers of ice because, riverlike, they flow downward through valleys which they are constantly enlarging. But many of their effects are so different from those of true rivers that it is not difficult to determine whether a mountain landscape has been carved by ice or by water. Glaciated slopes are likely to be steeper than those eroded by water, and to have more concave surfaces. The rocks upon them often show the long parallel scratches which the moving ice has wrought. Furthermore, there are many hummocks or ridges to be observed in glaciated territory, composed of rock fragments of all sizes, indiscriminately mingled. These are the moraines already discussed.

Mountain glaciers are formed of snow swept by the winds from ridges and summits into sloping gullies and ravines. When a sufficient quantity has been accumulated, increasing weight and partial melting cause the snow to be fused into ice. The ice, as a solid, does not flow readily, so that a glacier will often fill an entire valley from rim to rim before it begins grinding its way downward at any considerable rate of speed. The rate of flow may be only a few inches or feet a day, depending on the angle of slope, the season, and the amount of snowfall.

Through their fluidity and comparatively rapid run-off, rivers do most of their erosive work at the lowest part of the valley centers. River valleys are consequently V-shaped in cross section. Glacial ice, however, moves so slowly and with such even distribution of pressure that it has great grinding power even at the edges of its flow. Glacial valleys, therefore, tend to be eroded in broad curves at their bottoms, looking in cross section like the letter "U."

LANDS OF THE PRESENT ICE AGE

Though the ice sheets long ago acknowledged their defeat over most parts of the earth, they still have absolute domination over two great land areas, the Antarctic Continent, and Greenland. Upon these immense wastes of glaciation the Ice Age is a present reality.

Antarctica, at the center of which is the South Pole, has an area of about five million square miles. It is nearly as large as the combined areas of Europe and Australia. In all this vast region, nearly valueless to man, there is not one tree, nor a single land animal larger than an insect. For most of its extent it is a lofty plateau, rising at the South Pole to an altitude of eleven thousand feet. Probably not more than one hundred square miles of Antarctica are exposed to the atmosphere. The rest is permanently covered with a glacial icecap, sloping very gradually on all sides from the center toward the sea.

The ice at the middle of the continent is either stationary or else moves with extreme slowness. The rate of movement increases toward the margins of the land. The ice meets the sea as towering walls, from which great chunks are torn during storms to form icebergs. On some coasts, instead of coming to an end at the continental margin, the ice extends from the land in an unbroken mass stretching far out over the surface of the sea. The Ross Barrier, a floating ice sheet of this kind, covers an area as large as France, and presents to explorers an unbroken cliff face rising from fifty to two hundred feet above the water.

Greenland, though not the continent it appears to be on a Mercator's projection, is still the largest island in the world, with a total area of 827,000 square miles. Except for a narrow coastline which is ice-free during the brief summer, Greenland is entirely overlaid with a single continuous glacier through which only a few elevated rock masses protrude. The ice is believed to be over one thousand feet thick, and slopes very gradually toward the coasts. As in Antarctica, the ice advances most rapidly at the edges of the mass, moving down into coastal valleys and fiords with a speed which sometimes reaches 125 feet per day. Here too, icebergs are formed, and as they move down into shipping lanes they threaten ocean liners with collisions such as that which sank the Titanic.

Both Greenland and Antarctica have very important influences on the weather of the entire earth. From their icecaps cold winds sweep out in all directions, and because of the power and constancy of the air currents, these regions are known as the earth's "wind poles." The fiercest winds in the world are regularly present in the Antarctic regions, in certain portions of which *average* annual wind velocity is fifty miles per hour.

DIASTROPHISM

Wind, water, and ice, the leveling forces of earth, which are always seeking to lower the land, are sometimes abetted and sometimes counteracted by diastrophism, the deformation of the earth's crust.

The northern part of the Atlantic coast of the United States is sinking slowly, through diastrophism. This sinking is especially great from Connecticut to Virginia, where Chesapeake Bay and New York Bay are the outstanding coastal features. They are both the channels of former rivers, which eroded the land down so near sea-level that a slight sinking of the coast land caused their submergence below the sea. Soundings in the waters south of Long Island show the existence of a deep channel cut like a groove across the continental shelf. This channel is interpreted as a former part of the Hudson River valley, when the entire coast was much higher than at present. As the land sank, the ocean forced itself up into the channel, so that today the waters of the Hudson River are affected by the tides as far north as Albany.

Courtesy R. W. Coad, Buhl, Idaho

THE MYSTERIOUS SINKING LANDS OF IDAHO

Farther down the Atlantic coast, Florida exhibits an upraised shore line, with few indentations or islands. The Pacific coast has a similar simple outline. Coasts of this simple contour are continental shelves of recent uplift. Since the shelves have been made more or less regular by underwater deposits of eroded materials, when first raised, coastlines have few bays or inlets. They are then worn down by erosion into valleys and low plains only a little above sea-level. A slight sinking of the land thereafter will produce a coast of deep indentations and many islands.

What are the causes for these movements of the earth's crust? This question, like some of the other most basic ones of geology, has been answered in a number of different ways. The earth is believed to be shrinking, either through progressive cooling (a process now open to considerable doubt), by a rearrangement under pressure of the atoms of the materials near the earth's center, or by the rise of lava, which causes the earth above the lava bed to sink to fill the resulting cavity.

Movements of the earth's crust may be in three directions, toward the center of the earth, away from the center, or sideward along the earth's circumference. The segments of the lithosphere underlying the oceans have a greater specific gravity than the continental portions, as has been ascertained by comparing the weight of a given mass over land and over the oceans. As the earth shrinks the wedge-shaped segments of the earth readjust themselves inwardly. The oceanic segments, descending with greater force, crowd in ahead of the continental segments, forcing them upward with relation to the heavier segments under water. Since the ocean beds are deepened by this movement toward the earth's center, some of the ocean water is drained off the continental shelves, exposing more land to the atmosphere. So the eroded and lowered continents are partially restored to man again.

THE SEA: MOTHER OF MOUNTAINS

The sinking of earth segments toward the center of the globe makes the arcs of the outer surface of the lithosphere too large to be crowded into the new and smaller circumference. The result is that the outer edges of the segments thrust against one another, bending and wrinkling them. Wherever the surface rocks are exceptionally weak, or the side thrust of the crust is especially strong, there folding and wrinkling will take place. Such a process is especially likely to occur at the edges of continents, where the beds of soft sedimentary rock are the thickest. Furthermore, the powerful thrusts given by the large and heavy oceanic segments have their most intense effect at the continental shelves. The intense compression upon the beds of sedimentary or volcanic rock in these regions forces them to yield upward. By this process the rock layers may be closely folded, broken through, or even overturned, so that the rock strata visible in exposed mountain sides frequently depart greatly from their originally more or less horizontal position. If the compressed rock layers are so thin that they can be wrinkled or tightly folded, a mountain range is the result; if the rock layers are thick and highly resistant, they are bulged outward as plateaus.

The uplifting of rock beds to form mountains or plateaus should not be thought of as a process occurring with extreme

Courtesy Northern Pacific Railway

MOUNTAINS ARE GIGANTIC WRINKLES IN EARTH'S CRUST

violence at present. Some of the geologic ages were distinguished by periods of great and widespread diastrophic adjustments of the earth's crust, and perhaps at these times the earth was continuously and violently convulsed in mountain-building movements of great breadth. The present adjustments, however, while occasionally of great violence from the human point of view, producing disastrous earthquakes, are almost insignificant compared with the extent of movement necessary to lift mountain systems.

Earthquakes, which are associated both with diastrophism and with volcanic activity, are perpetually occurring. The earth's crust is trembling somewhere at all times, but most of these movements are too slight to be detected except by very sensitive instruments.

One of the greatest earthquakes within the memory of man occurred at Lisbon, Portugal, in 1755. Not only were great destruction and loss of life wrought in the city itself, but more than a million square miles were shaken in Portugal, Spain, southern France and northern Africa. Great waves produced by the earth movements (the so-called "tidal waves") rose forty feet high on the Portuguese coast, and raced across the broad Atlantic to the West Indies, where they were observed hours later.

The greatest known height which such a wave has attained is ninety-three feet, observed during the Japanese earthquake of 1896. After an earthquake on the west coast of South America, the resulting waves were noted in Japan, ten thousand miles away.

Another great quake with which we are all familiar was the Japanese catastrophe of 1923. The center of the quake, where most violent motion occurred, was under water. Part of the sea bottom was raised nearly three-quarters of a mile relative to neighboring portions. The island of Oshima was moved twelve and one-half feet to the northeast.

VULCANISM

Of all the sudden manifestations of earth processes, there is none to compare with volcanic eruptions in sublimity and terrifying splendor. Volcanoes have so impressed human beings wherever they occurred that they figure largely in the mythology and superstitions of many nations. Volcanic vents were regarded by the ancients as the openings into Hades. In the quaint miracle plays of the Middle Ages, the stage device called "Hell Mouth," from which issued roaring sounds and painted flames, and into which the Devil pitchforked sinful mortals, was probably a representation of a volcanic opening, which these simple people believed led into Hell. To us who live today volcanoes are no less impressive, but we try to understand their geological meaning and their significance to human beings.

We have read how the volcanic mountains of Jorullo in Mexico and Camiguin in the Philippine Islands were rapidly produced by lava rising to the earth's surface. These occurrences are examples of the process called *vulcanism*. The ejection of lava and cinders into the atmosphere, like upward diastrophic movements, has added large areas to the earth's habitable land surface.

The material of vulcanism is known as *magma* when under the earth's crust. As it is forced toward the outermost layers of the lithosphere by the pressure of the gases within it, if it finds no outlet to the surface it may solidify between strata as beds of igneous rock. But if it succeeds in finding an opening, an eruption, gentle or violent but always impressive, is the result.

The consistency of the magma, its internal pressure, and the size of the volcanic opening determine the type of eruption. The enormous volcanoes which built the Hawaiian Islands up from the ocean floor seldom erupt with extreme destructiveness. This is because their openings are large, permitting the lava to well

Courtesy Field Museum of Natural History

SOLIDIFIED LAVA

quietly up to the surface. If the lava rises high enough in the Hawaiian craters, it overflows their rims and solidifies on the upper slopes of the volcanic cones. When the quantity of lava is greater, it flows as a fiery river many miles down the Hawaiian slopes, burning forests and villages in its path. Though the lava-covered land is temporarily unfit for agriculture, the disintegration of the lava finally forms a soil of extreme richness.

But if the vent of the volcano is constricted, or the magma is under great pressure, the eruption may be of explosive violence, bursting volcanic mountains asunder, blowing islands completely out of existence, or destroying large cities and their inhabitants.

Vesuvius is probably the most famous volcano in the world because of the frequency of its eruptions and the literature written about them. It is of the explosive type, and ejects both lava and cinders, such as those under which the Roman cities of Pompeii and Herculaneum were smothered.

Probably no eruption since history was written compares in magnitude and violence with the Krakatoa eruption in 1883. Krakatoa is a small island in Sunda Strait between Java and Sumatra. Prior to the eruption of its volcano, earthquakes and subterranean rumblings were noticed on the island for several months. At length three terrific explosions occurred, blowing about two-thirds of the island into the sea, with a concussion that was heard three thousand miles distant. The waves which were produced traveled halfway around the globe, climbing far up low coasts and drowning over thirty thousand people. The volcanic dust was projected twenty miles high, and circulated through the atmosphere for more than a year, producing markedly brilliant sunsets all over the globe.

Still more recent and nearer home was the eruption in 1902 of Mount Pelée, a volcano which dominates the north end of Martinique in the French West Indies. On the west coast the populous and charming city of St. Pierre was built just under the mountain's shoulder. Many eruptions before 1902 should have warned the inhabitants of their danger, but although the mountain showered dust, rumbled, and shook the earth, the people expected to have time to flee should any serious peril threaten.

Courtesy Field Museum of Natural History

AN ERUPTION OF MOUNT VESUVIUS

For two days the signs of approaching violence increased. Clouds of gas and cinders belched high into the air above the mountain; horses were suffocated by gas in the St. Pierre streets, and all the telegraph cables from the island were broken.

The climax occurred on the morning of May 8, 1902. With explosive sounds a great cloud of hot gas, ashes, and burning dust grew high into the air above the summit. The cloud was described as being like a huge cauliflower in shape, and with purplish folds shot through with brilliant flashes of lightning. Rushing down the mountain side with the speed of a hurricane wind, the hot cloud swept through St. Pierre with such violence that many buildings were knocked down. The inhabitants, with two known exceptions, were all killed in a very few minutes, either by suffocation, or by the heat of the incandescent dust, which burned off clothing and seared flesh almost instantly. Such parts of the

Courtesy Union Pacific System

THE FAMOUS GEYSER, "OLD FAITHFUL"

city as were not burned or overturned were half buried under cinders and ash.

Today the city is still a desolate ruin, though a few courageous natives have established themselves there, building their huts from the ruins of the former buildings. Recent advances in the science of the behavior of volcanoes, known as vulcanology, make it possible to predict with more or less accuracy when eruptions of craters of the Pelée type are about to occur. With this assurance human beings may again find it worth while to invest their toil in buildings and farms on volcanic slopes once considered unsafe for habitation.

In addition to volcanic eruptions, geysers and hot springs are processes of vulcanism, since their heat is derived from slowly cooling masses of igneous rock hidden under the earth's surface. Geysers are water pools or natural wells which hurl columns of water or steam into the air at more or less regular intervals, under the pressure of closely confined steam. Hot springs differ from geysers mainly in the fact that they flow continuously, a fact due either to the size of their outlets or to their low steam pressure. Within recent years many geysers of the western United States have become hot springs, losing eruptive vigor as the rock beneath them cooled. Neither geysers nor hot springs are volcanic phenomena of great geological importance, since they add nothing but a few local deposits of mineral salts to the earth's exterior.

GEOLOGY'S GIFT TO MODERN MAN

Because of the tireless curiosity and the scientific devotion of the founders of modern geology, we who live today are the inheritors of a large body of geological fact and theory, through which we can understand many of the processes which have produced and are still modifying the present contours of our world. So many of the data of geology have been lost through the course of ages, that our record is, and always will be, incomplete; yet we have learned enough to control certain geological processes in part, and can adjust our human program to the much larger number of factors beyond our control. In any case, geology enables us to look at the earth's features from a profitable viewpoint: not as being the result of a single act of divine creation, nor of the mysterious union and interaction of Plato's four "elements"; but as the product of a continuous process, whose past effects we can understand, and whose future we can in some measure predict.

In the realm of knowledge for its own sake, we have been granted an understanding of the creation of the globe as a detached fragment of the sun, and of the division of this globe's surface into areas of land and water. We believe we know the approximate age of the earth and how life developed from its earliest and simplest forms to its last and most complex ones. On the practical side, geology has made our lives both richer and more secure. It enables us to trace broken strata to the places where mineral treasures such as coal, gold, or petroleum are hidden, and to determine the condition of the bedrock on which we erect our skyscrapers. Modern geology showed us how to map out the areas subject to destructive earthquakes. Today it is even becoming possible to warn people living in volcanic regions when dangerous eruptions are impending.

ENIGMAS FOR GEOLOGISTS

Despite the great advances made by geology in the last 150 years, we are realizing more and more how great is the number of riddles awaiting solution. Every new fact learned seems to widen the scope of the unknown, and beckons us onward to realms of science not yet even charted.

The dim hints of cosmic radiations whose definite existence has been proved by Compton and others, have raised new problems of interest to scientists in many fields. We are far from knowing the effect upon earth's geological and life processes of these rays, so powerful that scientists can locate few spots to which they do not penetrate. Nor can any shields be devised dense enough to exclude them from the laboratory.

If the moon really was torn bodily from the Pacific, as has been hypothesized, what effect did so great a cataclysm have upon the rotation, water-distribution, and climates of the shuddering earth?

Was there indeed in Paleozoic time a Gondwanaland—the super-continent believed to have spanned the southern oceans, linking Africa, South America, Australia, India, and Antarctica in one mighty whole? Acceptance of this hypothesis would help to explain for biologists the surprising likenesses of plant and animal species now widely separated by the oceans.

Look at a model of the globe, as did Wegener, the modern German geologist, and note the astonishing dovetailing of the Atlantic coasts of Africa and South America. Were these two continents, like battered pieces of a jigsaw puzzle, once united in a single mighty land-mass? Are the lands of the New World and the Old still drifting apart, as Wegener claimed, widening the Atlantic rift of "unplumbed, salt, estranging sea"?

The origin of life is a problem for the geologist as well as for the biologist. Modern science raised this problem by looking for a more precise and less symbolic explanation than the religious account of the Creation. As yet it has found no satisfactory answer. But men of learning deny that life is anywhere capable

THE HOT WATER BASINS OF MAMMOTH HOT SPRINGS
Limestone and other minerals are deposited by the cooling water in broad terraces or basins. Sometimes these basins are brilliantly colored by the presence of algae and diatoms.

of arising spontaneously at present. All life being born today, it is claimed, from the simplest to the most complex forms, is originated by the reproduction of organisms already existing. But was there truly an epoch of creation sometime in the shadowy past, when a favorable combination of temperature, pressure, and radiation permitted inorganic matter to assume the complex chemical forms and the adaptive behavior which we know as life?

Such enigmas as these are awaiting solution, and the advancing front of geological science seems destined to do its part in solving them, even though other problems as great be raised in their train.

EARTH'S UNPLUMBED CENTER

Since we can penetrate the earth only to a short distance, our direct knowledge of it is confined to a mere surface film, extremely thin compared with the earth's total volume. Our beliefs about the earth's interior are therefore based on inferences from known facts, rather than on direct observations of this most impenetrable portion of our globe.

By comparing temperatures at different depths in mine shafts we have learned that the temperature increases about one degree centigrade for every hundred feet of depth, at least as far as we have gone down. If the geothermal gradient, as this increase of temperature is called, continued at the same rate all the way to the central core the heat of the interior would be terrific. But the hottest temperature is not likely to be much more than from 7000° to 9000° Fahrenheit, for greater heat would tend to destroy the outer crust.

The density of materials inside the earth, like the temperature, increases with greater depth. Because of the enormous weight of layer pressing upon layer, the density of the inner core is about five times as great as that of surface rock. If we could duplicate this pressure in a laboratory, we might be able to demonstrate how it must affect the materials deep within the earth. But such a pressure is far beyond our present power to create.

We can divide the earth's interior roughly into three concentric zones or shells. The outer shell, about 750 miles thick, con-

Courtesy Field Museum of Natural History

MODEL ILLUSTRATING THE GEOLOGISTS' CONCEPTION OF THE EARTH'S INTERIOR

tains primarily rocks of various kinds. The next shell, about as thick as the first, probably consists of combinations of sulphur with iron and nickel. Finally, the inside core, with a radius of about 2,200 miles, is supposed to be made up principally of iron and nickel in a solid state.

EARTH'S CENTER: LIQUID OR SOLID?

A number of scientists, some of them of considerable prestige, deny the solidity of the earth's core. They argue that the great heat within the earth would melt even the metals with the highest melting points, and that the earth's interior must therefore be molten. The majority of scientists, however, insist that the pressure of the earth's outer shells upon the core is so great that iron and nickel would be held in a solid state no matter how hot they might be.

The seismograph is an instrument based on the principle of a pendulum, by which a written record is made of the duration, intensity, and location of earthquakes. It is proving very use-

THE CAUSE OF EARTH TIDES

Although we ordinarily think of tides as phenomena of the oceans, the pull of the moon acts on the land as well.

Courtesy Yerkes Observatory

ful in solving the problem of subterranean conditions. By measuring the velocities and types of earthquake waves recorded by the seismograph, we can conclude with some assurance that the earth is solid. A liquid can transmit only those earthquake waves which are of a compressional type. The seismograph, however, intercepts both compressional earthquake waves and those of a second type, the distortional or transverse waves. Only a solid is capable of transmitting waves of this second type, so that we know that for at least a depth of hundreds of miles the earth is solid.

The moon's gravitational pull, which causes tides, acts upon the solid part of the earth as well as upon the oceans. It has been found that the earth's crust at Pittsburgh sometimes bulges outward in a tidal movement as much as two feet. The earth-tides do not disprove the rigidity of the earth, since rigidity is a variable quantity, depending on the distorting force. Steel, although very strong, would not be completely rigid if subjected to the same attraction which the moon exerts upon the earth. It is claimed that if the earth were liquid its tidal distortion from a spherical form would be far greater than it is.

ELEMENTS OF THE EARTH'S CORE

How do we know that the central core of our planet is made up of iron and nickel? The composition of meteorites, which have come plunging down to earth from interplanetary space as "shooting stars," furnishes us with our evidence. They consist primarily of solid iron and nickel. Since all astronomical bodies are composed of similar materials, meteorites and the earth might be expected to contain about the same proportions of elements. Since the earth's surface layer contains only five per cent iron and very little nickel, we must look elsewhere for the great quantities of these metals which the earth must contain. Where, then, should we expect the metals to be, if not in the inaccessible inner portions of the earth?

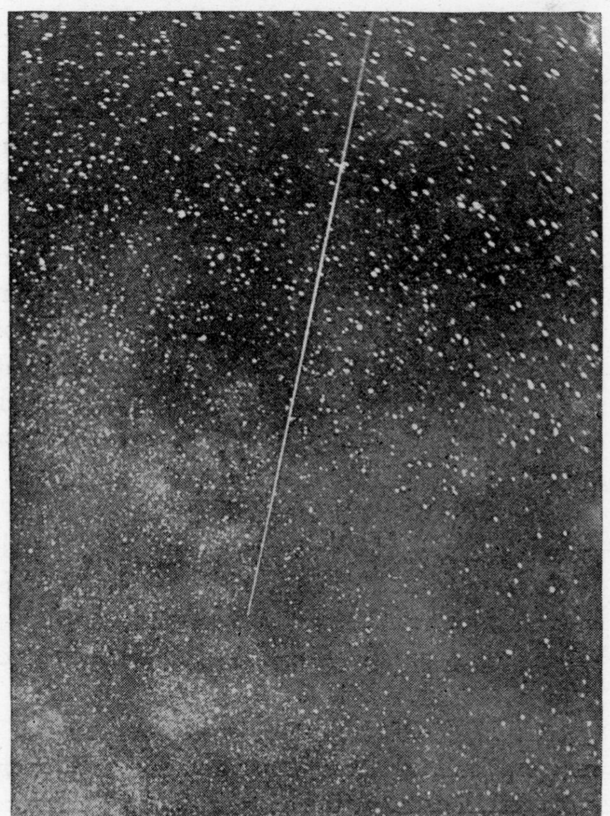

A METEOR TRAIL
Meteors may be clues to substances in the earth's interior.

Courtesy Yerkes Observatory

Finally, a comparison of densities leads us to conclude that the iron and nickel are concentrated in the central core, since the average density of the earth is about five times that of water, while the density of a surface rock is only about twice that of water. It is reasonable to assume, then, that the heavier metals, iron and nickel, are located at the center, to bring the density of the earth as a whole up to its known value.

Conflicting and partial evidence makes it impossible for us to come to a definite conclusion as to either the solidity or the material of the earth's interior at present. We must, therefore, content ourselves with leaving this riddle unsolved until we are enlightened by future scientific discoveries.

THE EARTH-MAGNET

Most children are more or less familiar with magnets, which they regard as toys to be used in picking up tacks or iron filings. This power of magnets to attract other metals to them has been known for ages, but until recent centuries magnetism was little understood. It was considered a curiosity rather than a potential tool for mankind.

Today we know that magnetism is produced in certain metals including iron, steel, chromium, and nickel, by a rearrangement of their molecules. This rearrangement may be produced either by bringing the metals into contact with existing magnets, or by electricity. The second process produces an electro-magnet, an indispensable unit in telephones, phonographs, and radio loud-speakers.

It is not generally recognized that the earth itself is a gigantic magnet. Somehow, by a process we do not fully understand, the iron and nickel of the earth's interior became magnetized. By comparing terrestrial magnetic readings of the past with those of the present, we find that the magnetic power of the earth's core is slowly being dissipated.

All magnets, including horseshoe and bar magnets, electro-magnets, and the earth itself, have areas where the attraction is the strongest, located at the ends or poles. Therefore, a compass, con-

DIAGRAMMATIC REPRESENTATION OF THE MAGNETIC FIELD SURROUNDING THE EARTH

Courtesy Carnegie Institution of Washington

sisting of a magnetized needle which is free to move about, always tries to align itself in a north and south direction, that is, so that its long axis will be parallel to the long axis of the earth-magnet.

GEOGRAPHICAL POLES AND MAGNETIC POLES

We should expect the magnetic poles of the earth to be located at the North and South Poles, the two extremities of the earth's axis of rotation. Indeed, as long as the use of the compass was known to navigators, it was believed until 1492 to point due north and south. Slight variations of the compass needle from true north had been noted before that year, but were attributed to transient causes or to careless reading of the compass. But in 1492, when Columbus' vessels beat their way out into the dreaded and un-

Courtesy U. S. Geological Survey

SWELTERING DEATH VALLEY, 276 FEET BELOW SEA-LEVEL
This is the lowest dip known in dry land.

known Atlantic, the compass began to behave queerly, veering farther and farther from the position the terrified navigators believed it should occupy. This nearly provoked a panic among the sailors, who thought that malignant spirits were wilfully twisting the compass to confuse them.

Today we know that the magnetic poles of the earth, where the forces of attraction are vertically downward, are not located at the North and South Poles at the ends of the earth's axis. For some reason, the north pole of magnetism is an area far distant from the North Pole and is located in the Boothia Peninsula northwest of Hudson's Bay. The South Magnetic Pole is 250 miles inland on the Antarctic Continent, west of the Ross Sea. Now that we know the approximate locations of these areas, we can make allowance for the variation of the compass, and so navigate accurately.

Expressed in map-makers' terms, the North Magnetic Pole is located at approximately 71 degrees north latitude, and 96 degrees west longitude. The South Magnetic Pole is at about 72 degrees south latitude and 156 degrees east longitude.

THEORIES OF EARTH MAGNETISM

Returning to the problem of how the earth became magnetized, we are faced with the fact that high temperatures seem to destroy the power of magnets entirely. Since the earth's interior is extremely hot, according to our present knowledge the metallic core ought to be incapable of magnetization. It may be that the intense pressure at the earth's center makes magnetism possible at a higher temperature there than at the earth's surface. If this is not the case, then the magnetic portions must consist of a layer of matter nearer the surface where the heat is less great. If this should be the case, an irregular distribution of the layer might account for the distance between the geographical poles and the magnetic poles.

One of the most interesting theories as to terrestrial magnetism suggests that it arises from the rotation of the earth at great speed. Rotation of an electrically charged body in a laboratory produces a magnetic field; but rotation of an uncharged body does not do so, at least not at speeds attainable at present. Perhaps a new set of conditions arises under rotation at the earth's speed, producing a magnetic field. In that case, however, we should expect the poles of magnetism to be at the ends of the axis of rotation, that is, at the North and South Poles.

THE UNDERGROUND FRONTIER

Little by little man has pushed outward the periphery of his knowledge. Most parts of the dry land, even many of the inhospitable glacial areas of Greenland and Antarctica, have been explored. The frontiers of the earth's surface are nearly at an end.

Where then shall the thirst for scientific adventure and exploration be quenched? There are proposals to visit space outside the planet by means of rocket-ships, but these are as yet purely fanciful, and will be realized only in the very distant future, if at all. Turning our eyes downward instead of upward, we see the possibility of exploration far deeper into the earth than has ever yet been attempted. Serious proposals have been made to drill shafts for laboratory and experimental purposes considerably deeper into the earth's crust than our deepest wells and mines.

The two principal handicaps to any such enterprise are, of course, the great heat and pressure which would be encountered before we could get very far. But these handicaps are much more likely to be overcome than the inescapable one of the great distances to be spanned in making lunar or interplanetary voyages. Even scientists would scarcely wish to spend lifetimes or years on these trips, far from their bases of supplies where conditions are controlled. Compared with those of space, the distances to be traversed within the earth are very small.

Exploration of the earth's depths may be expected to furnish us with better evidence than any yet known as to the state of its inner materials. It may also solve the mystery of terrestrial magnetism. In a more practical way, by having access to the earth's deeply buried portions we may some day be able to tap the vast fund of heat waiting for our use. We can then cease worrying about the depletion of the natural resources of the earth's surface

Courtesy Yerkes Observatory

THE PLANET JUPITER

NEW IDEAS OF TIME

THE STREAM OF TIME

THE WHOLE LIQUID, ever-changing mass of society is like a great river—broad, deep, and long, flowing in an unending sweep down the long valley of time. Unlike a river, however, which ordinarily moves more rapidly at its surface than in its depths, the surface waters of society are slow. It is the swift thought of the dreamers in the deeps—the Platos, the Lucretiuses, the Leibnitzes, the Newtons, the Einsteins—that flows on ahead, carrying along in its wake the minds of the masses. It is the waters of the channel beneath that must meet the obstacles of the bottom, the sunken trees, the boulders, and the submerged rocky ledges. The great minds find ways to conquer these obstacles of ignorance and superstition and prejudice and fear. It is leadership of the great minds which presses ahead, and it is their ideas which diffuse gradually through the waters of the world.

One of the striking things that stand out in the history of great thinkers is the prominent position of mathematicians. They speak a language of high structural efficiency and have been able in many cases to surmount thought difficulties more easily than men who speak in the clumsy language of everyday life.

Courtesy Lick Observatory

WHERE MEN STUDY PROBLEMS OF TIME AND SPACE
The facts of time and space are discovered at the great observatories.

A NEW BROOM FOR THE STAR-SWEEPERS

One of the fields for thought which fascinated the minds of men from the earliest periods of the evolution of civilization, was that of the unfathomed sky over their heads. Pythagoras, Kepler, and Newton all puzzled their way toward solutions of the problems of the heavens. Newton's monumental work was made possible by the invention of mathematical techniques by Descartes; in a similar way, it was the work of a German geometrician named Riemann which made possible to a considerable extent the startling advances of Minkowski, Einstein, and the other scientists who brought forth the theories of relativity. Einstein, whose name has come to symbolize the obscure, the mysterious, and the profound, actually founded a system which, although it is not simple and still generally not understood, explains such phenomena as space, time, and matter in a much more rational and satisfying way than could that of Newton. Relativity is merely a tool in the hands of scientists; it is a complex tool, to be sure, but its complexity is like that of a microscope—a device which is confusing at first, but ultimately useful. Without a microscope a drop of water is a deceptively simple thing. It looks like an empty globule of clear liquid. But through a microscope, a complex instrument, the drop of water takes on an entirely different aspect, one considerably nearer the truth than the impression received by the naked eye. The crystal clarity of the water drop becomes a complicated little world of swimming creatures which the poor power of human senses cannot detect.

Newton, dealing with a set of absolutes, like empty drops of water, perfected a picture of the universe which seemed to be a simple and easily understood whole. But the universe is not simple—no more than is the drop of water. Any picture of it which seems so is necessarily an inaccurate representation. With the advent of the relativity theorists, all the absolutes began to fade away; the old notions of absolute space, time, and matter were doomed. Peculiar contradictions which had puzzled the scientists armed only with the Newtonian hypotheses were explained under the new theories. One of the most thought-provoking of the new concepts was that of a space-time which did away with the artificial distinction of the Newtonian mechanics. The old ideas of space and time were only "common sense," anyone could understand them. Time, according to the old idea, was merely a thing which could be measured on clocks and calendars. Space was merely an empty place in which things happened.

But the physicists, bringing forth their atom-bombarding machines and their graphs, were saying that space was not empty. This was a notion which conflicted with common sense. Anyone could tell that space was empty; if one reached out one's fingers to touch it there was nothing there. One could certainly see through it, and odors and sounds seemed to travel through it unhampered. In short, the evidence which common sense used was merely that of the senses. But fruitful hypotheses, stirring stimulants to men's imaginations, asserted that there was something in space, something so finely divided that the crude sense of

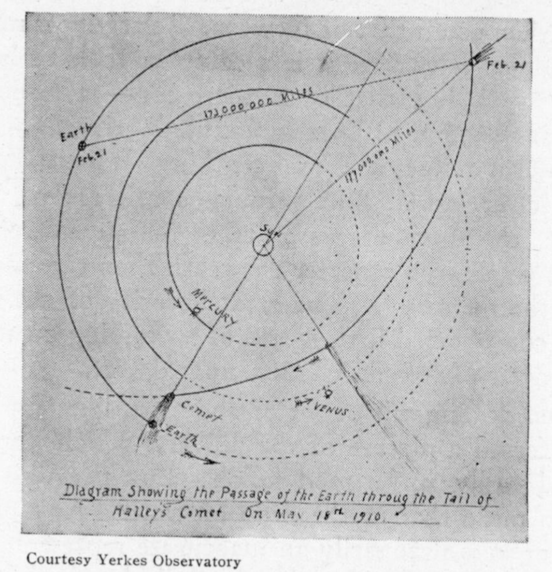

Courtesy Yerkes Observatory

THE EARTH AND THE COMET'S TAIL

A visible meteor shower from the tail of Halley's comet proved that it contained meteoric matter.

man could not perceive it. Floating about in the air, in the churning network of waves and rays and atoms and forces, are many things which the senses cannot pick out for man, but they are there, none the less. For example, the air is now filled with a hundred different voices and sounds which the ear cannot hear. These are the tones of radio, borne on electromagnetic waves. Without a radio receiver they can not be heard; relying solely on his senses, man would scarcely believe that they were there. But whether or not man has a radio receiver, the waves are there. Like horsemen in cloaks of invisibility they ride their waves constantly, whether the human senses can perceive them or not.

THE MOVING MOMENT

In a similar way, the senses give an inaccurate idea of what time is. These primitive ideas, frozen into a primitive language, have done much to hinder the growth of intelligent understanding of the world. Thought of as an *object,* time, by dint of the associations and implications of the name, is a separate entity, endowed with such qualities as beginning and ending, which are common to objects. The senses perceive time as such an objective reality, but here again the evidence of common sense is in error.

Time is no objective reality. Everyone has a sensation of time, but this sense of time is in reality a series of times, a rhythm which characterizes life itself. For individuals time is divided into three intervals, the past, the future, and a moving moment of the present which is sensed relentlessly gliding from the past into the future. A person knows the "now," the present moment, in which he is taking a bite in his apple, swinging a golf club to meet the ball, or standing with his hand on a doorknob. These moments fall into a definite series, an order: the moments of twisting the doorknob, the moments of pulling the door open, and the moments of walking through the doorway. One dot of time follows after another, and man measures time in terms of this order, which is real and definite for him. He measures it with his wrist watch or with his calendar; he also measures it in changes which take place in his own physical life—he ages moment by moment, he watches a cut heal over, and he feels the pulsation of his heart.

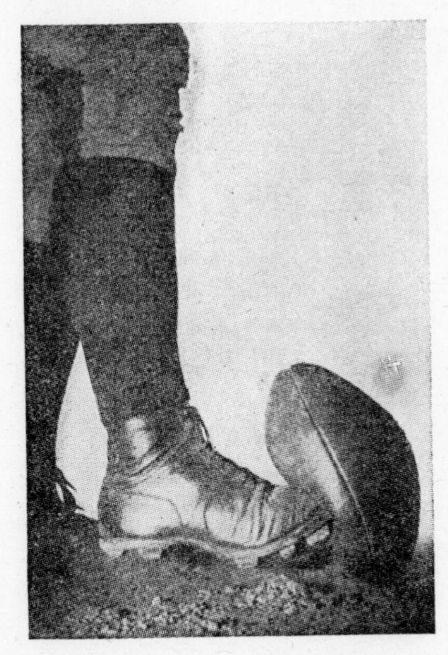

"NOW" IS BUT A FLEETING INSTANT

Even as the camera recorded the impact of the player's toe against the football, the action became a thing of the past.

Courtesy Massachusetts Institute of Technology

MEASUREMENT OF TIME
Man can not measure time itself, but only a series of events which he senses as occurring in time.

Courtesy Galloway Terra-Cotta Company

This concept of time is organic in man, apparently, and some sort of rhythmic pulsation is inherent in the processes of life itself. Man also sees it taking place in the physical world about him. In unending rhythmic succession the waves of the sea break toward him as he stands on the windy beach. Day follows night, and spring follows winter in ceaseless cycle. Man expresses the rhythmic quality of his life in art—in his dancing, his poetry, and his song. He delights in the hum of the pulsation of a well-tuned motor, and an aesthetic urge for order is part of his make-up. As far as it goes there is nothing wrong in this; for a primitive mind it is the natural way to think of time. But when the force of contemplation and of scientific thought began to be felt, there was another aspect of time which entered his consciousness.

This was brought about by the fact that while he saw things move, or perceived with his senses the unending motion and change of himself and the world about him, as soon as he labeled an apparently moving wall of water with the word "wave," he stopped the motion. Instead of a ceaselessly pounding surf which never stood still to be examined, he had a concept. This new game of labels fascinated his mind. He wanted to discuss waves and trees and men, and the terms which he could utter to denote the things he perceived about him became real to him. They were useful, and he made them still more useful until he began to believe that the terms had existences in themselves instead of being mere tools with which he might more easily examine and generalize about the world.

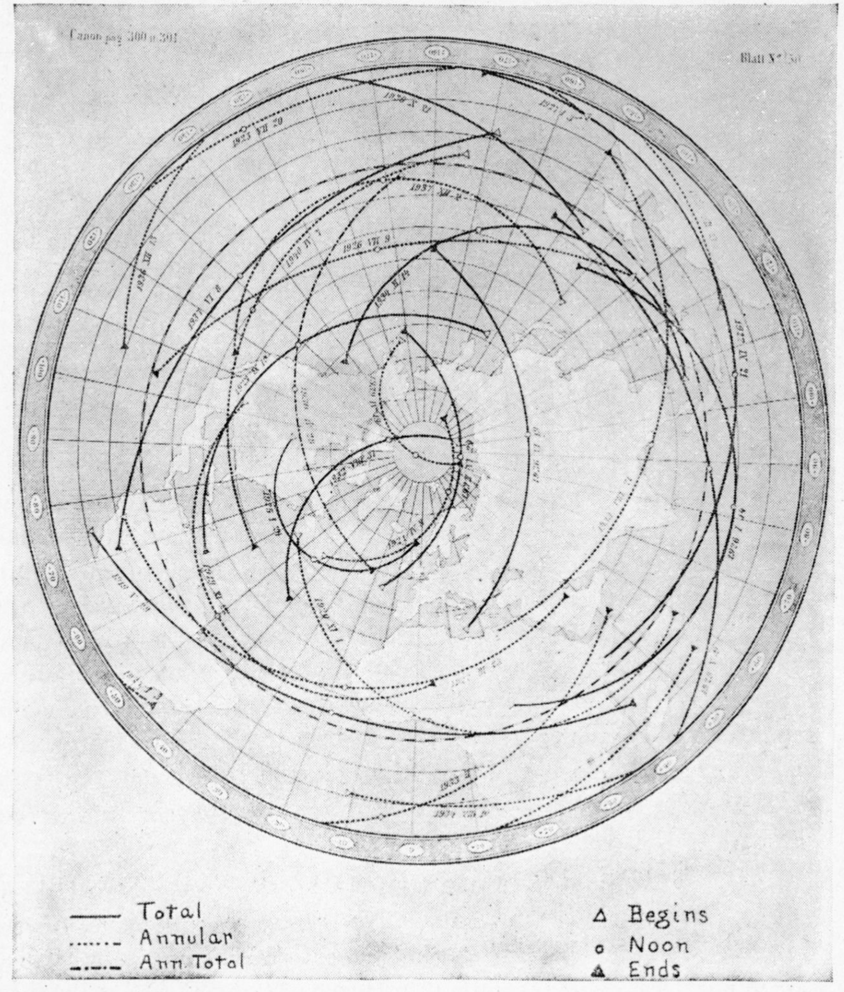

Courtesy Yerkes Observatory

A PROBLEM OF TIME AND SPACE

Astronomers have determined the location and time of eclipses for the years from 1919 to 1940.

He invented three terms, ice, water, and vapor. He saw the three—floating on the wintry seas, rolling in great rivers, and rising from boiling springs. These were words for three stages in a process which depended on applications of outside forces on one thing. If he had continued to realize that the three were really nothing but names for phases of the same actual reality, he would have been using language as a tool, but he invested the three terms with an objective reality which they did not have. Water was water—liquid, solid, or gaseous; however, under the unconscious but relentless domination of his thinking by an outmoded, primitive language he still thought in old terms even when he had learned better by experiments.

THE REVOLVING SIGN

With time it was the same story. Man became confused by the world he had created. Various schools of thought sprang up, some holding to the idea that the world was in constant change and that any thinking in "static" terms was a foolish waste of time because the world was not like that. Other schools of thought endlessly discussed their concepts, in which the world stood still for them; they ignored the constant flux in which a dynamic world exists. As usual both were right as well as wrong, for, like the water and ice and steam, both were merely different aspects of the same problem.

If a nearsighted man looks some distance away at an electric theater sign which seems to revolve, he is apt to believe, on the strength of the old saying that "seeing is believing," that the border of the sign actually moves around; so deceptive are his senses. If he draws nearer and watches closely, he sees that there is nothing in the sign but a set of individual blinking electric light bulbs. So it is with time. Time, like the revolving sign, flows endlessly for a given person with a given point of view and facts based on the evidence of his senses. But examined from a different point of view, with refined data, the sign does not revolve at all.

In problems of time the refined data could not be those of the senses; the poor ability of eyesight was soon exhausted by

MOVIES ARE A SUCCESSION OF STILL PICTURES

When these "frames" are projected in speedy succession, an illusion of movement is created.

Courtesy Paramount Pictures, Inc.

billions and trillions of miles. The more refined data were given by the mind. Realizing that "dynamic" and "static" are only mere labels pasted on the facts to be examined, men could understand that a wave of the ocean is actually a changing thing. It is not the same from moment to moment, and on the scale of atoms there is even less constancy than in that of the dimensions which the eyes make possible. But it is often useless merely to stand beside the ocean blinking at it because it is constantly

Courtesy American Museum of Natural History

THIS INSTRUMENT CAN TURN THE CLOCK BACKWARD!
The planetarium projector can show the motions of stars over long periods of years, in a few minutes. Similarly, it can show us how the sky looked a thousand years ago!

in a state of flux. Words which crystallize the process are productive instruments. They do the same thing to dynamic processes that suddenly stopping a rolling wave would do—stopping it still, with the spume hanging in the air, the foam about to wash over the top of the billow, and the surging water and restless energy of the watery body held motionless. By these techniques and only by these techniques is it possible to understand the action of the phenomena of the world.

It is a powerful ability which men's minds have, and as a matter of fact it is actually the ability which makes it possible for men to discover the extent and method of change which is going on. Thus, men would never have made their refinement of elements and molecules and atoms and electrons had it not been for this ability to examine things which do not stop by stopping them mentally, and thinking about them in the abstract. As long as men are conscious of what they are doing when they stop processes in order to examine them, it is a fine and valuable technique; but when they begin to believe that there is an absolute validity in something, simply because it is a word, they soon run amuck, especially if it is a word the only basis of which is "seeing is believing."

AT THE SAME TIME? NO!

An example of this sort of thing is found in the word "simultaneity." In everyday life it seems obvious to the average person that things happen at the same time—that is simultaneously. As an individual stands before his mirror, the image in the mirror seems to move exactly with him; when he picks up the hairbrush, so does the image; when he lifts it up and makes it go through his hair, so does his other self in the mirror. Apparently it is stroke for stroke action at exactly the same time, and no matter how quickly he moves the brush, the figure opposite does not lag and fall behind.

There are a thousand other cases in which the word "simultaneous" seems to have a real meaning. To the scientists, however, it became clear that the word was misleading and an actual impossibility. If the speed of light were infinitely great, there might have been some hope for the discredited word. But the speed of light is not infinitely great, and neither is the speed of nervous impulses traveling through the human body. Thus, although the extent to which the image in the mirror falls behind is so small that it is an impossible thing for human observation to perceive, it is none the less a measurable quantity. It takes a definite, although extremely small amount of time for the light reflected by the person to reach the surface of the looking glass, and it takes another approximately equal interval for the light from the mirror to be carried back to the eye of the person. Another negligible instant is used in the transference of the light image from the eye to the brain. But all these instants added together still consume an amount of time so short that it is impossible for the human perceptions to notice it.

It was when vast distances, such as those from star to star, and earth to star, began to be measured in light-years that strange errors and discrepancies began to appear. It became clear to

Courtesy Lick Observatory

A SOLAR ECLIPSE

The sun looked like this eight minutes before this image registered on the photographic plate.

scientists that the term "simultaneity" would have to be abandoned if a true and undistorted picture of the world were to be achieved. Taking the giant view of the cosmos which has come to be called the Minkowski world, there were obviously no two things which ever happened at one time for all observers. This notion of simultaneous action would necessarily have to mean that for all people, wherever they might be, there could not be two occurrences which took place at identical moments.

If there could conceivably be a dweller on the great golden star Betelgeuse, although except for purposes of explanation there certainly could not be such a person, he might have his notion of two simultaneous happenings. Standing on his fiery home-star he might point his telescope toward the gleaming whiteness of Rigel and see an explosive tremor sweep over the great star. Then turning his glass over the sky he might focus it on the sun which

THE ABERRATION OF LIGHT, A CONSEQUENCE OF THE FACT THAT IT TAKES TIME FOR LIGHT TO MOVE

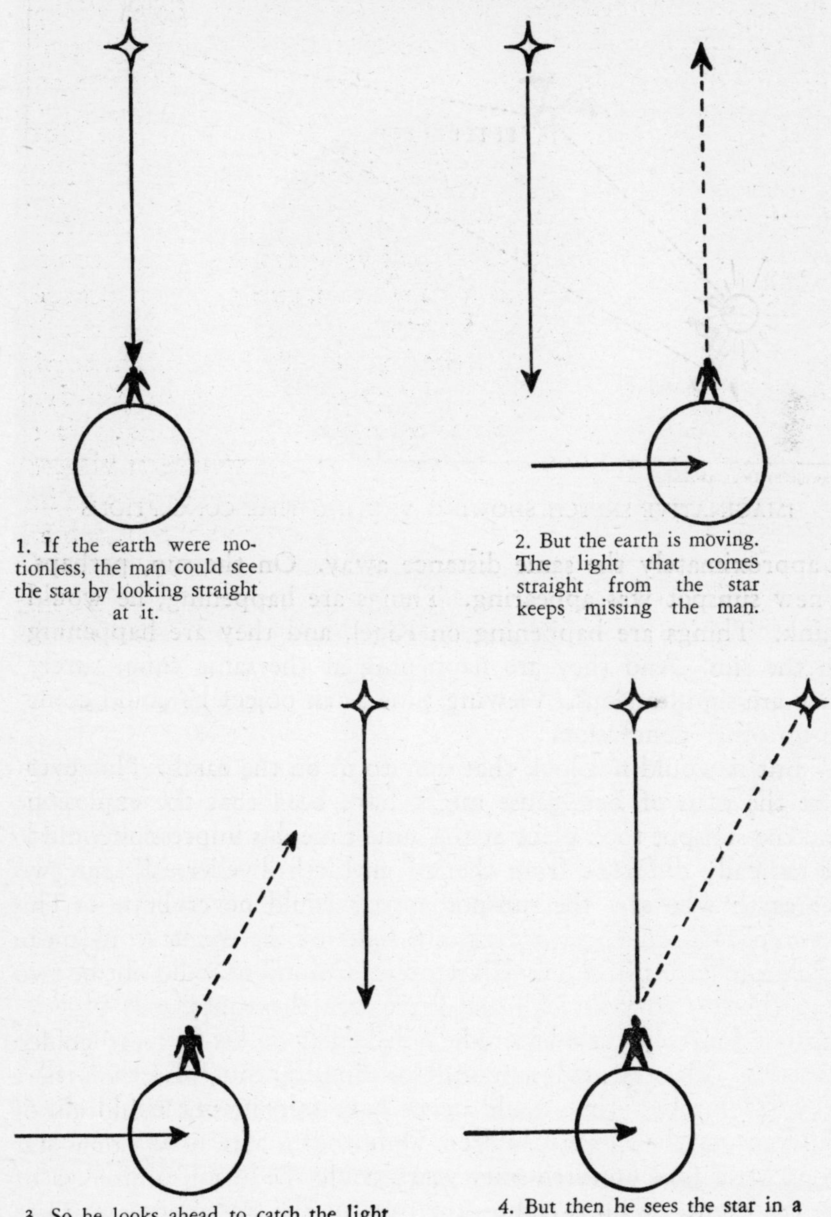

1. If the earth were motionless, the man could see the star by looking straight at it.

2. But the earth is moving. The light that comes straight from the star keeps missing the man.

3. So he looks ahead to catch the light on the fly.

4. But then he sees the star in a position ahead of where it actually is!

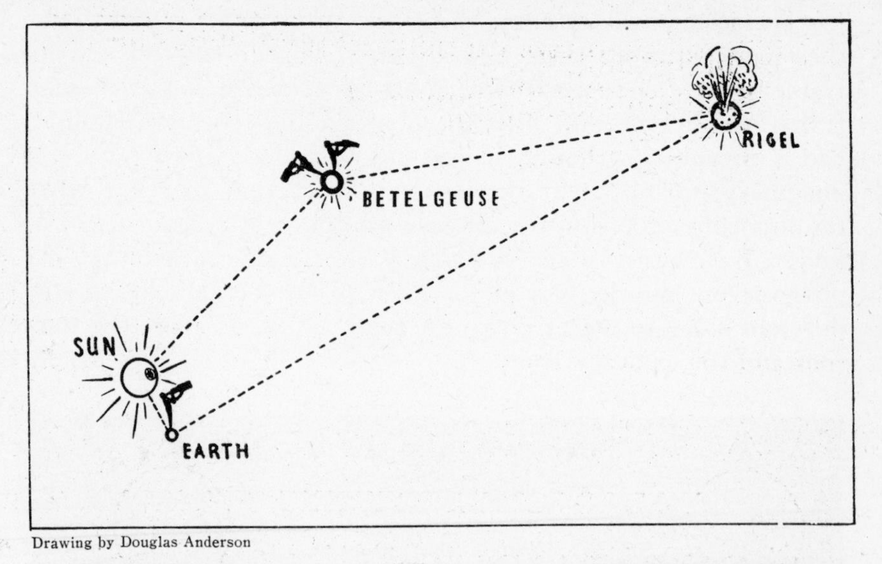

Drawing by Douglas Anderson

IMAGINATIVE SKETCH SHOWING VARYING TIME CONCEPTIONS

is approximately the same distance away. On the sun, perhaps, a new sunspot was appearing. Things are happening, he would think. Things are happening on Rigel, and they are happening on the sun. And they are happening at the same time; surely they are simultaneous. Viewing time as an object he could come to no other conclusion.

But it would not look that way to us on the earth. However sure the man of Betelgeuse might have been that the explosion and the sunspot took place at the same time, his impression would be radically different from that of an earth dweller. A man on the earth who saw the sunspot appear could never hope to see the explosion on Rigel because the light of the event would not reach him in his lifetime. Christopher Columbus, when he was a man thirty-two years old, may have seen the appearance of this sunspot fourteen years before he sailed away on his first voyage to America. Was the explosion on Rigel simultaneous? Earth dwellers of Columbus' time could never have seen it, nor could their children nor their grandchildren. Only today, after many generations, after four hundred sixty years, could the people of the earth see the event. Who is right—the man of the star or the man of the earth? Four hundred sixty years is not a trifling interval.

The scientists have come to believe that neither is right, and they have explained their view by saying that it depends on the frame of reference used. The inhabitant of the earth had one frame of reference; in his limited world the term simultaneity had a meaning, although it was not a general meaning. The imaginary inhabitant of Betelgeuse believed that he knew what simultaneous actions were; for his own frame of reference he *did* know. But neither of the two frames of reference is absolute. An observer on another star or another planet would have a still different story to tell of how near together or far apart the sunspot and the explosion were.

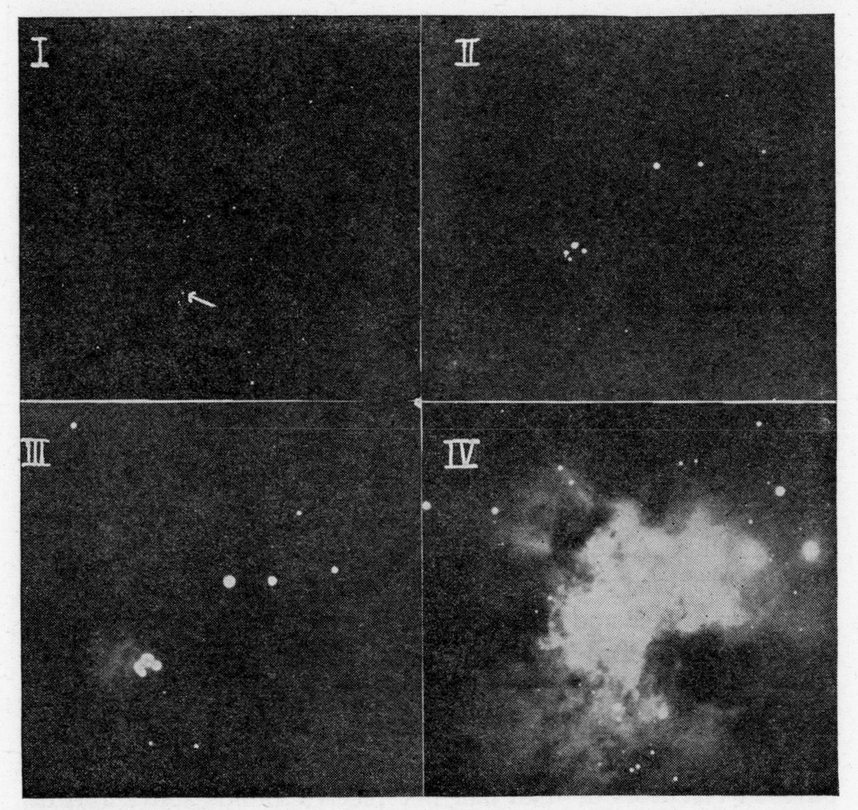

Courtesy Yerkes Observatory

LIGHT, TIME, AND THE PHOTOGRAPHIC PLATE

The first picture is a snapshot; the second frame was exposed twenty minutes; the third, an hour and a half; the fourth, three hours.

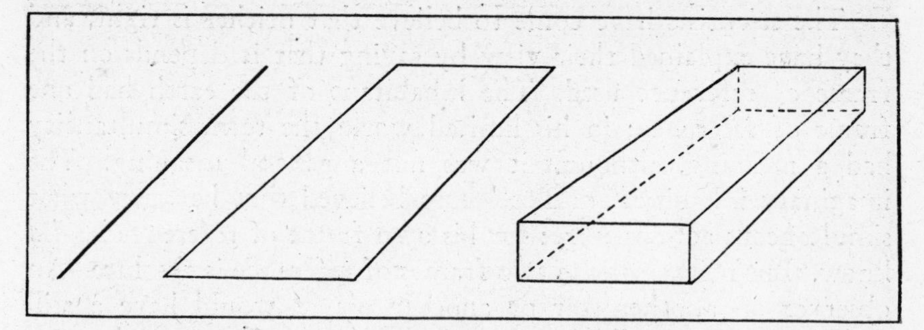

DIAGRAMMATIC REPRESENTATION OF THREE DIMENSIONS
Left, one dimension—the line; center, two dimensions—the plane; right, three dimensions—a solid.

FOUR WAYS TO THINK OF A PIECE OF CAKE

The world of the old thinkers was a world of three dimensions—three mathematical, geometrical directions. One dimension was a line, a dimension of length. The second dimension supplemented the first; it was a plane, a dimension of length and width, measured in square feet or inches or miles. The third dimension included the depth, along with length and width. These three dimensions were the real world as the senses brought it to men. A piece of cake was so long, so wide, and so thick; and so was anything else which men saw and used in everyday life. The map of the three-dimensional world was the Cartesian system of co-ordinates used by mathematicians in the analytical geometry of solids. All of this simple "common sense" geometry fitted in well with the simple world of Newton, the world in which matter and space and time were absolutes. But the absolutes were absolute on woefully weak foundations, for they relied on few more facts than the senses of man could give. And the senses of man can perceive only a small range of the forces abroad in the world. Besides the electromagnetic waves of radio, the unaided physical receptors of man can not receive sounds above and below a certain limited range of tones; there is no apparatus in the human body which can tell an individual directly of the existence and effect of Hertzian waves, X-rays, gamma rays, cosmic rays,

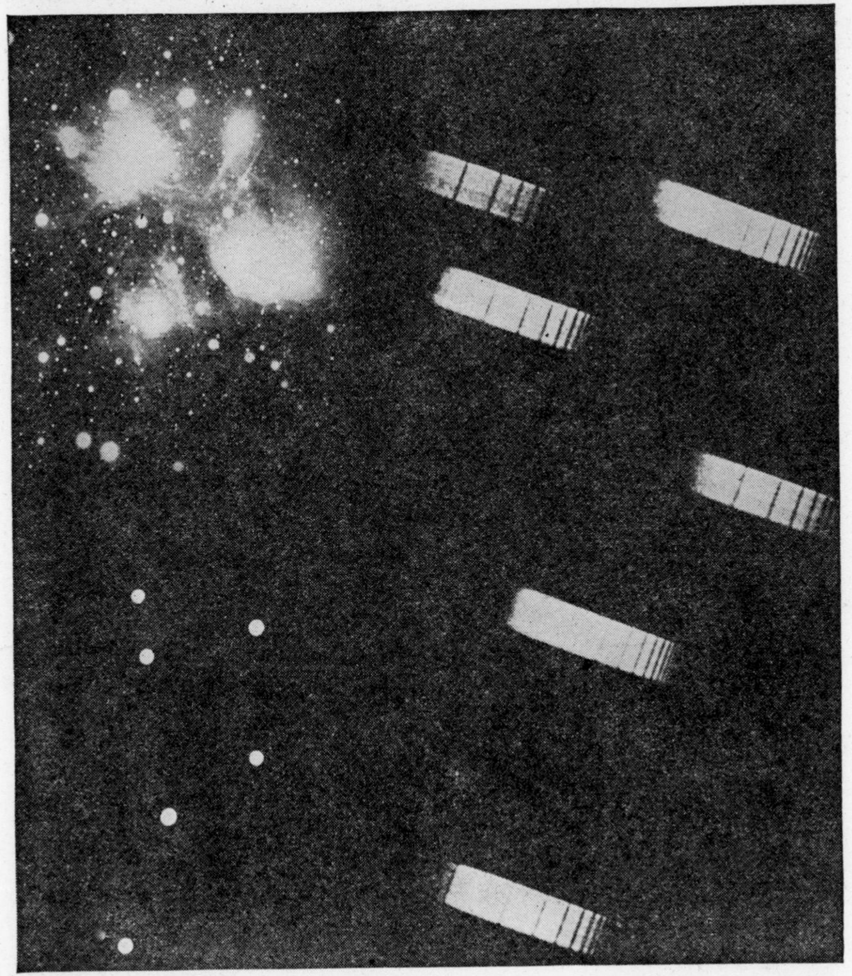

Courtesy Yerkes Observatory

THE COLORS OF LIGHT

The light of the stars at the left appears white. With the spectroscope, we find that their light is not white, but blue, green, yellow and red.

Courtesy Lick Observatory

THE MILLS SPECTROGRAPH
This instrument, shown attached to a telescope, records the color of light from the stars.

and of many other natural manifestations. The vision of man is as limited in perceiving the sweep of things which exist as is the sight of a completely colorblind man, whose world is made up of black and white trees, black flowers, black grass, and white brick houses.

With the new tool of relativity the scientists erected a new vision of the cosmos. The old, word-dominated absolutes gave way before the relentless onward march of mathematically based relative ideas; the world took on a new aspect. The word "time," which had hitherto been regarded as a separate and absolute entity, was incorporated into a world picture, a complete cosmos. This is the space-time continuum which has been so confusing to the world at large and which has led to general misunderstandings and fear of the relativity theories.

Remembering the impossibility of absolute simultaneity, and

keeping in mind the imaginary men on Betelgeuse and the other stars, it is really rather easy to construct in the mind a very large series of frames of reference in which time is only an aspect of space, and space is only an aspect of time.

This new space-time presents a concept of the world which is more true to facts—facts of mechanics, mathematics, electromagnetics, and others—than any word-system could hope to be. With virtually no exceptions, man can think of space in no terms except those of time; a given space is measured by the length of time required to traverse it, or to run the eye across it or for light to pass through it. Time, as men think of it, can be measured only in terms of space—the distance through which the hands of a clock pass, or a candle burns, or the shadow of a sundial moves. The two are inseparable except in the abstract thinkings and verbalizations of men.

An interesting example of how earth-time—time in the frame of reference in which human beings live—is still very closely bound up with space on the earth, is the striping which man has "painted" around the earth to divide it into zones of changing time and zones of geographical space. One series of lines, the meridians of longitude, serve sea captains and explorers in two ways. There are three hundred sixty degrees in a circle. They begin with the zero meridian, which passes through Greenwich, a suburb of London, and extends from the North Pole to the South Pole. The earth, as it rotates before the sun like a spinning top, is subjected to the steady gaze of the sun. The edges of the sunlit area sweep around the revolving earth, passing across fifteen of the meridian lines in each hour. Here the same lines which denote space also mark time for the earth. The new day, however, does not begin at the prime meridian. It was wiser to place this time line far off in the Pacific Ocean, half way around the world from Greenwich, rather than confuse the time-relations of European life.

This fascinating line is called the International Date Line, a wall between yesterday and today, between today and tomorrow. On one side of the line is Wednesday; on the other is Thursday. The traveler sailing westward and crossing the date line at midnight passes from Wednesday night into Friday morning, and the voyager traveling east may have two Thursdays. Here is the collision of time and space measuring. The indivisibility of the two is represented here.

A USELESS TOY BECOMES A USEFUL TOOL

When the world is considered as a space-time continuum, very large and unimaginably complex, the notions of space and time fuse together inextricably. There is still a difference in the categories of the first three and the fourth dimension, however. Mathematically the scientists discovered that there was a definite way to express this difference while still including time among four equally important dimensions. This mathematical technique was the expression of time in all space-time formulas by imaginary numbers. Imaginary numbers are so called not because they are really impossibilities, but because if they are rephrased in words they seem to be impossible. The product obtained when a number is multiplied by itself is called the square of the number. Whether the number which is multiplied by itself is a positive or a negative number, that is, whether it is "above or below zero," its product always is positive—"above zero."

Courtesy Yerkes Observatory

OLE ROEMER

Courtesy Yerkes Observatory

PERCIVAL LOWELL

Mathematicians for many years had, in the process of their computations, run across peculiar things which were the square roots of negative numbers. Now the square root of a number is that number which multiplied by itself produces the original number. Since the square of a root is always positive, these freaks, the square roots of negative numbers, were called imaginary because it was believed that they were nothing but some sort of accidents.

The relativity experimenters, however, discovered that in their formulas this seemingly impossible "imaginary" number fulfilled all the requirements for being a symbol for time. The workers in electromagnetics had already found imaginaries useful. Here is an example of the way in which mathematics, a language whose symbols are those of relationships rather than of objects, is superior in many sorts of thinking to everyday language, which often fails miserably and indeed confuses issues. In the equations of relativity the speed of light is the limiting velocity. Other events in the space-time continuum of the world leave a world-streak, bounded by space and measured by time. They race endlessly with swift-footed light, but they never catch up. They are like a pack of greyhounds on a race track, chasing a toy rabbit; however fast the panting dogs may run, they cannot catch up with it.

The speed of light is the greatest of all speeds; at least it is the greatest speed now known. As it passes through the world it leaves no world-streak, and it is the velocity against which all other velocities are measured. There is no such thing as watching the progress of light, for the speed of light is the limit of watching. It is not infinite, but it is very great. It is the link between the two components of the vast world of Minkowski and the others, the hyphen between space and time in space-time. The relationship is expressed in their wonderful language of mathematics by the scientists when they call time an imaginary number, for when the time and space components, the positive and negative, cancel out in their formulas, as they do in the expression for the speed of light, there is nothing to see. Seeing is itself limited by the swift progress of light.

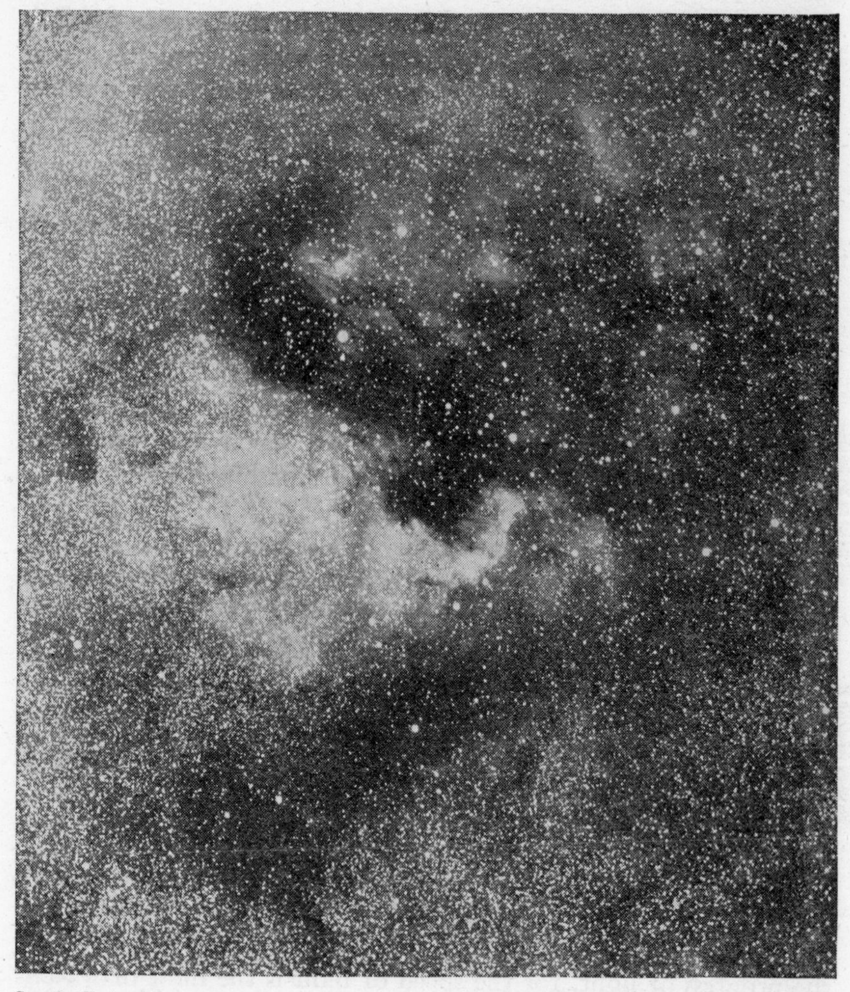

Courtesy Yerkes Observatory

IS THERE A LIMIT TO THE UNIVERSE?
It is difficult to conceive of the distances to the furthermost stars, but it is even more difficult to imagine a place in space beyond which there are no stars. "Beginning" and "end" mean little when we talk about the universe.

WHAT'S IN A NAME?

In the concept of the wide world-view, scientists often use the old space and time terms interchangeably. In designating the same interval in space-time, the same streak, they sometimes say "one second," and they sometimes say "three hundred thousand kilometers." The use of the term "light-year" as the designation of a streak in both space and time is another illustration of the actual indivisibility of the two components of space-time.

Under the leadership of the men of relativity and of quantum mechanics, the picture of the world has been radically changed for modern men and women. The universe is no longer space, emptiness, but is now a fulness. Space is a complex sort of network in which forces and energies are constantly at play, bending rays of light and twisting with the passage of the heavenly bodies just as water is thrust back by an ocean liner passing through it. All matter is apparently energy, some kinds being "thicker" than others.

The universe is like a kettle of thick soup on the stove, endlessly bubbling and boiling about, thin but never clear through considerable distances of its depth, with lumps moving about in it made of the same stuff but different only in the denseness of their composition. The universe, however, is different. The kettle has definite walls—its sides; if there are any walls bounding the universe no one has ever seen them or shown any other evidence of them. Men used to believe that some such walls did exist, because of the illusion that space was an object; therefore, like other objects had a beginning and an end. Men of later centuries began to believe and say that space was infinite and that the universe was boundless. This is a possibility, to be sure, just as it is possible that on the moon there is a rock formation like the Great Stone Face. Since, however, there is no way to find out whether these things are true or not, scientists today are content to say that the universe is unbounded rather than boundless, and exceedingly large rather than infinite.

Man in the cosmos is like a solitary walker at night in the deep fog of a strange city. He can make out the glistening pavement beneath his feet and dimly he can see the dripping bushes that he passes and the bleary, half-visible street lamps nearby. What lies beyond these things he can only guess.

DESIGNER'S NOTE

The text of this volume of "The University of Knowledge" is set in twelve point Linotype Garamond. The design and treatment of illustrations in this book were selected by the authors in order that each chart or picture might add to the presentation of the text.

The signs of the Zodiac at the head of each chapter are from the famous woodcuts by Fritz Kredel.

OTTO M. FORKERT
Director of Design and Layout

Stanley Mucick
3397 Piquette
Detroit Mich